Listen to Leaders in
ENGINEERING

Listen to Leaders in

ENGINEERING

Edited by

ALBERT LOVE and

JAMES SAXON CHILDERS

TUPPER AND LOVE/*Atlanta*

DAVID McKAY COMPANY/*New York*

Library of Congress Catalog Card Number: 64-23488

Manufactured in the United States of America

Van Rees Press   •   New York

Contents

v

Foreword

THE engineers writing in this book have presented not only the expected classifications of engineering—civil, chemical, structural, and so on—but they have gone further and have explored the newest areas in present-day engineering. They have gone from "Aeronautical and Astronautical Engineering" to "Nuclear Engineering," from "Electronics" to "Rocket Propulsion," from "Systems Engineering" to "Engineering in the Sciences of Life and Man"—and this latter chapter, we promise you, is really advanced. Yet it is a part of the new engineering of today and indicates both its extent and variety.

This book is for keeps. It is not a lap book, not a dozing book. It is vividly written by some of the greatest engineers, who tell what engineering as a profession has really become. It is a remarkable story of findings and inventions—and also of failures and frustrations that have finally been overcome by the engineers as they opened whole new areas of exploration. Engineers still build bridges and roads and skyscrapers, continuing in these essential assignments; but they are now also engaged in experiments and functions that previously were not associated in any way with them or their profession.

Actually, the engineers of today not only send their creations to explore the skies and probe the seas, but increasingly they are conducting research and are making discoveries that magnificently advance man's knowledge and his use of that knowledge. This is the story that this book tells.

It is written for every person who is interested in a giant bridge swinging across space, in a submarine months under the sea, in a rocket speeding to its swift target, and in the seeming miracle of the computers. The book is written for everyone who wants to learn the facts and progress of today's engineering; but particularly, we believe, it is written for those persons, of whatever age, who have glimpsed the accomplishments and the future of engineering and wish to be a part of it.

                                                                —A.L. and J.S.C.

Listen to Leaders in
ENGINEERING

1 The Engineer

BY VANNEVAR BUSH
HONORARY CHAIRMAN OF THE CORPORATION
Massachusetts Institute of Technology

VANNEVAR BUSH

Born: 1890, Everett, Massachusetts

Tufts College: B.S., M.S., 1913; Hon. Sc.D., 1932
Harvard University: D.Eng., 1916
Massachusetts Institute of Technology: D.Eng., 1916
Numerous honorary degrees

General Electric Company, Test Department, 1913
U.S. Navy, Inspection Department, 1914
Tufts College: Instructor of Mathematics, 1914–15
  Asst. Prof. Electrical Engineering, 1916–17
U.S. Navy: Research in connection with submarine detection for special
  board, 1917–19
Massachusetts Institute of Technology: Associate Professor of Electric
  Power Transmission, 1919–23
  Professor, 1923–32
  Vice President and Dean of School of Engineering, 1932–38
  Honorary Chairman of the Corporation, 1959
Carnegie Institution of Washington, D.C.: President, 1938–55

Chairman: National Defense Research Committee, 1940
  National Advisory Committee for Aeronautics, 1939–41
  Joint Research and Development Board of War and Navy Departments,
  1946–47
  Research and Development Board of the National Military Establish-
  ment, 1947–48
  Policy Committee of Manhattan Project
Director: Office of Scientific Research and Development, 1941–47
Member: National Science Foundation Advisory Committee on Govern-
  ment-University Relationships, 1953–55

Author: *Principles of Electrical Engineering* (with W. H. Timbie)
  Operational Circuit Analysis
  Endless Horizons
  Modern Arms and Free Men

AN OLD definition of an engineer is this: he is one who applies science for man's use in an economic manner. It is not a bad definition, but it is too limited from a modern standpoint, and if we wish to understand well what is now involved in engineering we need to look into the question more deeply than this.

For one thing, the engineer today not only uses science, he extends and modifies it for his purpose. The relationship between engineering and science will be discussed later, and the use of science by the engineer is a part of engineering research about which I will also have more to say. However, there are factors that need to be considered before we come to any of this. At the present time, before we go on to consider engineering and the engineer, let us examine the knowledge used by all professional men, engineers or any others. We will take into account not only the knowledge and understanding that a professional man acquires in the classroom but also that which he acquires by continuing study after leaving school, and throughout his life by reading, conversation, and observing the world around him.

Let us pin one point down at once, in order not to be misunderstood. There are two kinds of knowledge, two sorts of culture if you wish, which an individual acquires. Both are important but in very different ways. First, there is the professional knowledge already mentioned, which is a working tool in a man's career, the background which enables him to work effectively, to be successful, and to enjoy his work. It enables him to become a

3

leader among his fellows, to merit their respect, and to contribute to the well-being of those about him.

But there is a second sort of culture, and by no means should it be neglected if one wishes to lead a successful and happy life. This second culture, the higher one, takes many forms according to individual talents and tastes, but it is always divorced from the mere task of earning a living. Some find pleasure in good music, listening or even contributing to it; some find pleasure in reading great literature or poetry, and by contemplating the subtle art by which Shakespeare, for a great example, could select and use words for his purpose of stirring the emotions. Many, especially young men, find joy in participating in sports, climbing mountains, for instance, or sliding down them on skis. Many derive their greatest pleasure from very simple things in nature. They go fishing in a brook, but find their true enjoyment in the sparkle of sun on water, or the gliding flight of a bird, or tiny flowers peeping timidly out of the grass. Some wish a more virile satisfaction and guide a spirited horse over a jump, or manage a sailboat in a stiff breeze on a turbulent sea. Many, indeed, enjoy above all else a quiet evening of conversation with kindred friends, puzzling about some of the questions which have intrigued philosophers, and, in fact, all thinking men since civilization began.

We shall not treat here this second type of culture, except to say that it calls for the acquisition of certain special kinds of knowledge for its full enjoyment and satisfaction, and this knowledge, essential to a full life, is acquired over the years in many ways. Our purpose here is primarily to consider the type of knowledge that is useful in a professional career, but I have mentioned the other kind because I do not wish you to think that I disregard it.

What is this knowledge that a professional man should acquire in order to succeed in his profession? It is primarily a knowledge of *things* and of *men*. In whatever profession, whether medicine, law, engineering, or whatever it may be, the knowing of things—that is, the understanding of nature—involves science and technology; and this can range over a very wide area, stretching all the way from fundamental science to useful devices, from identifying flashing particles in space to the building of an engine.

The knowledge of things extends over such an enormous range that no man can master all of it. He can select, in accordance with his professional plans, and dig deeply into specialized fields. But he can also maintain an interest over a broad scope, and be prepared at any time to delve and study, seeking to acquire the knowledge he needs in some special situation. In fact, the skill of a professional man is likely to depend considerably on the facility with which he can acquire new knowledge as he needs it.

The knowledge of men, and the need for this knowledge, is just as broad and as varied as the knowledge of things. It involves all the ways in which men react individually to their environment, and the ways in which they interact together in their complex organizations. Again there is a broad range from fundamental theory to everyday practice. No man can hope to grasp all this knowledge fully, and it is necessary to choose areas where one will concentrate attention. Whatever this concentration may be, it should be mentioned that no one can wisely neglect the more intimate and earthy aspects of the subject.

There are places, of course, where knowledge of things and of men become closely mixed. Take, for example, the introduction by a commercial company of a modern digital computer, for the purpose of handling the payroll, the billing, the inventory, and so on. The executive in charge does not need to understand the full technical details of the device, the functioning of its transistors, its storage toroids, its magnetic tapes. Nor does he need to understand completely the means by which the device is programmed to cause it to perform as desired. Specialists will know these things fully; but, on the other hand, if the executive does not talk their language at all he is not likely to get a shining result. Besides some knowledge in this technical area of things, he also needs to know how the men in his organization fulfill their duties, what various men do, what they themselves need to know, and when they need it. Moreover, he probably needs to understand the attitude of labor organizations within his plant toward all automation, including the digital computer. Here is a case where knowledge of things and of men is intimately interconnected. In fact, such interconnection is the rule rather than the exception, and there are no professional men today who operate entirely at only one end of the spectrum of knowledge.

Now, after this slight excursion, we are in a better position, I believe, to understand the profession of engineering. The engineer stands in the middle of the spectrum between men and things, not only in his objectives, but also in the ways in which he uses science, and in the ways he operates in organizations. The science he uses is generally much more matured, less complex, and most subject to explicit analysis. The organizations with which he deals are broadly those of industry and government. His object is to form a bridge, and, by causing scientific knowledge to be used for meeting human needs and wishes, to bring about valuable results at reasonable costs.

He is concerned with improving man's shelter, food, clothing, and health, and with meeting the desires of men for better communication, transport, even entertainment and relaxation. All this he does by understanding science sufficiently to apply it sensibly, and by understanding men and their organizations well enough to fit plans together so that they will work in practice. With all this to do he can hardly expect also to be a scientist, although some engineers become genuine scientists in some specialized field. Rather he acquires a broad grasp of science, plus an intimate grasp in his special area, and, most important, he gains a versatility that enables him rapidly to extend his grasp as he finds himself immersed in new problems. Often his engineering career leads him into management in industry, for his understanding of organization, essential to his functioning as an engineer, is valuable in its own right, and sought after.

There is a great deal of misunderstanding, especially among young men, of the difference between a scientist and an engineer; and, in an effort to render the position of the engineer clearer, let us take an example. Consider the launching of Telstar, the first satellite placed in orbit to provide channels of comunication between widely separated countries. Here is one of the finest achievements that we have seen in many years. A small spherical object was launched by powerful rockets. These boosted its speed to around 20,000 miles per hour. Complex radar systems followed it as it rose, precisely evaluating its path and speed. Equally complex command systems caused it to steer itself properly so that it entered into an orbital path around the earth, circling as does the moon, but only a few hundred miles out in space. Then a message, or a television program, was beamed to it from this country. The minute energy it received was amplified and rebroadcast at high power, the energy for this purpose being derived from batteries kept charged by solar cells. This enhanced message was received in Europe, and, for the first time, viewers in Europe could see first-hand something that was happening in this country.

It was a magnificent achievement, but there was more to come. After a while, fortunately after it had supplied most of the experimental data for the obtaining of which it was built and launched, the satellite failed. The radiation in space damaged some of its transistors—which was one of the potential dangers that the satellite was built to learn about. However, men on the ground, listening to the story of its condition, which it still transmitted, could tell just where in its circuitry the failure had occurred. Then, by transmitting to it proper orders, they succeeded in bypassing this fault and causing it again to perform correctly. To diagnose a misfunction of an electric circuit, hundreds of miles out in space and speeding past at thousands of miles an hour, was one thing. Telling it how to cure itself was a feat that is almost, but not quite, unbelievable. From this experience, engineers knew better how to protect the transistors aboard the second Telstar.

Who did the Telstar job? The answer is scientists, businessmen, and engineers. But it was primarily a great engineering job. First and foremost, a small group of inspired engineers recognized that the tools were at hand to attempt a significant new engineering experiment, one that might lead to an important advance in world-wide communication. After careful study, they knew that available rockets, electronic devices, and radars were capable of the task, and that the operational problems of satellite tracking and personnel coordination were within reason. This alertness to new possibilities, mediated by a deep knowledge of science and human needs, is the hallmark of engineering. Recognizing this fact, let us look more deeply into the background of Telstar.

No great pioneering engineering task can be accomplished unless fundamental science has laid the groundwork for it, and this was true in the case of Telstar. Long ago basic scientists had developed the theory of electromagnetism, on which radar depends, the laws governing electrons in the solid state, the photoelectric effect, and so on. Long ago celestial mechanics had made possible the computation of trajectories of satellites. Chemical theory, the thermodynamics of gases, had laid the basis for rocket propulsion. All this, and much more, formed the scientific basis for advance.

Businessmen had to find and appropriate the money, make arrangements with government agencies for joint effort, and they had to provide the extensive organization for coordinating the efforts of the thousands of men involved.

The main job, however, was an engineering task. Solid-state physics had been applied to produce transistors, and photoelectric theory to make solar cells. The basic laws of electricity had been developed into working methods of analysis and synthesis of complex electrical networks. Chemical engineers had developed powerful rocket fuels; thermodynamicists had designed efficient nozzles. Radar had been refined. Telemetering circuitry had been rendered fast and reliable. These devices and methods had been developed into practical, reliable forms, produceable at reasonable cost.

In addition, engineers had to design and fit together all the elements in a working affair, to estimate costs and control performance to meet those estimates, to design so as to minimize weight, and, above all, to test every element in an elaborate system to ensure its reliability at critical moments. They had to build powerful stations in remote places, man and supply them, and tie the whole thing together so that every device and every part would operate as planned, so that nothing would be left out. The result was an achievement of which every American can be proud.

Having now written at some length about Telstar as an *achievement*, let me go back to an earlier period in Telstar's creation and write of it for a moment as a piece of engineering *research*, a product of a lesser known area of engineering.

Actually, from Telstar's initial bits and pieces to the completed job there was essentially the research approach, which is the judicial combining of theory and experiment. As we said earlier, Telstar was conceived and planned, as well as produced, by engineers. Of course the scientists should have credit for their part in the achievement, but engineers pioneered the development of the transistors and solar cells employed in the satellite. The traveling-wave tube, which is the heart of its repeater, was invented and developed by an engineer. The essential ground stations, with their horn reflector antennas and feedback FM receivers, were largely invented by engineers. The maser, which performed the first amplification, was discovered by a scientist, but was put into a usable form by engineers. Also, engineers conceived, planned, and experimented with Echo I, the metallized balloon which preceded Telstar as a satellite.

Even more important than any single experiment was the combining of multiple components into a significant system. The development of this system was beset with uncertainties and called for research of the highest order, necessarily involving a deep appreciation of natural processes plus the ability to formulate and carry out crucial experiments. Such work, called systems engineering, is an important part of the work of engineers.

With these achievements for us to consider, and a great many more than these, I suggest that engineering is a good deal broader in its concept and function than ordinarily is realized, and the relationship between engineering and science needs clarification. The heart of this relationship is the recognition of the functions of both engineering and science, and of their interrelationship.

As a classical example of this working together, this combining of efforts resulting in a shared success, there was the development and achievement of the atomic bomb. Here science laid the groundwork and performed essential services. Organization within government was also important. But the main effort, the building of great new plants, the introduction of new untried processes on a large scale, the interrelation of thousands of suppliers and widely separated organizations into an integrated whole, was to a very large extent an engineering undertaking.

We do not need to trace all this in detail, for the story has often been told; but it is important to realize that when science becomes applied to great objectives, so that the problems of organization, costs, scheduling, become paramount, we have then to deal with engineering. The professional engineer is the man who can turn one way toward science, and the other way toward men, and tie together a plan and an effort to produce results in a practical manner.

As was said in connection with Telstar, perhaps the most vital function of the engineer today is to recognize and act upon opportunities for new achievement, on one hand within the technical possibilities and on the other answering a human need. In its finest and most creative phase, engineering at times may actually be ahead of the related sciences. This is not usual, however, and, as Dr. Jerome Wiesner,* a distinguished engineer, formerly Chairman of the President's Science Advisory Committee and now Dean of the School of Science at Massachusetts Institute of Technology, once said: "Technology can outrun science, but not by much."

The truth of the matter is that the goal of the engineer is to keep the ability *to do* and *to control* ahead of, or at least even with, the ability of the scientist to predict experimental results and reconcile bare facts with basic principles. In this, as in all associations between engineers and scientists, engineering is more a partner than a child of science. This emphasizes the responsibility of engineering in today's world of creative effort, indicating

* Author of this book's final chapter.

clearly that engineering has its own initiative and does not merely follow along behind science, does not merely make use of science's discoveries in the building of engineering "gadgetry."

Engineering often operates by combining disciplines into new fields of study. From these fields of combined disciplines there flow both new sciences and new technology. For instance, the engineers' study of information-processing in human and animal nervous eystems is today opening up a whole new horizon of knowledge, which will have profound effects on biological science as well as on the applied fields of medicine and communication. Indeed, engineers are playing a major role through research in filling the void between their traditional professional concern, which is the physical sciences, and the newly-emerging behavioral, social, and informational sciences.

In the area we are discussing at the moment, which is the relationship between engineering and science, we should point out that while everyone knows that engineering is concerned with the conversion of science into technology, everyone does not know that engineering also does just the opposite and translates technology into new science and mathematics.

There are numerous examples. Karl Jansky created the new science of radio astronomy while engaged in engineering research on antennas and electromagnetic wave propagation. Digital computers, which are an engineering tour-de-force, have provided mathematicians with a new tool for carrying out symbolic manipulation, and have provided scientists with a new experimental medium for gaining insight into the nature of the world.*

Another area of engineering concern is that of information processing. Basically, research in this area concerns the handling of information in meaningful fashion by machine, including such topics as information retrieval, automatic language translation, man-machine communication, and the coding of information for transmission and display for human consumption. A related area

* EDITOR'S NOTE: Dr. Bush's own contributions to this area have been fundamental. His development of the differential analyzer led to the modern analog computer, which was the forerunner of a whole family of computers and analytical machines.

concerns the extraction of information from radar, sonar, seismic, heart, video, and other signals.

My main point is that the challenge of modern engineering lies in adapting research techniques and the methods of science to the goals of engineering. In meeting this challenge, the engineer must be both worldly and wise. Certainly an engineer is concerned with science, but not only with science; he is concerned with knowledge in its broadest sense. Moreover, he is concerned with more than the development of the knowledge we already have; he is engaged in research for new knowledge. At all times, too, he has an interest in ideas and understanding deeper than merely an interest for its own sake; he is concerned with the use of these ideas and this understanding, in doing something with them. Gordon Brown, Dean of the Engineering School at the Massachusetts Institute of Technology and author of the second chapter in this book, once said: "An engineer is a worldly scientist." It is this image of the engineer that I would like to see clearly recognized and understood.

Now let me go on to point out that there are many kinds of engineering. To begin with, they differ in the fields of science upon which they principally lean. They differ also in the relative emphasis they place upon the knowledge of things and of men. In the various chapters of this volume will be told the story of different kinds of engineering, but there are two facts which apply to all, and which need final emphasis.

First, in any engineering career there is likely to be a gradual shift from emphasis on knowledge of *things* to emphasis on knowledge of *men*. The young engineer, in his first post, is not likely to be called upon to expound a program to a board of directors. His initial advancement may depend much more upon whether he can design a circuit, or a part of an engine, or a step in a chemical process, in a sensible manner. His advancement will also depend upon whether he can work harmoniously with his fellows, his helpers, and his boss. Despite this need for satisfactory human relationships, there is a tendency among young engineers to discount the knowledge of men in favor of things, merely because things come first in their experience. It is well, however, for the young engineer to realize that, while his work at first may lean considerably toward that of the applied scientist, it is likely to lean later, if he is truly a professional engineer, in the other direction.

The final point is an important one. Many years ago there were stone walls which separated civil, mechanical, electrical, and chemical engineering. These walls have now disappeared, and, instead of fixed compartments, we have a dozen new varieties of engineering such as nuclear engineering or biological engineering. The keynote today is versatility. This has come about for several reasons. First, disciplines have become intermingled. Step into a laboratory today and often you cannot tell whether you are in an electrical, chemical, or biological laboratory. For one thing, wherever you are, the place is likely to be full of electrical gadgetry.

Second, employers who can give a young engineer his start have gradually come to realize that the man who can tackle varied problems in the beginning of his career is likely to be a valuable engineer. In regard to this matter of versatility, take the situation of an engineer faced with the task of designing a control system for a new type of intricate machine tool. At the outset, he had better consider whether he will make his signals and his control impulses electrical, mechanical, hydraulic, pneumatic, or a combination. If he does not take all this variety into account, he may have the sad experience of seeing his competitor produce a better and a less expensive system. The ability to think, plan, and work in a versatile manner is attained if the student, while in college, discovers more than merely the knack of learning about the immediate subject of some given course. Versatility is attained when a person, on his own, in a pinch, can learn fast about something that he never studied formally. Versatility also involves the ability to step quickly from a subject in which the emphasis is primarily on things to one in which the emphasis is largely on men.

Engineering is a great profession. For the person who likes both things and men it presents fine opportunities. It calls for hard work, of course, making its demands by the very range of

its study and work. However, it rewards well, and, in the terms
of this world's goods, it sometimes rewards very well. More important, it can provide a life of genuine satisfaction in many ways,
especially through ministering in a practical manner to the needs
and welfare of mankind.

2 Engineering School — and Preparation for Engineering

BY GORDON STANLEY BROWN

DEAN OF THE SCHOOL OF ENGINEERING
Massachusetts Institute of Technology

GORDON STANLEY BROWN

Born: 1907, Drummoyne, New South Wales, Australia

Royal Melbourne Institute of Technology: Diploma of Mech. & Elec. Engrg., 1925

Massachusetts Institute of Technology: S.B., 1931; S.M., 1934; Sc.D., 1938 (All in Department of Electrical Engineering)

Purdue University: D.Eng., 1958 (Honorary); Dartmouth College, Sc.D., 1964 (Honorary)

Massachusetts Institute of Technology:
Research Assistant in Electrical Engineering, 1931
Instructor, 1932
Assistant Professor, 1939
Associate Professor, 1941
Professor, 1946
Head of the Department of Electrical Engineering, 1952
Chairman of the Faculty of the Institute, 1951–52
Dean of Engineering, 1959
Founder and Director Servomechanisms Laboratory, 1941–52

Purdue University: Exchange Professor, 1935

University of California at Berkeley: Visiting Mackay Professor of Electrical Engineering, 1956

University of Sydney (Australia): J. I. Carroll Memorial Fellow, 1958

First Chairman, Committee on Feedback Control Systems, American Institute of Electrical Engineers, 1946–48

Fellow: American Academy of Arts and Sciences
Institution of Electrical and Electronic Engineers

Member: American Society for Engineering Education
President's Committee on the National Medal of Science
Board of Overseers of the Thayer School of Dartmouth College

Director: Baird-Atomic, Inc.; Gorham Corporation; Allegheny Ludlum Steel Corporation; United-Carr Fastener Corporation; Commission on Engineering Education

Sigma Xi
Tau Beta Pi
Eta Kappa Nu: Eminent Member, March 25, 1963

George Westinghouse Award, American Society for Engineering Education, 1952

Lamme Medal, American Society for Engineering Education, 1959

Medal in Engineering Education, American Institute of Electrical Engineers, 1959

Author: *Principles of Servomechanisms* (with Donald P. Campell) Numerous technical papers and articles on engineering education

IF YOU will look closely at the character of engineering work to about the years 1400–1600, you will note that the craftsmanship which a father taught his son was good enough to permit the son to work as an engineer throughout most of his lifetime. Each generation of craftsmen worked under a master, learned a little more by experience, and passed its know-how on to the next.

Admittedly, the practice of design gradually became better established and knowledge of how to perform many of the processes whereby bricks were made, metals were mined, melted, and formed, and so forth, became more refined. But the basic principles upon which rested much of the engineering of that era were understood by relatively few people until about 1700, about the time of the Industrial Revolution. Experience and intuition, rather than quantitatively exact technical knowledge, were until then the principal attributes of the engineer.

Even during the first hundred or so years of the Industrial Revolution many of the early patterns continued. Great technological advances were made by engineers who worked without the benefit of organized education. But when the early craft schools appeared in Europe around 1750, a multiplying factor took effect. More engineers were schooled in their skills; they learned them at an earlier age and with more exactness; their number and their competence began to grow at an ever-advancing rate. It was perhaps the establishment of the Ecole Polytechnique in Paris in 1794—the first technical institution of university rank—that gave us the seeds of today's flourishing profession.

Until about the beginning of the twentieth century, however, many engineering schools concerned themselves mainly with teaching students about the technology or the industrial practice of their own day. They operated on the doctrine that what a student learned in college would serve him throughout most of his professional career. This early theory of education stemmed perhaps from the philosophy that technology would not change appreciably during an engineer's lifetime. It assumed, falsely, that engineers would merely build more machines to a conventional pattern and keep them running.

The early doctrine of education also overlooked a subtle but important fact of technology; namely, that whereas prior to the turn of the twentieth century scientists were extensively concerned with documenting basic theory and explaining many things which engineers had already done by the application of art and intuition, the era was dawning when the discoveries of scientists would evolve *new* theories that would lead to numerous advances in engineering. The old doctrine failed to recognize that, under the pressures exerted by the aspirations of man, the skill of engineers at innovation would exploit new findings of science to unsettle steadily the shape of technology. The old doctrine also failed to recognize that the tempo of this unsettling would increase.

During the early days of engineering education, the content of a curriculum was predominantly technical. Students learned about what we now view as elementary mathematics, physics, and chemistry. They were taught the skills of mechanical drawing, foundry, shop, woodworking, and many other crafts. Whenever there were courses in English or composition, they were invariably elementary. But as engineering matured, and as the work of engineers became more sophisticated and ranged more widely, it became clear that engineers dealt both with science and with society. In addition to dealing with facts and scientific principles, they had to be prepared to become leaders because society realized that they held within their grasp much of the destiny of mankind.

About forty years ago, it was agreed that an engineering curriculum should embrace many elements of a liberal education.

As a consequence, every school where an accredited four- or five-year bachelor's degree program is now offered stipulates that approximately twenty per cent of the student's time shall be allocated to studies in the humanities and social sciences. Similar requirements prevail in the accredited technical institutes that offer the two-year program leading to the Associate Degree in Engineering Technology. Every engineer should have a keen awareness of the social, the political, and the economic consequences of his work.

Today, in America, students who aspire to become engineers, who have a flair for physics, mathematics, or chemistry, who have an innate curiosity about how things work and an urge to build things, may choose from nearly two hundred schools. Graduates from high school with grades that place them in the upper quartile of their class in mathematics and science, and skill at communicating ideas both orally and in writing, should not find it difficult to gain admission to one of several schools of their choice.

Every state university in the nation provides a school or college in engineering within its system. Almost all are expanding their facilities as rapidly as possible so that they can accept more of the students who apply. There are also a great many privately endowed universities, institutes of technology, or polytechnic institutes where a student can acquire a basic education for a career in engineering. Many of these schools are also expanding, though to a lesser extent than the state institutions. Although admission to all of them is competitive, no student should feel deterred from applying to whichever one he prefers. While engineering schools require that students have performed well on the requisite entrance examinations, all admissions officers feel that top grades are not the only criteria for admission. Interests in extracurricular activities, an urge to continue an education, a potential for leadership in engineering, and personal qualities are all weighed in the selection process.

I want now to say that I consider it unnecessary and even unwise to worry excessively about making an early commitment to enter a particular specialty of engineering. This may sound surprising, for I suspect that often, when trying to decide whether you want to go into engineering, or whether you should apply for admission to an engineering college, you have been asked by well-meaning persons, "What kind of engineering?"

If you happen to have asked people—even practicing engineers —to tell you something about engineering or to describe what a such-and-such engineer does, you have probably been disappointed. I, too, find it difficult to tell young men in a convincing way what even a narrow specialty in engineering is all about.

It is for this reason that the editors of this book have asked a number of leading engineers from many different fields to write down in their own words what they do, or what a field embraces, and to tell how they view their work.

Students who have a chance to work with engineers during summers, or those whose fathers or intimate friends are engineers, will probably have had some of the flavor of engineering rub off onto them. But even their view of what they will eventually do as engineers could very likely be incorrect.

A student might conclude, for instance, that he should enter mechanical engineering because gas turbines interest him at the moment, or because he thinks it would be a glamorous field, or because the Sunday edition of the *New York Times* carries a lot of announcements by companies seeking to employ these engineers. The choice of mechanical engineering for a program of study may be and, in fact, could well be the right one, but all the above reasons for the choice would be wrong.

What the student perhaps does not know is that the character of almost every specialized field will change markedly during the next decade or two. In fact, any particular specialty may not even exist by then. Therefore, please do not choose a college just because it offers a course in such a narrow area as gas-turbine engineering.

Let me put this problem into better perspective by saying that statistics show that within five or so years after graduation from college a substantial fraction of graduates will be working in a discipline different from their college major. Let me also say that they will invariably make this cross-over from one field to another on their own iniative because of improved opportunities or changes in their choice of work. The ease with which they will make it will depend greatly on their mastery of the fundamentals of science and applied science taught during their undergraduate education.

As you read what the other contributors to this book say, you can put their stories into appropriate perspective by remembering that if you graduate in the 1960's, you will not reach the summit of your career until about the 1980's. You will not retire before about the year 2010. Because you have a long career ahead, and because of the certainty that scientists will make new discoveries, we are becoming less and less certain of our ability to predict with any precision the exact nature of the knowledge you will need.

There is, however, one indisputable fact, and it may sound paradoxical; namely, that professional achievement—success, if you wish—in any field of engineering, whether it be the newest and most glamorous specialized field of your generation, or an older changing field, is only assured when it is built on a sound fundamental training in the oldest of our technical disciplines—physics, mathematics, and chemistry—and some skill at using them.

There is a much higher probability, for example, that Newton's laws will be of value in 1980 than some particular test code about materials or some existing manufacturing practice will be applicable. To the older, classical versions of physics, mathematics, and chemistry are now added all the most recent discoveries. Modern curricula also comprise many of the applied or engineering sciences, such as mechanics and dynamics in the broad sense; thermodynamics and statistical mechanics; electrical science with emphasis on both network and field phenomena; the processing of energy; mass momentum and heat transfer; the processing of information, especially by modern computers; information theory; and the microscopic nature of materials as they point to a relationship between structure and property.

To a surprising degree the programs offered in any of the accredited curricula—for example, mechanical, electrical, chemical, metallurgical, civil, aeronautical—in the degree-granting colleges or universities in America include substantial coverage of all of the above engineering sciences. The differences, if any, exist more as a means for providing groupings of topics in order to provide motivation, and to relate the work to engineering, than for any other reason.

My advice to you at this stage in your career is that you say, "I intend to become a good engineer." Defer, if possible, making the choice of a department or field of study until about halfway through your program. But if your school policy requires that, as a freshman, you affiliate with a particular department or discipline, choose what appeals to you at the moment and relax. Do not regard this decision as permanently tying you to that discipline.

Many students who enter a university are totally unaware of the university's true role. Early in their programs they frequently become critical of the teaching and say that the professors are too interested in research. Actually they are discovering, for the first time, that the ability to learn on one's own is a major asset and that many of the procedures of an institution of higher learning are oriented toward developing that ability.

It is not sufficient for a boy or girl to enter college and merely attend lectures—to soak up facts and figures like a sponge. If you appear in class merely to the extent that you can be counted, you are at best merely a pupil. If, however, you are showing some skill at learning what you have been told to learn and have mastered the game of taking examinations to the extent that you can convince your teacher that you know what you have been told to learn, then I would call you a student. But if you have progressed to the stage where, with some skill, you can decide what it is you ought to know and have acquired the capacity to learn it essentially by your own resources, you have become a scholar. You will then have the inherent capability for lifelong learning.* When you have achieved this ultimate status,

* I am indebted to Professor Paul Chenea of Purdue for this viewpoint as it was explained in his talk presented before the Design Engineering Conference, April 30, 1962, American Institute of Mechanical Engineers.

you should try to make yourself part of the environment, to become a contributor in your own right—to conduct yourself so as to add one more brick to the total edifice of knowledge.

Your college experience will be much more rewarding if you have an appreciation of the institution's total role in society and if you can identify the factors that give it strength. You will then be able to share in the fulfillment of its mission.

Stated simply, in addition to being a place where knowledge is taught, a university or an engineering college must be a powerful element for the self-generation of new knowledge, new philosophies, and new doctrines to meet the needs of the future as well as the present. This means that the professors must be true scholars; they must be engaged in both research and teaching. Their main focus must be on learning. Too often the young student assumes that their only function is to teach him what he is prepared to learn.

Many changes have been made recently in high-school science courses. Also, many freshman and sophomore college courses in physics, mathematics, and chemistry are becoming out of date, with the result that faculties everywhere are taking drastic steps to redirect their outlook, their methodologies, their organizational structure, and the content of their programs of instruction and research. The curricula offered by engineering schools throughout the nation have been almost completely rebuilt during the last decade. It is certain that they will change even more during succeeding decades because the scientist is forever making new discoveries and the engineer is forever evolving new technologies.

It is essential that you realize this situation. You should not be puzzled, nor should you become annoyed by the changes you will see professors constantly making in their courses and methods of teaching. Changes in courses inevitably cause confusion to a student. Frequently a professor must teach the old while also beginning to teach the new. This task is difficult. But change is so inevitable that if by the time you graduate the courses then being taught to the entering freshmen are not superior to the courses you were taught, you should be critical of your school.

It is usually a shock to an engineering student, when he first enters a bachelor's degree program, to find that he is expected to devote his major efforts to the study of science—physics, mathematics, and chemistry—apparently to the exclusion of engineering. Invariably these subjects are taught by scientists or mathematicians who, viewed superficially, appear to care little about the engineering usefulness of their subject matter. But you should realize that by learning about science from scientists you are assured of learning what is now going on in science, and of being given an insight into how a scientist thinks. As a prospective engineer, you need to be exposed to the most modern science, and the best is none too good.

Some engineering schools are experimenting with courses that aim to teach freshmen about engineering. Some schools provide an elective for freshmen in which they can study under an engineering professor, get to know him, and get some taste of engineering. Whenever such courses are offered, I suggest that you take them, but at the same time you should learn all you can about the sciences offered you as freshmen and sophomores. Accept the fact that you are laying the foundations of knowledge on which your career will be built and that you are in a situation where learning to think and learning how to learn about intellectual matters are the major goals. Your fascination with gadgetry and engineering applications, which may have been what initially motivated you toward engineering, will be better satisfied after you have broadened your foundation in fundamentals. During your freshman and sophomore years, perhaps only in the laboratories will you find much opportunity for contact with physically tangible things.

I hope you will learn that mathematics is not a gimmick but an orderly, exciting, and powerful tool that engineers use to conduct a theoretical investigation of a situation. You should realize that engineers often begin a paper study of a physical problem by formulating a mathematical model. They then use tools such as calculus, Laplace transform methods, the laws of probability, statistics, number theory, Boolean algebra, or vector analysis and other components of higher mathematics together with computers in order to explore the abstract or to analyze situations and obtain numerical results from their mathematical models.

You should not assume that a mathematics preparation that terminates with differential equations is adequate. You should understand higher mathematics. It is my opinion that the measure of the amount of mathematics you should take is the amount that will lift you to your mathematical asymptote. And one piece of advice I would like to inject here is that whenever you get a numerical answer to a problem, pause for a moment and size it up. Ask yourself if the answer really makes sense. By developing this habit, you will quickly cultivate one of the key qualities of a great engineer, namely, the knack of estimating the reasonableness of things and of keeping in touch with reality.

You will help yourself by taking an imaginative view toward laboratory instruction. The practice of relating laboratory work closely with classroom work is followed not merely to help you understand theory or to prove to you that the theory you were taught in class is correct. This objective could not justify the cost in either money or in your time. You should realize that the experimental method is one of the powerful ways whereby the technologist explores the mysteries of nature or conducts investigations of complicated physical situations. When you appreciate that the laboratory provides a way to model a physical situation for the purposes of learning, you will have increased your total competence.

Experimentation is one of the powerful arts of both the engineer and the scientist. Sometimes, as in a laboratory, it can be performed skillfully in miniature without being grossly expensive. But sometimes, as for example when evaluating the performance of actual massive machines or in probing outer space, experimentation may cost millions of dollars.

Theoretical analysis, then, provides a way to model mathematically, and the laboratory provides a way to model experimentally. It is essential to have instruction in both classroom and laboratory and to develop both skills as your mastery of the content of your studies is increased. In this way each skill serves as a vitamin to pep up the other.

There is abundant evidence that today's technology has over-taxed the capabilities of many materials which engineers use. Many problems of production, such as control of product quality, yield to solution only as engineers learn more about the materials with which they work. Mere instruction in, or tabulation of, the experimentally measured macro-physical properties of materials is not enough. During the past few decades scientists have clarified many earlier abstruse concepts about matter and energy and about the relation between structure and properties. Much that once was vague is now well understood. Solid-state physics, physical chemistry, the concepts of quantum mechanics, and a host of new techniques for making measurements about structure and property have injected a high degree of microscopic quantitative exactness into the knowledge of materials. You cannot over-estimate the importance of gaining the most up-to-date knowledge about materials and materials science, because every good design of a machine inherently taxes the materials to the tolerable limit of their capability. Courses on empiricism and testing of standard materials are giving way more and more to courses on solid-state physics, on atomic and nuclear physics, and on the broad aspects of materials science. The presentation of these courses is becoming commonplace in engineering curricula of all specialties.

I want also to make a few remarks about the role that electronic computers are likely to play both in your education and in your career. Computer technology, both analog and digital, has been progressing by leaps and bounds over the last decade. The speed of operation of computers and their capability to handle complex problems have increased enormously. Their reliability has increased, and their size and cost for any given capability have been reduced.

Because of the great capability of today's electronic computers, let alone tomorrow's, computational methods for investigating engineering problems are becoming much more powerful. Regardless of whether engineers work in laboratories, in design, in production, or in business, computers are taking an increasingly important place in the solution of their problems.

On many college campuses professors and students are working together to develop techniques for exploiting computers both for carrying out straightforward numerical information-processing and for incorporation into man-machine systems involving non-numerical information. Problem-oriented computer languages are being developed so that engineers can talk to the computer in just about the same way they talk to one another. As the computer performs the routine calculations, the teacher and student are free to concentrate on the creative aspects of engineering, to carry out designs, or to optimize designs. Already computers can be made to prepare engineering drawings, to plot curves, and to tell machine tools what to do. Research is underway to develop new patterns of logic, new programming aids, and new input, output, and display equipment to enable engineers to enhance their broad decision capability.

As you progress through your program of studies, you will encounter no difficulty in learning the technique of how to program a computer in order that it can give lightning-quick numerical answers to traditional problems. But if you will also acquire an understanding of how a computer can extend the cognitive capabilities of human beings, you will be in step with one of the greatest developments in engineering that we have seen for a long time.

Let me conclude this topic by saying that one of the challenges that confronts an engineering professor is to devise courses that contain material of enduring value and to teach them in ways that will cultivate in a student the knack of being innovative or will spark his creativity. Professors aim to teach that science has given us an organized and objective documentation of the laws of nature so that you may know as precisely as possible what happens and how it takes place. They aim to teach both science and the scientific method, to teach procedures whereby you may bring together in common logical sequence the multitude of observed and seemingly unrelated events of nature. This quantitative organization of physical phenomena, which is often called model making, is the key to much of what is called engineering analysis and synthesis. Professors also aim to teach you how to predict the quality and the quantity of the outcome of the designs not yet made so that you may project your efforts into the future. They aim to enhance your future ability to create and to devise new technologies.

It is clear that an undergraduate program cannot include all that an engineer needs to know; hence, it is becoming widely accepted that a student who is headed for a highly technical career will continue with graduate study. I take it for granted that you will join a professional society and keep abreast of developments in the technical literature.

In 1962 President Kennedy, in releasing a report from his Science Advisory Committee, said, "Requirements for the more highly trained engineers, mathematicians, and physical scientists are rapidly outstripping our capability to produce them." The Committee's report recommended steps to encourage engineering students to go on to graduate schools.

As I write this story, the Congress of the United States is studying many proposals submitted to it by the National Science Foundation, the Atomic Energy Commission, the National Aeronautics and Space Administration, and other agencies to furnish fellowships in engineering. I want to point out, however, that if you hastily scan their announcements, you might assume falsely that they make awards only in science. Engineering is included in a very substantial way under the designation "engineering sciences." These actions greatly aid a student in meeting the cost of obtaining an advanced degree. In fact it is almost possible to predict that we are approaching the time when scholarships and fellowships from either government or private industry, and assistantships in either teaching or research offered by the graduate schools in engineering, will be available in sufficient numbers to permit every student who can benefit from advanced study to work toward his master's or doctor's degree in engineering with negligible financial cost to him.

But inevitably you will have to learn anew as you go through life, and it becomes crucial whether you will have the inherent capability to identify what you should learn or whether you will have to be told by someone else. It is important therefore for you to decide now that you are to become a scholar and not merely a student.

I have deliberately restricted most of my remarks to a discussion of the scientific and professional aspects of engineering education. The place of the humanities, the social sciences, and the life sciences are very important to an engineer's professional future. They will also serve to increase the role of cultural interests in his life. He must act to integrate these elements into his total education as he proceeds with his technical program.

As my colleague, Professor Elting E. Morison, speaking as an historian points out, any engineer trained broadly in the principles, in the theories, and in the highest creative expression of his own field will tend naturally to act as a liberal influence in his community. His attitude toward himself and toward his profession, his capacity to proceed from the particular to the general, and his training in establishing connections between things not superficially relatable will naturally tend to give him a broader sense of proportion and to make him a truly civilizing influence in the society of which he is a member.

You will find that an engineering education is both a liberal and a powerful one.

3 _Engineering and Research_

BY FREDERICK EMMONS TERMAN

VICE PRESIDENT AND PROVOST

Stanford University

FREDERICK EMMONS TERMAN

Born: 1900, English, Indiana

Stanford: B.A., 1920; Engr., 1922
Massachusetts Institute of Technology: Sc.D., 1924
Sc.D. (honorary): Harvard, British Columbia, Syracuse

Stanford University:
   Assistant Professor to Professor, 1925–37
   Executive Head, Electrical Engineering Department, 1937–45
   Dean of Engineering, 1945–58
   Provost, 1955–
   Vice President, 1959–
Radio Research Laboratory, Harvard University: Director, 1942–45

Institute of Radio Engineers (now IEEE):
   Vice President, 1940; President, 1941
   Medal of Honor, 1950; Founders Award, 1962
American Society for Engineering Education: Vice President, 1949–51
Member: Air Force STAG and TAPEC Committees on Electronic
      Countermeasures, 1950–56
   Signal Corps Research and Development Advisory Committee, 1954–62
   Naval Research Advisory Committee, 1956–64; Chairman, 1957–58
   Defense Science Board, 1957–58
   NSF Divisional Committee for MPE, 1955–59
   Board of Foreign Scholarships, 1960–
   Consultant, President's Science Advisory Committee, 1959–
   National Academy of Sciences
   American Philosophical Society
Director: Hewlett-Packard Company; Watkins-Johnson Company; Granger
   Associates; Stanford Research Institute
Trustee: Institute for Defense Analyses

U.S. Medal for Merit, 1948
Decorated by British Government, 1946

Author: *Transmission Line Theory* (with W. S. Franklin)
   Electronic and Radio Engineering (formerly *Radio Engineering*)
   Measurements in Radio Engineering
   Fundamentals of Radio
   Radio Engineers Handbook
   Electronic Measurements (with J. M. Pettit)
   Numerous articles on electrical engineering and electronic subjects,
      and on education

RESEARCH and related creative activities occupy the attention of an increasing number of young engineers. For those with the interest and proper qualifications, such work is both intellectually stimulating and financially rewarding. It also provides an excellent background for subsequent participation in other types of engineering activity, including management responsibilities.

The term research as used in this chapter denotes a broad group of creative activities in which engineers engage. These include the search for new facts of nature without regard to the utilitarian value of these facts—this is the *basic* research of the scientist and engineer. In addition, research is here used to include innovation and advanced development, *i.e.* original ways to use new knowledge, and likewise creative systems work in which the objective is to determine the best way in which to use new knowledge to obtain a desired end result.

Research in engineering therefore spans a breadth of creative activities that is greater and often more exacting than is required in research carried on in a laboratory, or with pencil and paper or computer, to discover new facts of nature. It does not satisfy the engineer that there be a scientific demonstration that flight is possible; he demands that the airplane also be safe, reliable, fast, comfortable, economical, and capable of carrying large loads. In the process of achieving such a result, the engineer commonly finds it necessary to acquire an understanding of the basic principles involved that is more intimate and more complete than that of the research scientists and research engineers who made the original discoveries.

33

To do this the engineer is often required to perform research that will bring to light and make clear additional facts of nature that bear on the subject with which he is concerned; this is the applied research of the engineer. It differs from basic research only in that it is more sharply focused toward an immediately useful goal.

The strong emphasis that now exists in the engineering profession on those creative activities, which we have grouped together under the term research, is new. It began with World War II, but the full impact has been felt by the engineering profession only since the early 1950's. This trend toward research is still present and is increasing rather than leveling off.

The engineering profession is today in the midst of a revolution. The character of the work performed by engineers is changing, as is the training that engineers now receive. This has come about so recently that the public image of the engineer, and of the engineering profession, lags behind the facts. The popular concept of the engineer is far less exciting than is the actual profession that the young engineers enter today as they complete their training at our colleges and universities. In particular, high-school counselors too often look at the total spectrum of engineering, including the activities of both the pre-war and post-war engineering graduates, and fail to realize that the recent graduates receive training and enter into activities that are quite different from the experiences of their fathers. A true picture of the engineering profession, insofar as young people are concerned, can be gained only by observing how our colleges are training engineers *today,* and what the young graduate now does with this training in the first few years after he completes his formal education. Only in this way can one obtain an idea of what lies ahead of young people planning a career in engineering.

In the later chapters of this book that deal with specific engineering activities, the reader will find a recurring emphasis on creative work, *i.e.,* research, by the engineer. This is an easily distinguishable thread, common to all areas of engineering that are developing or changing, whether electronics, astronautics, materials, energy conversion, or structural engineering. It is this creative activity that challenges the best of the young engineers today—a fact of great significance to the engineering profession of the future. It is also this creative activity that gives the engineering profession today a character quite different from that it possessed during the first half of this century.

The growing importance of research activities in the engineering profession is indicated by the national expenditures for research and development. In the period from 1953 to 1961 such expenditure increased from 5 billion dollars in 1953–54 to 14 billion in 1960–61,* and for 1963–64 it has been projected to be about 20 billion. These figures include all research and development, irrespective of whether performed by industry, universities, non-profit organizations, or government laboratories, and irrespective of the source of funds. They represent 1.4%, 2.8%, and over 3.5% of the gross national product for these respective years; the corresponding figure for the years before World War II would be only a small fraction of one per cent. The investment this nation is making in new ideas and in the development of new and more advanced technologies is growing rapidly.

This investment in new knowledge is already producing goods and services that have a value many times the investment cost. As a consequence, a significant fraction of today's gross national product is a result of the postwar expenditures made for research as here broadly defined. The increase in the gross national product during these postwar years has been even more a result of the creative activities of the engineer and the scientist.

The great expansion that has taken place in engineering research since the end of World War II is a result of several factors:

1. There has been an enormous expansion of knowledge in recent decades.

2. The world of technology is becoming increasingly complex.

3. Society has found that it pays to invest in research.

4. Society can afford to invest in devices and systems that are technologically sophisticated.

New knowledge provides a basis for creating new things that

---

* From data published by the National Science Foundation.

are useful to society. Examples are electronic computers, nuclear power plants, jet engines, radar, and so forth, all of which have been made possible as a result of expansion of knowledge.

New knowledge also provides better ways to do old things. Thus new knowledge of materials, thermodynamics, and fluid mechanics has made it possible to increase the speed of the airplane from the 100 miles per hour of Lindbergh's plane to a speed greater than that of a shell shot from a high velocity gun. New knowledge of the electrical behavior of materials led to the invention and development of the transistor as a practical replacement of the vacuum tube in many applications. Furthermore, the transistor not only provides in many instances a better way to obtain a particular end result, it also makes possible new end results not previously possible, for example, microminiature electronic equipment.

As the knowledge of nature increases, the increments of new knowledge that man gains become progressively more complex. The easier and more obvious things are discovered and used first. The result is that the frontiers of discovery and advanced development are characterized by a level of sophistication that increases with time. The last twenty-five years of rapid expansion of knowledge has thus seen a profound change in the role of research in the engineering profession.

Today, major advances in such important areas as computers, satellites, radar, jet engines, nuclear power, and so forth are not made as a result of chance observations, or as incidental byproducts of other work, or by tinkering evenings and weekends in a basement shop. Rather, significant advances in engineering are now gained as a result of carefully planned and intensive research effort in its broadest sense. As a result, research in engineering has in recent years become an activity of major significance in its own right. This is in contrast with the situation of twenty-five or more years ago, when most engineering research was satellite to and often incidental to more conventional and less creative engineering work.

The growing complexity of the world in which the engineer operates can be illustrated by a few examples. The nuclear power plant is more sophisticated than the old-fashioned steam plant, the giant electronic computer is in a different class from a hand computer or a slide rule. The transistor employs principles that are more difficult to understand and to apply than does the vacuum tube that it is rapidly replacing. The creation of the supersonic airplane involved more sophisticated mental activity than the creation of the slow-speed plane, and an intercontinental ballistic missile is far more complex than a big gun.

Our society is characterized by an intensive use of scientific and technological developments and devices. This is responsible for its high productivity and consequent high standard of living. In such an environment things that are useful have a high value. Hence, a development or device that adds only a small percentage to this usefulness is applied to such a large base that in absolute terms the value of the increment is great.

Our society can thus afford rapid and highly reliable air transportation because the ability to travel fast and safely on a dependable schedule has a large economic value. We can afford a telephone system in which every office and almost every home in the entire United States can be dialed directly because the ability to do this improves the effectiveness in which our civilization functions, and hence contributes significantly to its productivity.

In contrast, it would have contributed very little to the standard of living of the early Modoc Indian of California to have been able to make a five-hour airplane trip to visit the Iroquois tribe in New York. Neither would it have had much economic value for him to have been able to talk by telephone to someone in the Iroquois tribe, even without direct dialing.

The value to an advanced society of creative work that expands its intellectual and economic frontiers is so great that to such a society as a whole the effort expended in research is a dividend-paying investment rather than an expense. A clear realization of this fact has existed only in recent years. For generations this country operated in the belief that while research was nice, it was a luxury that nourished the soul rather than the body. The view was strongly held that the body benefited only from highly practical work in which the potentially valuable results were close at hand and easily visible. The experience of World War II changed this concept. The efforts of the engineers and scientists introduced radar, rockets, proximity fuses, new and better airplanes, the ballistic missile, new electronic devices such as electronic computers, pulse communications systems, and finally and ultimately, the atomic bomb. The contribution that such devices made to winning the war and saving lives was so great and so obvious that it became apparent that in the years before the war this nation had been under-investing in creative work, not only from the point of view of military security, but also for the good of our entire industrial economy.

The resulting reaction has been for the government to provide increasing funds in the postwar years for support of research by the scientist and the engineer—research in both the narrow and the broad sense. Concurrently, industry has greatly expanded its own expenditures for research; the number of industry dollars devoted to research more than doubled between 1953–54 and 1960–61. In this connection the late Sumner Slichter, a noted economist, has said: "The discovery that an enormous amount of research can be carried out for profit is surely one of the most revolutionary discoveries of this century."

The reason for the government involvement in research is that the social value of the results of research is in most cases far greater than the private value. This is because the value of a particular research activity to our society as a whole is usually far greater than the private gain that can accrue to any one individual or any one corporation. Under the circumstances, there are many research activities that in relation to their costs are profitable for society to underwrite, whereas the same investment could not be justified on the basis of the financial return to an individual or a private gain to a corporation. Involved in this is also the fact that as our society, the government, spends money for research, the opportunity for profitable private investment in research increases.

The fact that our society is affluent enables it to use the results of research. An intercontinental ballistic missile with hydrogen warhead would have been very useful to the Crusaders, but even had they known enough to make such a device, the total resources of all Europe in the Middle Ages would not have been sufficient to produce it and still support the people. Today we have intercontinental ballistic missiles and butter, too, and also pie, and likewise strawberry shortcake in January.

Again, the money that a secretary receives for one hour of work will pay for a transcontinental telephone call. A secretary, or almost anyone else for that matter, can accordingly afford to make transcontinental telephone calls if only for family chit-chat. Still again, the fact that a round trip between the Hawaiian Islands and the mainland takes only ten hours and costs $200 makes possible a one- or two-week vacation in Hawaii for almost everyone who really wants one. The jet airplane and our telephone system are the results of vast creative engineering efforts that have over the years cost our country billions of dollars. However, because of our high income level we can afford to make such extensive use of these fruits of research that the actual cost to the individual who makes use of them is quite within his means.

This is not true in the underdeveloped and newly emerging nations of this earth. They can make only limited use of the results of research, even when they make no contribution to the costs of the research and are given heavy subsidies to help pay for its use. The need for research, and the ability to pay for its results, increases exponentially with affluence.

The young man who wishes to participate in the exciting world of engineering research will require formal training that preferably extends to the doctor's degree. The combination of inspiration and perspiration characteristic of Edison, Bell, and others is no longer enough. The technological world today is simply too complex for untutored genius, however great, to make many significant contributions.

The bachelor's degree in engineering is no longer adequate to provide even a reasonable beginning. A four-year bachelor's degree program includes only about one year of work in a particular area of engineering. The rest of the time is devoted to obtaining the necessary background in mathematics, chemistry, physics, related fields of engineering, and some general education in the social sciences and humanities. The bachelor's degree accordingly represents training in general engineering with a mild specialization.

A master's degree provides an additional year of study, all of which can be directly applicable to a particular area of specialization. The master's degree thus greatly increases the technical competence in the chosen field, and is essential for every bright engineer who wishes to follow a career that emphasizes the more technical aspects of engineering. Without the knowledge represented by a master's degree, an engineer does not have the technical tools with which to come to grips with many of the new and more interesting engineering activities of today. Yet, while the master's degree can serve as a preparation for research, it places severe responsibilities for further self-education upon its holder if he is to be fully effective in doing creative work in engineering.

The doctor's degree provides technical depth and breadth substantially beyond the master's degree, and in addition, through the thesis research under the supervision of a faculty member, gives the student some organized training in carrying on creative work. The Ph.D. degree today symbolizes training for research and is rapidly becoming regarded as the *sine qua non* for the young person who has ambitions to be a leader in engineering research.

Graduate study today stresses fundamental knowledge that will be of continuing value to the engineer. It de-emphasizes the "how to do it" aspect of engineering, such as design procedures, current engineering practices, detailed properties of existing apparatus and equipment, etc., all of which a bright man can readily learn on the job as he needs these particular facts. On the other hand, a thorough grounding in the mechanics, dynamics, circuitry, science of materials, mathematics, statistics, and physics that are applicable to one's particular area of engineering interest, represent the kind of knowledge that can be gained in a graduate program and can be of continuing value throughout a lifetime. Again, familiarity with computers and how to use them is something that will be valuable to an engineer for his entire career, even though the technology of computers and the details of computer programming will change over the years. Likewise, a little contact during graduate years with such topics as business accounting, industrial organization, and similar courses, as offered in graduate schools of business and in some industrial engineering curricula, will do no harm and may ultimately prove very valuable to those who develop an interest in administration as their careers advance.

It is possible through such individual study as the reading of books and reports, attending organized lecture series, and so forth, to acquire the equivalent of an advanced degree, but this is a very hard path to follow and requires rigid self-discipline. While such study can successfully bridge the gap that exists today between a master's degree and the competence represented by a doctor's degree, it is becoming increasingly difficult for an individual with only a bachelor's degree to make himself into a competent research worker in engineering by any reasonable effort at individual study.

The young person contemplating a career in engineering research must also be prepared to carry on a continuing lifelong program of individual study. This is true even for the man with a doctor's degree. Knowledge becomes obsolete and the very rapid rate at which new knowledge is being gained today makes the rate of obsolescence of old knowledge especially high. Most men who received their Ph.D. in electrical engineering in the late 1940's are today working with transistors, or lasers, or microwave ferrites, or something else that had not yet even been thought of at the time they received the highest level of training that a college then had to offer them. However, this does not mean that their education was wasted. Quite the contrary. The extensive training represented by a properly planned doctoral program provides a foundation that makes it possible readily to acquire new knowledge of a sophisticated character. In contrast, the man with only a bachelor's degree training does not have a sufficient background to be able to acquire a real understanding of these new developments with any reasonable amount of study.

In response to the needs and opportunities of today, many engineers go on for graduate work, and the number who do is steadily increasing. At present more than 20% of all engineers who obtain the bachelor's degree will sooner or later complete graduate work for the master's degree. Of those engineers who graduated five years ago, aproximately 4% will obtain the doctor's degree. It is anticipated that of those who will graduate in 1970, at least 40% and probably more will carry their formal studies to the master's level, and that something over 10% will obtain the doctor's degree.

This is a great change from the situation that existed in the early 1920's when I graduated from college. At that time the advice to the young engineer was to go out and get practical experience as quickly as possible after graduation. Those who wanted to get the best possible preparation for a career as a teacher of engineering, or for research, were given half-hearted encouragement to work for a master's degree. Only a rare non-conformist carried his studies further, with the result that a doctor's degree in engineering was then an oddity.

For example, MIT's total contribution of Ph.D.'s in electrical engineering to the U.S. economy during the six-year period 1919–1925 consisted of only one Ph.D., namely the one earned by the writer of this chapter. Today MIT awards some twenty-five such degrees at each June commencement. Similarly, Stanford University, from its opening in 1891 until the beginning of World War II, had trained a total of exactly eighteen men to the doctorate level in engineering; in contrast, the June, 1963, commencement program listed ninety doctor's degrees in engineering awarded by Stanford in a single year. These changes are typical of what has happened throughout the country and are indicative of the transformation that has taken place in engineering since the beginning of World War II.

The student who has had a hard financial struggle to obtain a bachelor's degree may be appalled at the thought of more years of schoolwork, even though the advantages of graduate training are apparent. He has perhaps received all the help it is reasonable to expect his parents to provide, he may be contemplating marriage, and with his bachelor's degree he can earn around $7,000 a year as a starting salary. Under such circumstances, does it make sense to go on for graduate work?

The answer is an emphatic *yes*, provided the individual is qualified to do graduate work successfully, and to benefit from it. Moreover, graduate work in engineering, at least to the master's degree level, is today within the financial possibility of every graduating senior qualified for undertaking advanced study, because many sources of financial assistance are available to students qualified for graduate work in engineering.

Research, as here defined to include all creative work of a technological character, is carried on in many places and in many ways. There are great industrial, government, and non-profit laboratories in the country which concentrate almost exclusively in such work. There are in addition literally thousands of small companies that carry on creative work of high order. These small companies are of considerable significance in the total national scene because many of them are specialists in some particular area, and as such compete with the larger companies on even and often superior terms. Engineering research is also often carried on in association with the operations of manufacturing plants, particularly when the product being manufactured relates to some of the newer technologies.

Research activities involving engineers are widely distributed throughout the United States. They are to be found north, east, south, and west; in large cities, in small towns, in heavily industrialized areas, and in thinly populated regions.

There is a growing tendency, however, for the more sophisticated intellectual activities to concentrate in centers. These commonly have as their nucleus a great university with a strong graduate program. Such universities as Stanford, MIT, California Institute of Technology, and so forth, are increasingly becoming centers for creative industry. This is because in research there is a strong emphasis on intellectual activity, and the most desirable location is therefore a center of brains, such as the region around a strong university. Industries in such a location find that if they exploit the situation properly, they are generally more successful in their creative work than competitors located where there is less local intellectual stimulation.

In other cases, industrial research centers have been built up in the absence of a university, and have now become large enough to be self-sustaining in terms of intellectual attractiveness. In some instances, as for example in missile testing, the location of the creative activities has been dictated by considerations relating to the nature of the work being performed. In cases where centers of creative work have developed in the absence of local educational opportunities at graduate level, there is a tendency to bring the university to the work through the establishment of branch campuses, or the development of graduate programs in local educational institutions that had previously devoted their principal attention to education at the undergraduate level.

There is also a tendency for creative work to build up around the suburbs of large cities rather than in the centers of the city. This provides the opportunity for pleasant living conditions, and at the same time avoids the commuter life.

There is a shortage of engineers with the qualifications required for performing research; that is, men who combine good ability with graduate training. University campuses swarm each year with recruiters looking for such men. The want-ad sections of Sunday papers in industrialized metropolitan areas are filled with job opportunities requiring creative talents. Accordingly, the young person who has something to offer his employer in terms of ability and graduate training finds that his problem is to decide which opportunity to accept. He can generally choose the field of specialization in which he would like to start, the geographical area of the country where he would like to live, and in many cases even the particular employer for whom he would like to work.

While the discussion up to this point has been in the context of a position in industry, the young person who combines qualifications in research with an interest in teaching others will do well to consider the possibility of an academic career as a member of a faculty in a university that offers graduate and undergraduate work in engineering. The qualifications required for success in such a career are somewhat narrower and more exacting than for success in industry; they depend more upon intellectual qualities and an interest and ability in communicating ideas to others, and less upon other personal characteristics. A Ph.D. degree is now almost essential if one is to capitalize fully on the opportunities and satisfactions that are available in an academic career.

The career of a college professor in a good university is one that contains many satisfactions. There is the opportunity to contribute to the development of young people, while enjoying a degree of personal freedom in one's professional activities, including research, that is seldom possible in industry. Although the financial expectations of a successful college professor are usually less than the same man would find in an industrial career, the difference is not overwhelming; in these days embarking on an academic career does not imply taking a vow of poverty.

An attractive feature of an engineering career that begins with research is that the well-qualified young person has the opportunity to make significant contributions relatively early in his career. In the newer fields of engineering, the ability to do important work does not depend upon accumulation of years of experience and upon judgment gained through maturity. The young man with good training for research can make important contributions very early in his career because he is working in areas where there is no extensive backlog of experience involving related situations and judgments. In a short time, the alert and capable young man can catch up with about all that is known in a new field, and can therefore quickly hold his own with others.

Things were not always this way. Before World War II the young engineer, irrespective of his training, usually started out in field work, or shoveling ore in a mine, or doing routine drawing in a drafting room, all to gain practical experience. In such work he was not likely to make much direct use of his college training. From such a start the young engineer, if he had the talent, worked his way up to become a great bridge designer, or an industrial executive, an inventor, or even President of the United States.

Herbert Hoover's first job after graduation from Stanford as a mining engineer was as a laborer in a gold mine near Grass Valley, California. From this start he went on to a notable career first in engineering and then in public service. No one has better phrased the personal satisfaction that can come to an individual from creative work in engineering than Mr. Hoover,* when he said of engineers and engineering:

> It is a great profession. There is the fascination of watching a figment of the imagination emerge through the aid of science to a plan on paper. Then it moves to realization in stone or metal or energy. Then it brings jobs and homes to men. Then it elevates the standards of living and adds to the comforts of life. That is the engineer's high privilege.
>
> The great liability of the engineer compared to men of other professions is that his works are out in the open where all can see them. His acts, step by step, are in hard substance. He cannot bury his mistakes in the grave like the doctors. He cannot argue them into thin air or blame the judge like the lawyers. He cannot, like the architects, cover his failures with trees and vines. He cannot, like the politicians, screen his shortcomings by blaming his opponents and hope that the people will forget. The engineer simply cannot deny that he did it. If his works do not work, he is damned.
>
> Unlike the doctor his is not a life among the weak. Unlike the soldier, destruction is not his purpose. Unlike the lawyer, quarrels are not his daily bread. To the engineer falls the job of clothing the bare bones of science with life, comfort, and hope. No doubt as years go by people forget which engineer did it, even if they ever knew. Or some politician puts his name on it. Or they credit it to some promoter who used other people's money with which to finance it. But the engineer himself looks back at the unending stream of goodness which flows from his successes with satisfac-

* From *The Memoirs of Herbert Hoover—Years of Adventure, 1874–1920* (New York: The Macmillan Company, 1951), pp. 132–134. Used by permission.

tions that few professions may know. And the verdict of his
fellow professionals is all the accolade he wants.

The engineer performs many public functions from which he
gets only philosophical satisfactions. Most people do not know
it, but he is an economic and social force. Every time he discovers
a new application of science, thereby creating a new industry, providing new jobs, adding to the standards of living, he also disturbs
everything that is. New laws and regulations have to be made
and new sorts of wickedness curbed. He is also the person who
really corrects monopolies and redistributes national wealth.

4 Industrial Engineering

BY ANDREW S. SCHULTZ, JR.
DEAN OF THE COLLEGE OF ENGINEERING
Cornell University

ANDREW S. SCHULTZ, JR.

Born: 1913, Harrisburg, Pennsylvania

Phillips Academy, Andover, Massachusetts
Cornell University: B.S. in Engineering, 1936; Ph.D., 1941

U.S. Army: 1941–46 (Lt. Col. U.S. Army Reserve until 1953)

Cornell University:
  Instructor and graduate student, 1937–41
  Assistant Professor, Associate Professor, Professor, 1946–
  Head, Department of Industrial Engineering and Administration, College of Engineering, 1951–64
  Dean, College of Engineering

Johns Hopkins University, Operations Research Office: Operations Analyst, 1953

New Jersey Bell Telephone Company, Plant Department, 1936–37
Western Electric Company, Engineering Research Center, Full-time Consultant, 1960
Logistics Management Institute, Washington: Vice President and Director of Research, 1962–63

J UST recently a young engineering student who had decided to begin his career in industrial engineering confessed to me that his main fear was that he would end up on his first job working alone in an office pushing a slide rule all day. He asked me what he should expect to experience in industrial engineering. In answer to him I attempted to run down quickly the types of activities in which a number of industrial engineers with whom I had recently come in contact were engaged. They went something like this.

One young industrial engineer was employed by an industrial manufacturing firm and worked in a large factory. When I last saw him he was standing in the middle of the plant, talking to a time-study man who was observing and recording the time required to perform certain work operations. Evidently the problem my friend faced was to make modification of work assignments and methods so that the product flowing from one assembly line meshed into the demands of another. If successful, he could save the company considerable money by eliminating the need for intermediate handling, storage space, and inventory.

The second was employed in a consulting engineering firm and was occupied on a problem concerned with traffic measurement in a city. The objective of the study was to obtain information that would facilitate a better decision as to the type of bridge or tunnel to construct. He was busy directing a crew making traffic observations and obtaining information about traffic flows and then later had to spend a good deal of time developing the mathematical representation of this data.

Another was involved in the design of a complex control system which made use of electrical circuits, various types of electronic computing and data processing equipment, and input devices at work stations throughout the factory. The purpose was to provide a system which could report when a job was complete, the number of completed units, and the work station, so that time and cost data could be computed and recorded and succeeding operations scheduled. The computer function was not merely to record such data but to indicate, based on other work in process and schedules received, what the next operation was, where it was to be performed, and what the expected time required to perform it was. On this basis, with a minimum of movement and delay, the work of the factory was to be controlled.

Another young industrial engineer spent most of his time in his office working on one specific problem. He was performing detailed statistical analyses of the distribution and sales processes of the firm, and was attempting to provide a sounder basis for decisions by the company's marketing managers with regard to advertising, sales, and promotional effort. His ultimate objective was to forecast market demands with greater accuracy. To do this he was utilizing complex statistical relationships which could be handled conveniently and successfully only by using a large digital computer.

Still another example is provided by a recent industrial engineering graduate who is employed as a manufacturing engineer in an automotive parts plant. His major responsibility, when I talked to him, was in the tooling of a manufacturing unit to produce certain bearings. He was much concerned with selection of equipment, with detailed design of tooling and fixtures, with quality control, and problems of tolerances, gauges, and measurements. He would have further responsibility for the continuing improvement of efficiency and quality of the process when his plan was put into operation.

Obviously industrial engineering is not just "pushing a slide rule," or even punching computer buttons. All engineering involves working with science and theory, ideas and origination, data and information, equipment and materials, and people.

It is clear from the examples given that the industrial engineer is management's engineer and that the products of his efforts, more than those of any other engineer, affect the management function. Broadly defined, the industrial engineer, by bringing together men, machines, materials, and information, is concerned with achieving an effective operating function. The process of creating and defining such an operating entity is called design. The entity designed is frequently called a system, since it is composed of many related elements which interact with each other.

The American Institute of Industrial Engineers has defined the industrial engineering function as follows: "Industrial engineering is concerned with the design, improvement, and installation of integrated systems of men, materials, and equipment. It draws upon specialized knowledge and skill in the mathematical, physical, and social sciences together with the principles and methods of engineering analysis and design, to specify, predict, and evaluate the results to be obtained from such systems."

This definition, of course, attempts to define not only the broad engineering function to which I have already alluded but also those aspects peculiar to industrial engineering. An automotive assembly line, a distribution warehouse, an automated freight terminal, a management control system, an airlines computer-based reservation system, a sales data processing system, all would fall equally well within this definition. In fact, industrial engineers are currently engaged in all of these areas, studying, analyzing, designing, or improving such systems.

The breadth and variety of problems and situations faced in industrial engineering are indicated further by such terms as production engineering, operations research, management engineering, administrative engineering, value engineering, quality control, automation, human engineering, manufacturing engineering, systems engineering, and many others that are used to describe functions performed by modern industrial engineers.

Industrial engineering began in the latter part of the nineteenth century. Frederick W. Taylor, a young mechanical engineer, had come to realize during his experience as a workman that many of his fellow workers produced but a fraction of the work they were capable of turning out; and, at the same time, the bosses evidently did not know what a proper day's work should be. When Taylor was made a foreman, he began a lifetime's work devoted to development of solutions to this problem.

An example of Taylor's efforts better to understand work, and how it should be performed, is provided by his experiments in the development of high-speed steel. He found that machinists, when assigned the job of turning railroad car wheels, were using different speeds, different cutting tool shapes, cutting tool positions, and tool feeds. As a result, both the time to do the job and the life of the tool between sharpenings varied considerably. He undertook, over many months, a series of well-designed experiments which exhaustively investigated the effects of these and other variables; and from these experiments he developed high-speed cutting steels which enabled American industry, over succeeding decades, to turn out vastly more production than otherwise might have been possible. He also developed the necessary knowledge to provide a basis for specifying the speed of the rotation of the work piece, shape of the cutting tool, and rate of advance of the cutting tool, all of which resulted in maximum economic output. Thus he could predict how much time was required to complete a specific machining job, if it was performed according to his specifications.

Besides specifying in detail the most effective way of performing a job, Taylor was equally painstaking in defining management's duties and in developing procedures which resulted in the acceptance and execution of what he regarded as management's responsibilities.

Taylor became world famous and was regarded as the creator of a new science—that of management. Other men, such as Towne, Barth, and Gilbreth, of *Cheaper by the Dozen* fame, also contributed to these developments and from their activities developed the movement termed "scientific management." The methods and ideas of these men were spread throughout industry, but unfortunately many who followed were unable or unwilling to do the thorough investigative and experimental work which Taylor's methods required, and some so-called "scientific" management consultants or engineers perverted Taylor's work to exploit labor. For a period of time such activity had a bad name and it took several decades for reputable consulting firms to live down the reputation of less scrupulous organizations.

Nevertheless, the problems of industrial management had been exposed by the scientific management movement, and rather clearly defined techniques, used in dealing with these problems, had been evolved. They included time study, wage incentive determination, job evaluation, engineering economy, cost accounting, and many others.

These methods largely had to do with manufacturing and were based on experience in mechanical manufacture, the category of most industrial activity in this particular period of industrial engineering development. It was natural, therefore, that most formal industrial teaching was a part of mechanical engineering and was especially concerned with its problems. The methods of instruction were generally of a very practical sort, largely derived from experience. Extensive use was made of graphs, exhaustive check lists, and "principles" for general rules and good practice. Experimental methods in most cases were rudimentary, and the engineer lacked the organized body of theory, along with its supporting science and precise techniques, that he needed in dealing with the problems he met in designing manufacturing systems. Thus in arriving at a plant layout, or location of machinery and equipment within a manufacturing facility, he would use templates or three-dimensional models in a cut-and-try procedure. Once an apparently acceptable layout was conceived, various forms of graphical analysis were used to consider the results. The methods clearly were qualitative, lacking the rigor and precision associated with quantitative or mathematical analysis.

However, during the period 1935–1950, perhaps accelerated by the national needs associated with World War II, a number of significant scientific and engineering achievements directly bearing on the field of industrial engineering occurred. One of these was the development of methods of statistical analysis through research in topics of probability and statistics, with resultant application to industrial problems. During World War II developments in both mathematical statistics and applied mathematics were accelerated. The Navy as well as the Army supported research directed toward providing more powerful methods of dealing with complex experimental or operational problems such as sampling inspection, non-destructive test methods, and other means of controlling the quality of the tremendous quantities of munitions being procured.

Concurrently, there was a recognition of the contributions possible from an activity termed operations research or operations analysis. For example, a problem faced by the Allies early in the war was to make effective use of the new patrol aircraft available to search out enemy surface ships and submarines. Engineers and scientists familiar with probability theory, and accustomed to the methods of physical research, attacked the problem. They gathered necessary data concerning the speed of the aircraft, their ranges, and the area to be patrolled. Mathematical relationships which expressed the probability of seeing a surface ship and other factors in the problem were developed. These were solved and tactics for search were based upon them. The tactics were found to be successful as measured by an increased number of sightings and also by predicted results in terms of enemy ships.

From this general activity of operations research, as applied to military operations, many applications to industrial and governmental activities have developed. At the same time, new theoretical concepts have been explored. As an example, a body of applied mathematical techniques known as search theory has evolved, resulting in the availability of a theoretically sound basis for directing limited efforts so as to locate such things as lost aircraft, ore bodies, or similar objects of search. The important result of all these earlier activities, however, was the realization that a systematic study of the type of complex operation found in modern industry, using modern research methods, could be most profitable to an organization.

A major beneficiary of these and many similar developments was the industrial engineer, who was thus provided with a new underlying body of mathematics and science, new abilities, new opportunities, and new tools. Since these abilities and techniques could be applied usefully in many areas other than manufacturing, his interests broadened as well. For example, they have been usefully applied in transportation, oil distribution, airline operation, marketing, and many other areas. Among the new tools, the great power of the automatic, electronic digital computer made it possible to work with mathematical relationships that could not otherwise be solved, as well as to use the computer itself as a model for complex system relationships and thus provide an experimental tool.

As already mentioned, the nature of the mathematics which the industrial engineer uses is relatively new and is different from that on which primary emphasis is placed by other engineers. Probability and statistics are of prime importance to him, as is linear algebra. The types of experiments he conducts to obtain design data are also different. An engineer's responsibility includes not only the design and specification of the system but also the prediction of its performance under variable conditions. In the case of many other engineering designs such as structures, mechanisms, and electrical or electronic circuits physical models can be constructed for this purpose. Laboratory experiments or "breadboarded" circuits can be used to test new ideas and designs to see if they work.

The industrial engineer seldom can experiment in a real environment in this physical sense. For example, he cannot reproduce a thousand-man factory just to try out a new idea. As a result, he must resort to some form of abstraction or model to demonstrate and validate his system designs. For this the computer is of the utmost importance, and the modern industrial engineer relies upon the computer in the same fashion that other engineers rely upon measuring instruments, slide rules, and other mechanical devices.

The net effect of these various developments in the underlying sciences, in methods of operational analysis, and in digital computation was the movement of industrial engineering out of mechanical engineering, the creation of separate curricula with different emphases in mathematics and other topics, and the application of these methods and knowledge developed to a broader range of problems than mechanical manufacture.

I have previously given an impression of the breadth of activity in industrial engineering. The following cases are indicative of the sort of knowledge and approaches that are required of an industrial engineer.

The first has to do with the process of automation. A particular electronic component used in considerable volume in the missile industry was manufactured by a series of successive operations in a variety of sizes. The resultant product, while satisfactory for normal commercial use, was inadequate for the purpose for which it was intended. A quick study indicated that both the cost and the operational reliability were unfavorably affected by the human operations. Rapid investigation of available equipment and manufacturing techniques indicated that the process might be carried out automatically.

On the basis of this initial study, the development of a process was authorized, funds were appropriated, and a project leader designated. He obtained assignment of a team of engineers, and, since it was clear that special equipment had to be designed for some of the operations, several of the engineers began to explore this possibility. When the designing appeared feasible, a preliminary or trial development of the process on an experimental, small-scale basis was planned. Once each proposed step in the process was accomplished, a complete manufacturing line was constructed and initial production tried. During this time the process was debugged and methods of automatic control, involving the use of a computer as part of the production line, were developed. The size characteristics and electrical characteristics of each unit were measured and recorded in the electronic memory of the computer. These measurements were then averaged for successive units and compared with the desired values of the specification. When they departed by a statistically significant amount from the standards set by the specification, the computer computed the required adjustments of the process, and this information was automatically provided. Some adjustments were made automatically. Others were printed out by an automatic typewriter and made by the man operating the process.

On the basis of the trial installation, it was possible to design additional lines that provided the volume of high-reliability parts that were required. The engineer in charge of the project had to recognize and define the crucial steps in the problem. He had to obtain the assistance of the necessary specialized engineers involved, to conceive the over-all solution, then to convince various responsible engineers and managers of the method's worth and of its savings. At all times he had to deal with the problem of equipment and people involved, and he also had to follow through on the project from its inception to its fulfillment.

Another engineer was faced with the problem of assisting the sales manager or marketing manager of a corporation in the introduction of modern electronic data-processing and computing equipment into the firm. The problem began with an investigation of what systems were already being used and a decision that a much improved method of statistical analysis was necessary to determine exactly what types of information would be most helpful in the marketing operation. This involved a good deal of mathematical and statistical work using data accumulated over the years and some rather elaborate computer analysis of this data. From this, a basis for the design of an integrated data-processing system was obtained that would provide not only the essential financial information to allow for order filling, shipment, and billing of customers for goods received but also factual information to enable the company to obtain maximum return in the deployment of selling, advertising, and merchandising activities throughout its marketing areas. The final outgrowth was a system designed to communicate in a matter of minutes information that formerly required weeks to process, beginning at the point of taking the order, through the sales order recording system, to the point of manufacture and shipment. Once installed, major changes in the personnel and organization of both the marketing and the production control functions of the firm resulted as the full impact of the new communication system was felt.

From these examples it can be seen that the industrial engineer may work in the engineering department, he may be involved in manufacturing, in production control, in cost control, in plant design, in problems of quality control, or be involved in sales and distribution activities. Obviously this varied area of opportunity leads to a broad range of opportunity for advancement, and to-day many industrial engineers are found in general management, most frequently obtaining the position of plant manager or director of manufacturing after having held the position of supervisor of the industrial engineering activity. The engineer who is forced to approach his design problem in the broad operational context must consider not only the physical aspects of the problem but also the complex economic criteria, as well as the personnel of the organization. This is evidently the best training for management, since the judgment that the engineer must exercise is similar to that required of the manager.

The practicing industrial engineer, while he must also have a good education in modern industrial engineering, will find certain additional characteristics of help. He should have a congenial personality and enjoy working with people, since people will be a major concern to him. He must possess those qualities of tact, persuasion, and sensitivity to others which are essential in persuading managers to study and adopt complex ideas. At the same time he must also be analytical and able and motivated to study so that he can keep pace with new techniques as they are developed. Perhaps most important, he must possess initiative, adaptability, and the desire to do a good job.

The successful industrial engineer is constantly seeking better ways of achieving economic gains for society—the basis of its strength and well-being. He has a constant, driving desire to do things well and to convince others that this is the way things should be done. In the last analysis, it is this wish to achieve maximum effectiveness that enables him to attack the challenging problems that complex operating systems provide. These characteristics provide an excellent foundation from which the industrial engineer can approach the towering problems of the modern world—problems of industrially underdeveloped areas, of the control of our environment, of better distribution of our products, and of the more effective use of human resources.

5 *Chemical*
Engineering

BY GEORGE E. HOLBROOK

VICE PRESIDENT
E. I. duPont de Nemours & Co., Inc.

GEORGE E. HOLBROOK

Born: 1909, St. Louis, Missouri

University of Michigan:
B.S. in Chemical Engineering, 1931
M.S. in Chemical Engineering, 1932
Ph.D. in Chemical Engineering, 1933

E. I. du Pont de Nemours & Company:
Organic Chemicals Department:
Chemical Engineer, 1933
Assistant Director, Jackson Laboratory, 1943
Assistant Director, Technical Division, 1949
Assistant General Manager, 1955
Development Department: Assistant Director, 1951–54
Elastomer Chemicals Department: General Manager, 1957
Vice President, 1958–

National Production Authority
Deputy Director, later Director, Chemical Division, 1952

Member: American Institute of Chemical Engineers Director, 1950–52,
1954–56; President, 1958; Treasurer, 1962
American Chemical Society
Americal Physical Society
Society of Chemical Industry
Franklin Institute
American Association for Advancement of Science
Visiting Committee, Department of Chemical Engineering, Carnegie
Institute of Technology
Chemical Society (London)
Institution of Chemical Engineers (London)
Phi Lambda Upsilon
Tau Beta Pi
Sigma Xi
Phi Kappa Phi
Phi Eta Sigma

Trustee: University of Delaware Research Foundation
Director: E. I. du Pont de Nemours & Company, 1958–
University of Michigan Development Council, 1962–
Engineers Joint Council
Manufacturing Chemists' Association

O F ALL the sciences, none penetrates so deeply into the structure of the human environment as chemistry. Chemical processes and principles are basic to life in all its phases. They appear in such familiar activities as building a fire, raising crops, preparing food, relieving illness, and in producing virtually every commodity of the commerce which has marked civilization's ascent from the cave.

For the better part of six thousand years of recorded history, however, men established their living conditions very much on the products of nature as they found them. They built with stone, wood or clay; they wove cloth from cotton, wool or silk; they made shoes, harnesses, and saddles from animal skins.

Gradually, they began to make changes in the products of nature to satisfy their desire for a better way of life. They won metals such as copper and iron from natural ores, made concrete, paper, and gunpowder. In the course of the past half century or so, this innovating process has been most radically accelerated. The natural directions of chemical reaction have been replaced or augmented by a series of induced reactions which rearrange the limited raw materials of nature into endless patterns of usefulness. Now we build with metal alloys, glass, hundreds of plastics; weave nylon and other synthetic fibers; manufacture countless dyes and pharmaceuticals; make fuels, rubber, automobiles, airplanes, and spacecraft largely from synthetic materials.

The process through which these opportunities have been seized and the benefits enlisted to the service of mankind is now recognized as chemical engineering, one of the newest of the professions. Some chemical techniques originated in antiquity, but their practice owed more to art than to science or engineering. The skills involved were rather like those of a cook, relying on intuition, experience and individual discretion. Not until the nineteenth century did an orderly discipline develop, based on scientific methods, and not until well into the present century did the chemical engineer take his place in the forefront of the new and creative technology.

Chemical engineering has an impact on practically everything that we do, and it is in every facet of the environment in which we live—the food we eat, the clothes we wear, the homes in which we live. In the modern household, for example, the roof, walls, plumbing, electrical system, interior furnishings, and almost everything in the house results from materials that have been through an evolutionary process of selection and development to provide properties best suited for an intended purpose. In each instance, other professions and other professional people have made major contributions toward the ultimate products, but in virtually all cases chemical engineering was involved in the blending of these contributions into the final process or product.

The modern automobile is another example of the chemical engineer's sphere of interest and influence. The operation of the motor involves the conversion of chemical energy into mechanical energy—a fundamental chemical engineering process. The performance of tires has been improved by the development of new and better cords, rubber, and rubber chemicals. The electrical system is more reliable because of better batteries, improved insulation, better ceramics and metals. Difficult lubrication problems have been solved by changes in the chemical composition of the lubricants. High performance gasoline results from products and processes to which chemical engineers have contributed. Even modern air conditioning involves chemical engineering processes and stems from chemical engineering achievements in refrigeration systems and synthetic refrigerants.

The scope of chemical engineering may prove to be the broadest of any profession. Applicability of this field of knowledge to everyday living is both intimate and diverse, ranging from the artist's studio to the mills and factories of heavy industry. When an artist paints a picture, his own contribution is largely an aesthetic one, but the things used to produce the interesting result he has in mind—the paints, canvas, paper, brushes, and so on —represent, in varying degrees, contributions of chemical engineering. The paint is better because it has had chemical engineering attention, contributing shades, physical properties and uniformity otherwise unattainable. The papers of the water colorist have been selected and prepared for the particular use intended, and again their strength, durability, and surface characteristics are properties that have been built in, to some extent, by the application of chemical engineering.

Far from the materials used by artists are the materials in the plants of heavy industry, yet here, too, the materials used and the processes employed reveal the touch and talent of the chemical engineers.

Even in the field of medicine, the impact of chemical engineering is appreciable and becoming increasingly important. The manufacture of drugs and medicines involves chemical engineering, and chemical engineers are needed to develop processes and production equipment. In recent years, however, even more spectacular developments have demonstrated the essential kinship and interdependence of science, chemical engineering, and medicine.

Many who have benefited from open heart surgery, for example, may justifiably feel an appreciation for chemical engineering contributions. The new plastic heart valves that are employed are made in most cases of "Teflon," TFE-fluoro carbon resin, a plastic discovered only recently, with physical properties making it compatible with the physiology of the human body. Though the discovery of "Teflon" was a significant scientific observation, the commercial development that converted it from a laboratory curiosity to a product broadly available for many uses was a chemical engineering achievement. The selection of this specific material and the design of the valves also represent chemical engineering functions, whether actually performed by scientists, physicians, or engineers. External circulation of blood during operations and the maintenance of controlled temperature and oxygen content are all chemical engineering processes. Some of the fascinating work being done in the medical field these days is through research teams that bring together the talents of physicians, physicists, chemists, and engineers. The chemical engineer, particularly because of his basic understanding of all these sciences, plus the general appreciation of engineering values, can be expected to make significant future contributions.

Moving a little farther afield, the whole nuclear energy program was largely expedited by contributions made by chemical engineers in blending all the sciences and talents necessary to produce this outstanding achievement in such a short time. From the mining of uranium through the development of the weapon, and now, under peacetime conditions, the development of sources of nuclear power, all of these were fertile fields for the participation of chemical engineers. This was an especially challenging experience under the stress and pressures of a wartime environment because seldom was there time for what we like to think of as normal steps in the development process. Under the prevailing circumstances, the chemical engineer frequently had to design without really adequate data, and on occasion had to build and operate full-scale facilities without benefit of pilot-plant operation—all this in a field of new and often hazardous technology. The application, however, of sound scientific and engineering principles, the wise extension of past experience, no matter how limited, the prudent use of intuition, and, I suppose, a certain amount of good luck, combined to spell success with safety in this tremendous undertaking.

In the space program, where the proper selection of materials of construction requiring lightweight strength and unusual thermal properties is so important, the chemical engineer is heavily involved, either in the selection from existing materials or in the design and development of special materials to meet the unusual environmental conditions. He is also engaged in the development, manufacture, and use of propellants. As a matter of fact, the success of the space program, while fundamentally dependent upon contributions of basic science over the years, is really a development operation where engineers and chemical engineers in particular are bringing existing knowledge together and using it in the most effective manner for solving the particular problems of the program.

The engineer's work today is a milestone in history, for it constitutes recognition of the fact that science is the beginning, rather than the end, of man's effort to improve his environment. While we appreciate the pure science that enlarges our knowledge and horizons, we have learned that its most meaningful function is fulfilled only when it can be translated into terms of utility for all members of society.

In the classical sense, of course, the aim of "science" is knowledge and the aim of "engineering" is the solution of material problems. My own feeling is that little is gained by an arbitrary separation of the two, for they are interrelated. I consider it more constructive to recognize that science and engineering are two parts of a single effort, each contributing its own strengths and insights, and not infrequently venturing unchallenged into each other's territory.

Accordingly, I like to think of chemical engineering as the process of blending chemistry, mathematics, physics, engineering, and economics into the solution of problems for the purpose of achieving useful results. Thus the chemical engineer finds his place in bringing to fruition the science that once was content to satisfy man's curiosity.

Of what manner of man is this chemical engineer? Well, in addition to his professional knowledge, he must know how to cooperate effectively with others. Some professions are characterized best by lonely vigil or by impersonal analysis—not so in this profession. In a technical age the creation of the goods and materials to fulfill human needs is almost by definition a complex team effort, requiring many contributions, many phases, and many considerations, synthesized into an acceptable whole. For example, when engaged in research the chemical engineer seeks and receives scientific information and data from chemists and physicists which he analyzes in terms of process, product or equipment development. Working then through skilled craftsmen

—electricians, pipe-fitters, machinists, and the like—he builds experimental equipment that is operated to establish the data for full-scale design. Cooperating with design specialists, some of whom are also chemical engineers, he participates in the plans for plant construction. Later, he collaborates with construction people in plant start-up and further process improvement. Whatever his role, he is a link in a chain of people and events that must be coordinated for maximum effectiveness, timeliness, and economy.

The chemical engineer is not only a cooperator but a communicator. Though the substance of his effort may involve complex data and advanced formulas, the success of his endeavors will depend in large measure on how well he can deal with people. This means how successfully he can explain and persuade, how he can recognize and comprehend the role of others, with an eye always on a result that balances the truly significant factors. The personal qualities that make for satisfying relationships in any activity find full expression in the chemical engineer's life. By no means is it a career for the hermit or the self-centered.

The chemical engineer is an innovator. The guidelines of his activity circumscribe neither his reach nor his grasp. To a degree that is unfortunately underrated, technical advances rest only in part on original discovery—the requirement is for innovation in detail as well as in outline.

In the development of nylon, for example, the problem was to transform a sticky mass at the bottom of a test tube into the textile fiber of extraordinary strength, elasticity, and aesthetic properties that imaginative research indicated could be achieved. Many people were enlisted in the project, many of them chemical engineers. It was necessary to invent a workable process for manufacturing the liquid polymer, to devise pumps that would handle the polymer under pressure, to invent a workable and economic spinning process, to develop commercial processes for new dyes and finishes. Ingenuity, inventiveness, and creativity were evident in every chapter of the dramatic story; and each contribution, large and small, was essential to the success of the whole.

Since nylon's introduction in 1939, the work of the chemical engineers in regard to it has continued in even greater intensity, extending the usefulness of the material, improving its economics, vastly improving its quality.

The nylon drama has its counterparts in many companies and industries, and chemical engineers are found in a wide range of modern industrial developments. A large number of those who enter industry gravitate to the chemical industry itself, an extremely large and dynamic segment of the economy. Many also enter closely related fields such as the petroleum, rubber, glass, paper, and pharmaceutical industries.

In these industries, chemical engineers find need for their services in virtually every phase of operation—in research and development work, design, construction, and in supervisory posts in manufacturing and sales. Many attain highly responsible executive positions. In fact, it would take some searching to find one of these companies that did not have one or more chemical engineers in the highest corporate echelons.

The chemical business is complex in terms of technology, and as a result there are many challenging opportunities in research and development. The function of chemical engineering here is usually one of developing the lowest cost process for manufacturing a product of specified quality. This means assembling process equipment so that experiments can be conducted to study the effect of such variables as pressure, temperature, and concentration on product quality and yield. Appropriate materials of construction have to be selected to minimize corrosion and avoid product contamination. Frequently, novel equipment has to be conceived, constructed, and tested to solve particular problems. Careful consideration must be given to safety factors and to air and stream pollution.

This is an intensely satisfying and rewarding function for the man who likes to experiment and to collaborate with scientists and other engineers toward innovation and improvement. A part of one's satisfaction is that the results of one's efforts are obvious and immediate and they beckon to even further improvements. One of the major contributions that the chemical engineer makes during this stage is in the field of economic analysis and appraisal.

The ability to develop rigorously, to appreciate fully, and to interpret effectively the economic aspects of a project is not only a trademark of the profession but a yardstick of one's value to an organization.

Some chemical engineers become specialists in design work, which broadly involves the analysis of experimental data and pilot-plant operations in order to specify the equipment necessary for large-scale commercial operations. Others may be involved in the actual construction of the plant facilities. When the plant is ready to produce, some may assist in its start-up and in the usual "de-bugging" operations; they may also assist subsequently in supervising the going operation to meet production schedules and quality and cost targets. Sometimes the same engineer plays multiple roles in the evolution from research through production.

Because chemical engineers have a lively appreciation of properties of materials, along with the economic features of a business and a thorough understanding of value in use, many of them at some stage of their careers find interest in the sales field, particularly in selling chemicals whose utility is based upon inherent properties. Their experience fits them admirably for this kind of technical service to customers, which is an essential feature of the chemical market.

Not all the opportunities for chemical engineers lie in large organizations or in strictly chemical producing companies. Many industries are of a character that requires relatively few people with backgrounds and aptitudes in technical matters. Although the technically trained people so employed may be relatively few in terms of the total number of employees in the organization, they are essential, and the broad balance of the chemical engineer's capabilities renders him particularly useful. I don't want to convey the idea that he can do anything or everything, but I do believe that there are few things he can't help to improve.

Besides the fields I have mentioned, there is the consulting practice, in which experienced chemical engineers as individuals or in partnership or corporate groups offer their professional services to industrial clients, usually on a project-by-project basis.

Finally, there is the rewarding field of teaching, to which we owe so much in terms of the propagation and continued vitalization of the profession.

One point should now be made crystal clear. Science and technology are advancing at such a rapid pace that unless one makes a determined, continuing effort to keep informed on technical progress, his knowledge will become inadequate and his usefulness diminished. This makes life exhilarating and satisfying, or frustrating and disappointing, depending on how one responds to this stimulus.

It has become increasingly apparent that without an understanding of the technological process and its high potential, one now lives in a dream world wholly apart from reality. It is therefore my conviction that a chemical engineering education will prove satisfying and rewarding even to one who does not subsequently make a lifelong career of direct professional practice.

Such an education provides the deep satisfaction that stems from an understanding of the world in which we live. In such an education one encounters the logic and order that are inherent in the study of scientific and engineering principles. They induce the state of mental discipline that forms a base for clear and constructive thinking. In our time when life is so complicated by the rapidity of change, and when the ends are so often confused with the means, logic and order and discipline are of value to anyone.

For those who do elect to follow the profession, the outlook as I see it is one of great promise and fascination. Impressive as our gains have been, the limitless possibilities of future development taunt even the most uninhibited imagination. There are challenges and excitement ahead in chemical engineering for those who choose to share in its practice.

6 *Structural Engineering*

BY NATHAN M. NEWMARK

DEPARTMENT OF CIVIL ENGINEERING
University of Illinois

NATHAN M. NEWMARK

Born: 1910, Plainfield, New Jersey

Rutgers University: B.S., 1930; Sc.D., 1955
University of Illinois: M.S., 1932; Ph.D., 1934

University of Illinois, Department of Civil Engineering:
  Research Assistant to Associate, 1930–37
  Research Assistant Professor, 1937–1943
  Research Professor, 1943–; Head of Department, 1956–

American Society for Engineering Education
  Vincent Bendix Award for Engineering Research, 1961
American Society of Civil Engineers
  Engineering Mechanics Division, Executive Committee, 1950–1953
  Committee on Research, 1961–1964; Chairman, 1962–1963
  J. James R. Croes Medal, 1945
  Moisseiff Award, 1950
  Norman Medal, 1958
  Ernest E. Howard Award, 1958
  Theodore von Karman Medal, 1962
American Society of Mechanical Engineers
  Applied Mechanics Division, 1950–1954; Fellow, 1963–
American Concrete Institute
  Board of Direction, 1949–1952
  Building Code Committee, 1936–
  Wason Medal, 1950
American Physical Society
Earthquake Engineering Research Institute
Seismological Society of America
International Association for Bridge and Structural Engineering
National Society of Professional Engineers
Other technical societies and committees

Fellow: American Academy of Arts and Sciences
Member: Scientific Advisory Board, USAF, 1945–1949
  Commerce Technical Advisory Board, U.S. Department of Commerce
Consultant: National Defense Research Committee, Division 2, 1940–1946
  Office of Field Service, OSRD, 1944–1945
  Awarded President's Certificate of Merit, 1948
Numerous engineering projects

Author: Numerous technical papers, monographs, and books
Editor: Series of texts in Civil Engineering and Engineering Mechanics

STRUCTURAL engineering has the oldest scientific and mathematical base of any of the branches of engineering, yet its dependence on analysis and calculation is only slightly over 100 years old. The major structures of antiquity, such as the pyramids of Egypt or the Colosseum at Rome, were designed by a combination of experience and intuitive reasoning dependent upon trial and error and learning from failures. The majestic temples of the Greeks were built without any real concepts of the magnitude of stress due to loading or of the strength of materials, in any rigorous mathematical sense. Even at the time of Galileo, although he had a rational concept of the stress distribution in a beam, there were serious quantitative errors in the methods then used in design or proportioning of structures. In a book first published in 1915 on the structural design of warships, William Hovgaard pointed out that naval vessels were designed by experience, essentially by comparing conventionally computed index stresses with those corresponding to a previously successful design, and that one could extrapolate only a little further than one's previous experience. In 1932, in his book, *Continuous Frames of Reinforced Concrete*, Hardy Cross, one of the greatest teachers of structural engineering in recent times, made a similar comment.

It is a significant fact that such a statement is no longer so completely true. Modern techniques of analysis and computation have made it possible to extrapolate much further beyond the range of experience, enabling us to predict the behavior of structures and to develop methods of proportioning them, both for configurations and materials beyond the bounds and limitations of the past. Nevertheless, structural engineering still involves much more than a mastery of analytical techniques. It requires judgment, tempered by experience, and willingness to learn from failures.

Structural engineering is the largest of the groups making up the entire field of civil engineering. Structural engineers often work with architects in the planning of major projects, and it is the responsibility of the engineer to select the materials and the configurations that can carry out successfully the architectural design concept. Structural engineers also work with contractors and constructors to carry out the intent of the design and to develop the methods of building the structure so that it will be of appropriate strength and form when it is completed.

On their own, structural engineers design bridges, buildings, towers, tunnels, dams, pavements for highways and air fields, missile bases, and launching platforms for space vehicles. They may often be involved in the design of the space vehicles themselves, space platforms, structures designed to be built on the moon or on the planets, and the great antennas that have been constructed to search for various types of radiation from space, or to send and receive signals from spacecraft. Structural engineers are often involved either directly or as consultants in the design of major or unusual pieces of equipment, machinery, or facilities such as large nuclear reactors, marine platforms, oil drilling rigs, the special equipment designed for drilling a very deep hole in the earth's crust for the Mohole project, the huge particle accelerators developed by the physicist to study the basic properties of matter, and the supports for the 200-inch mirror of the Mt. Palomar observatory.

To do these things properly the structural engineer must have a sound background in mathematics, mechanics, and classical physics, as well as a knowledge of chemistry and thermodynamics. He must have a good basic knowledge of the properties of materials, including such phenomena as fatigue, brittle fracture, plastic behavior, and effects of dynamic loads. And he must have enough knowledge of numerical analysis to be able to use effectively the high-speed digital computers that have virtually revolutionized the field of engineering in the past decade.

But these abilities are not enough. Many structures are of such size and cost, and their possible failure involves such hazard, that their designer has a responsibility far more critical than has the designer of a radio, or a refrigerator, or even an automobile or other vehicle, because any of these lesser creations can be proof-tested and checked out in detail before being put into general service. The structural engineer cannot possibly proof-test or check his completed work, and, in the design criteria for a structure, he must depend in considerable part on probabilities and statistics.

In most cases the details of environmental conditions involve uncertainties, and there is also necessarily a lack of knowledge about the future loadings to which a structure will be subjected because of new developments or changed conditions; yet these factors, and other elements of uncertainty, must be taken into account in the planning, for example, of a major highway bridge that will have to stay in service for as much as fifty years. In the planning of any structure, the engineer must remember that its loading can be affected by wind, wave action, earthquake motion, and, in recent years, blast forces from nuclear detonations or ground motions arising from such detonations. He must also consider the effect of rolling vehicles on a bridge or the effects of heavy loads that may occupy any particular areas in a building.

In the past, the structural engineer has often been forced to be more conservative than other engineers in providing for uncertainties; but in the years ahead, because of economic demands, because of the need to hold down costs, he will be called on to be less conservative. In doing so, however, he must become correspondingly more precise in his evaluation of environmental conditions, in his knowledge of the properties of the materials that he uses, and in his calculations of the stresses and deformations induced in the structure.

The reader should not get the impression that structural engineering will become an exact science, or that a lesser degree of conservatism can take into account all the uncertainties that we are almost sure to have with us. It will continue to be necessary for the structural engineer to apply judgment, common sense, ingenuity, and a sense of proportion. He must have these qualities, or must develop them by experience, to supplement his scientific and mathematical background.

Despite the need of judgment and experience in structural engineering, the great importance of the mathematical and scientific aspects of the field can enable a young man to play a significant role, and even make major contributions, while he acquires the experience and judgment that he needs to become a designer. I remember the deep personal satisfaction I derived, while still a graduate student not yet 21 at the University of Illinois, when I had the privilege of working under the direction of the late Harald M. Westergaard, the great expert in structural mechanics and the theory of elasticity. Without experience or engineering maturity, I was able to make investigations of the behavior of the intake towers at Hoover Dam in an earthquake and make studies of the deformation of the canyon walls due to the pressure on the walls caused by the reaction of the arched elements of the dam.

Although structural engineers have the reputation of being traditionally very conservative, which is probably a good thing, many of us have to some extent overcome this tendency because of experience in laboratory research, or in field tests, where we have had deliberately to design structures or elements that would fail under prescribed conditions, carrying out the tests in order to learn more about the strength and the behavior of the structure. This has been most important in connection with my work in the design of nuclear field test programs where it was fully as essential to know when failure would occur as it was, under other conditions, to avoid such failure. As a matter of fact, in most of my life as an engineering research worker and teacher I have had to plan tests in the laboratory where it was essential to know when and how the laboratory test structure would fail, so that I could properly plan the tests and design the equipment for them.

Because of the experience gained from research we have been able to learn how better to design structures; but while experience is a great teacher, not all experiences contribute to one's education. Many experienced engineers have unfortunately not been able to learn from their experience anything about the strength or the behavior of the structures they have designed. We probably learn more from our failures than from our successes, but it is much more pleasant to have the failures planned in advance. This we can often do in research.

There is still a great deal to be learned in structural engineering from experience. Through the years there have been major failures of structures, both in the process of construction and after they have been completed and put into service. The failure of the Quebec Bridge in 1907 led to major changes in the methods of design of compression members in trusses or in buildings. The failure of the Tacoma Narrows Bridge in 1940 emphasized the importance of aerodynamics even in the design of a fixed structure such as a bridge. The failure of the Texas Tower off the coast of New England indicated the need for more information regarding the action of waves and currents on underwater foundations. The failure of the Malpasset Dam in France in 1959 underlined the importance of more precise knowledge of foundation conditions in the abutments of an arch dam. And the catastrophe produced by massive landslides in the reservoir of the Vaiont Dam in Italy showed that the strength of a structure might have no direct relationship to the successful performance, or survival, of an entire facility or system in which the structure plays only a part. There is now and will always be need for men with ability and imagination to carry further the field of structural engineering and to learn more about those aspects which are not yet sufficiently well understood.

Among the accomplishments of the structural engineer, the most striking, and perhaps the most widely known, involve such monumental structures as the great modern skyscrapers or long-span bridges. The design of a structure like the Empire State Building takes courage and imagination to make it capable of resisting the wind forces, temperature differentials, and other influences that would be of only minor importance on a small building. It becomes a problem of even greater difficulty to design a multistory building in regions where earthquakes occur.

I had the good fortune to be associated with the design of the

Latino-Americana Tower in Mexico City, a forty-three-story office building that was completed less than ten years ago. Not only is the building in a region subjected to major earthquakes, but it is supported on probably the poorest subsoil material of any skyscraper in the world. The development of the unusual foundation system for this structure was made by one of our former students at the University of Illinois, Dr. Leonardo Zeevaert, probably the outstanding foundation engineer in Mexico City. Together with another of my students, Dr. Emilio Rosenblueth, one of the ablest structural engineers in Mexico, we developed a concept for the earthquake resistant design of a tower that, unexpectedly, was put to severe test during the earthquake of 1957 in Mexico City, when the building was virtually completed.

In order to study the behavior of the building we had instruments mounted at several elevations to record motions of the floor during wind or earthquake tremors. These were fully operative during the earthquake, which turned out to be of about the intensity for which the design had been made. The displacements recorded by the instruments were almost precisely those that we had computed as the most probable displacements for the maximum expected earthquake in the vicinity. The building suffered no damage from that earthquake, or from the subsequent one of 1962, and in 1958 it was given a special award by the American Institute of Steel Construction for its successful performance.

Much of my work in recent years has been associated with dynamic problems of a different sort, involving the design of structures, and equipment contained within structures, to resist the shock and blast forces arising from nuclear detonations. Many of these problems involved velocities and accelerations of orders of magnitude beyond any previous experience, and required a great deal of theoretical work, calculations, experiments, and even field tests under simulated actual conditions. Although I have little doubt that the structures I have designed would behave in the ways predicted by my analyses should they be subjected to an actual nuclear blast, I must confess that I would not derive the kind of satisfaction from such proof that I did from the successful performance of the Latino-Americana Tower!

One of the most striking structures in appearance to either an engineer or a layman is a long-span suspension bridge. The longest span in the world, when it is completed, will be that of the Verrazano Narrows Bridge in New York designed by the eminent Othmar H. Ammann, a Swiss engineer who came to the United States in 1904, who was responsible also for the design of the George Washington Bridge in New York, completed in 1931 when he was Chief Engineer of the Port of New York Authority.

Dr. Ammann was associated as a consultant with the design of the Golden Gate Bridge in San Francisco, completed in 1937, which now has the longest span in the world. I had the pleasure to serve with him and with Mr. Frank Masters, another eminent bridge engineer, on a board of consultants appointed some years ago to make a study of the possibility of operating rapid transit rail traffic on a proposed lower deck of the Golden Gate Bridge. We spent nearly six months on this work, during which time I learned a great deal from my colleagues, whose average age at the time was 80 years. In the course of this study I had occasion to make fatigue tests of wires cut from the cable near one of the anchorage shoes, to determine if any deterioration had occurred and to investigate whether increased stresses might cause difficulties in fatigue. Although it seemed fairly clear to me that the cables and the towers were amply strong to take the increased loads, there were problems associated with the fatigue strength and the flexibility of the stiffening truss which would have been unusually expensive to solve, and which caused the board finally to recommend that it was not feasible to add a deck to carry rail traffic under the roadway.

Structural engineering is in a rapidly developing and changing era, as are other branches of engineering. The pace of technological development is so fast, and the absorption of new scientific discoveries into technology proceeds so rapidly, that the future practice of structural engineering is sure to involve concepts and ideas that will be exciting and challenging. The use of new materials promises not only great economy and the possibility of building unusual structures, but presents new problems as well.

It may be possible, within the next few decades, to develop concrete with a high tensile strength, probably needing much less or certainly much different types of reinforcement. We shall see greater uses of high-strength steels and other metals, and perhaps a greatly increased use of structural plastics. Structures will be designed for unusual environments completely beyond our present experience. Space platforms and structures on the planets or on the moon will involve radically new design procedures to deal with temperature ranges and other conditions of unusual character, some of which we have as yet no means of knowing fully. One of my students is now writing a doctoral dissertation concerned with building structures to protect personnel against the environment on the moon. The unusual conditions of large temperature ranges, lack of atmosphere, and low gravity introduce novel and interesting problems, including the possibility of metals becoming virtually welded together at smooth surfaces of contact from only moderate pressures.

One of the most fascinating prospects in engineering is the increased use of high-speed digital computers. Already the availability of computers has made major changes in methods of analysis. The computation of stresses and deflections in structures can now be done on an almost routine basis with problem-oriented compilers for computer programs that require only a description of the structure, the location of its joints, the size of its members, and the description of the results desired for given loadings. Ten years ago the calculation of the modes of vibration of a structure was a relatively complex problem, requiring approximate calculations generally expected to give reasonably accurate results for only a few of the possible modes of vibration. Now by essentially standardized computer programs, it is almost as simple to compute at one time *all* the mode shapes and vibration frequencies as it is to compute the fundamental mode shape and frequency. The structural engineer in a few years will have so many new analytical tools at his disposal that he can afford to spend a great deal less time on the calculation of stresses and deflections, which heretofore have been the most tedious parts of his work. He will then be able to spend more time on the selection of the proper shape and configuration of the structure and on the selection of the materials of which it is to be made.

But there is an even greater revolution already in the offing, namely the use of computers in the actual design process. Methods still have to be developed for this, and the structural engineering students of the next few years will have the challenging problems of helping with these developments. Although there has been a tendency to move from procedures in which the man does all the work to procedures in which the machine does all the work, it appears likely that the best and most useful employment of the computers will be in an interaction between man and the computing machine in which there will be a continual feedback of information. In other words, as judgments are made by the engineer, he can query the machine from time to time and ask for the solution of the intermediate problems that are involved in the various steps that he makes, so that he can continually apply his knowledge and intuition during the design process, learning by experience, so to speak, as he proceeds.

We have already seen instances of going beyond even these predictions in simple cases where the machine has taken over the development of a design, and afterward the preparation of drawings and the preparation of the bill of material for the construction, on an entirely automatic basis.

In view of the complications in the loading and environment, the unavoidable uncertainties in the properties of the materials actually used, the changes that occur with time, and the problems involved in the construction of a structure, it is easy to understand that there may be no single best design. In common with other fields of engineering design, any of a wide range of designs of a structure may be satisfactory, and no one may be definitely most economical or lightest or safest. In treating the many facets of the problem, in trying to arrive at an optimum solution or a range of suitable solutions, the high-speed computer can prove extremely useful.

I could not complete this description of the profession of structural engineering without at least a brief discussion of education and research. I have had the good fortune not only to be involved in extremely interesting structural problems throughout my career, but I have been engaged also in the education of students and in the search for new knowledge through research. I would find it difficult to say which of these activities is the most interesting. Yet, if I had to choose only one aspect, I think I would prefer to keep the contact with education and research. It has been a source of great satisfaction to me to work closely with students and to see their development afterward. I have traveled all over the world and almost everywhere I go I can find a former student, if not of mine then of one of my colleagues at the University of Illinois. The large number of excellent graduate students in civil engineering, and especially in structural engineering, that we have had at Illinois has made my work interesting and exciting. I am sure that many young engineers will find a most rewarding career in college teaching and in the research that goes along with it; or, if they prefer, in the practice of structural engineering as a profession; or, in many cases in a combined career.

When I was graduated from college I had ambitions to design great bridges and to leave monuments to endure for years afterward. To do this, I felt that I needed more specialized knowledge and training and therefore came to Illinois to do graduate work under Hardy Cross and Harald Westergaard. Because of the Depression, after I had completed my graduate work, the kind of position I wanted was not available. But in the meantime I had become attracted to teaching and research and I have never regretted it. I have had contacts with major engineering works over the country and in various parts of the world. Although I have not had the sole responsibility for any major structure, I feel that the results of my research have had an influence on many structures of various kinds. But above all I take pride in the accomplishments and achievements of the many students that I have had. I know that they have found their careers interesting and rewarding, and I am sure that young men who select structural engineering as a career will find, in the next few decades, this choice to be equally interesting and rewarding.

7 _Civil Engineering_

BY ROLF ELIASSEN

DEPARTMENT OF CIVIL ENGINEERING

Stanford University

AND

PARTNER, METCALF & EDDY, ENGINEERS

ROLF ELIASSEN

Born: 1911, Brooklyn, New York

Massachusetts Institute of Technology: B.S., 1932; M.S., 1933; Sc.D., 1935

Illinois Institute of Technology: Assistant Professor, 1939–40
New York University, College of Engineering:
  Associate Professor, 1940–42
  Professor of Civil Engineering, 1946–49
Massachusetts Institute of Technology:
  Professor of Sanitary Engineering, 1949–60
  Acting Head, Department of Civil Engineering, 1960–61
Stanford University, School of Engineering:
  Professor of Civil Engineering, 1961–
Corps of Engineers, U.S. Army: Captain to Major, 1942–46
J. N. Chester Engineers, Pittsburgh, 1935
The Dorr Company, Engineers, Chicago and Los Angeles, 1936–39
Metcalf & Eddy, Engineers, Palo Alto, Partner, 1961–

Fellow: American Society of Civil Engineers
  American Academy of Sanitary Engineers
Member: American Water Works Association
  California Water Pollution Control Association
  Society of American Military Engineers
  California Society of Professional Engineers
  Consulting Engineers Association of California

Consultant:
  Board of Water Supply, City of New York, and many other municipalities and industries
  Department of Water Resources, State of California
  U.S. Atomic Energy Commission
  U.S. Public Health Service
  U.S. Department of the Interior
  The White House, Office of Science and Technology
  World Health Organization
  International Atomic Energy Agency

Author: Technical articles and chapters in books on the treatment of water, sewage, and industrial and radioactive wastes.

CIVIL ENGINEERING is of concern to all human beings because the facilities and systems that civil engineers design, construct, and operate have as their common objective the fulfillment of human needs. If you are interested in helping people to live in a better environment, and if mathematics and science are among your talents, civil engineering may be the field that has the greatest attraction for you.

Civil engineering is a difficult profession to describe in a few words. Dean L. E. Grinter of the University of Florida has defined the duties of the profession as: "The research, development, planning, design, and responsibility for construction of large facilities and systems in the public interest." The breadth of civil engineering is indicated by the technical divisions with which members of the American Society of Civil Engineers may affiliate: Aero-Space Transport, City Planning, Construction, Engineering Mechanics, Highways, Hydraulics, Irrigation and Drainage, Pipelines, Power, Sanitary Engineering, Soil Mechanics and Foundations, Structures, Surveying and Mapping, and Waterways and Harbors. There is great satisfaction in participating in a field where there is such breadth and variety.

In my travels around the world on civil engineering assignments, particularly in the underdeveloped countries, I have seen that the engineering discipline of most vital interest and concern to these nations is civil engineering. They have great needs for highways, railroads, airports, and harbor facilities for trade and for the development of their natural resources. The health of the people depends upon pure water and adequate sewage disposal, which can be obtained only by planned development of their

water resources. In the construction of buildings and other facilities, there is need for the development and utilization of native
materials, resources, and skills.

I recall a conversation with a public health official of India
when we were both on assignments to the World Health Organization in Geneva. The discussion turned to his opinions on the threat
of Communism in his country. He said: "Communism breeds on
hunger and disease. Give me *one pure water supply* in each of the
half million small villages of my country and you will do more to
combat Communism than by any other means. My people will
not be sick with intestinal diseases; hundreds of thousands will
not die prematurely each year; the farmers will be free of debilitat-
ing sicknesses that now hinder them from tilling their fields; and
much hunger and famine will be prevented."

Civil engineering is the oldest of the engineering professions.
It started as military engineering hundreds of years ago. Even up
to the present, military engineering work for the U.S. Army is performed by the U.S. Corps of Engineers, which is comprised mainly
of civil engineers.

There are many types of activities and specialties within the
profession and of these structural engineering is the largest. Civil
engineers in this category frequently are associated with architects
in the design of environmental structures such as buildings, public
works, public utilities, and industrial facilities. They must be
skilled in using many types of materials, including concrete,
steel, aluminum, plastics, brick, blocks, and any new material
that may exhibit structural strength and lightness as well as
economy. The structural engineer must be an excellent mathematician and must have a keen analytical mind.

Construction is the largest industry in the U.S.—a total of 85
billion dollars per year. This field taxes the imagination and resourcefulness of the engineer whose responsibilities are to use
men, materials, and machines to create a structure or a system
from a set of blueprints and written specifications. Each situation
presents a new problem to which the same fundamental principles
may be applied, but with widely different applications. An interesting example of this is the assignment given to our firm of

Metcalf & Eddy for the U.S. Air Force in 1950. The project involved the design and supervision of construction of a major bomber base at Thule in northern Greenland. Just listen to these environmental conditions: a harbor open to ocean shipping only three months a year and full of icebergs even then; sub-zero cold with winds of 150 miles per hour during long winters of total darkness; no local labor, no timber, no construction material except water, rock, and gravel; and all structures to be built on ground that is permanently frozen (except when thawed, as by warmth from a building, when it becomes a sea of mud). What an environment for the civil engineer to control!

Our firm, along with the architectural firm of Alfred Hopkins and Associates, was given the engineering assignment by the U.S. Army Engineers in December of 1950; we were told that the air base had to be in operation by October, 1951. As you might well imagine, the survey, design, logistics, housing, and construction problems were enormous and different from anything previously encountered. But the deadline was met by as hardy a crew as ever tackled such an impossible problem—a perfect example of one of the mottoes of the Army Corps of Engineers: "The difficult we do now; the impossible takes a little longer."

For the next ten years our firm worked on the design and supervision of construction in the enlargement of the air base and the Ballistic Missile Early Warning System. Each of the five antennae of this system had dimensions equal to the length and width of a football field, but they had to stand vertically and resist wind, snow, and ice. Other aircraft control and warning stations were designed and built on the icecap itself—huge steel structures supported on the ice by columns with built-in jacks so that the entire installation could be raised above the ever-changing snow surface. It was my privilege to make an inspection trip there one summer. What a thrill to see the Thule Air Base nestled between the glaciers and the sea! A group of us flew to one of the icecap stations from Thule. On the way we lost the power of one engine in a four-engine craft equipped with skis. The pilot reported back to us: "No sweat; the icecap is an airfield 1600 miles long and hundreds of miles wide on which we can land anywhere with our skis." And a wonderful landing he made in an August snow-storm, right on target! Such is the way that men, materials, and equipment were transported to this construction job.

Most structures built by civil engineers are set on soils, rather than rock. Therefore, a thorough understanding of the role of soil as a foundation material is of utmost importance to the civil engineer. Although ideal foundation materials, such as sands, gravels, and hard soils are sought on location surveys, the client frequently wants his buildings, facilities, or highways on land that has a less ideal foundation material. Soil mechanics is a funda-mental approach to knowledge of the behavior and characteristics of the engineering properties of soils, and the foundation engineer, by knowing the science of soil mechanics, can design sub-struc-tures with loadings and foundation conditions for soft clay and other less desirable materials, with full assurance of safety and economy. Soils have such a tremendous range of physical and chemical characteristics that the scientific approach is the only one that will solve the engineering foundation problems, whether they are for highways, railroads, buildings, industrial structures or dams, or for still other hydraulic structures such as pipelines and irrigation canals.

Foundation engineering starts where the soil mechanics engi-neer leaves off. The design and construction of mat foundations, footings, retaining walls, piles, and caissons are usually the re-sponsibility of the foundation engineer. The piledrivers you see operating in many cities with clay and other soils underneath them are placing the piles with proper length and spacing defined by the expert in soil mechanics. His knowledge is translated into experience by the foundation engineer, who specifies how the concrete foundation, with all of its reinforcing steel, will be de-signed to accept the configuration of the structure above.

As I write this in my office in Palo Alto, California, I can look out my window and see the Santa Cruz Mountains only a few miles to the west. Alongside these mountains lies the great San Andreas Fault. Occasionally, large bodies of the mountain slip by each other along this fault line and cause an earthquake in the manner of the one that virtually destroyed San Francisco in

1906. The foundation engineer, in preparing for a building, must assure all of us in California that he knows how to provide for the shock loads and stresses that will be caused by earthquakes. The earth may tremble, but buildings still stand as a tribute to the scientific knowledge and engineering ability of those who have designed the foundations, as well as of the structural engineers who designed the buildings.

Flow of water through the ground is another interest of the specialist in soil mechanics. He and the groundwater geologist combine to study the flow of water through porous media such as earth dams, underground water supplies, and the drainage of saturated lands. Thus, the mechanics of fluids, as well as the mechanics of solids, must be within the comprehension of the civil engineer specializing in this field. Laboratory testing programs of soils become a very important part of foundation engineering because, for one example, the compressibility of soils, particularly clays, must be predictable to a high degree in order that the foundation of a building will not settle under the greatest possible loads predicted for the structure. Loading in three dimensions must be considered, and elaborate testing devices, with electronic instrumentation, are used in laboratories to predict the behavior of soils under loading. Highway designers rely heavily on specialists in soil mechanics to learn the slope at which excavations and fills must be constructed to prevent landslides and excessive erosion, as well as settlement of the pavement.

As you drive along a great superhighway in hilly country, give some thought to the engineering sciences, such as soil mechanics and materials science, that have contributed to making your ride not only comfortable but safe and economical. This highway, as well as all other civil engineering structures you encounter every day, represents a distinct degree of coordination between theory and practice.

Highway engineering is a twelve-billion-dollar-a-year industry. The funds for this construction work come from public bodies, but the planning, design, construction, and maintenance is under the supervision of civil engineers. There is a great future in this field in the United States, since vehicular traffic is doubling every ten years. It is also a relatively untouched area in many of the underdeveloped nations of the world.

Hydraulic engineering, a division of civil engineering, has to do with the planning, design, construction, and operation of structures that are utilized to control water. Fluid mechanics is the basic tool of the hydraulic engineer. This is a highly mathematical subject that seeks to understand by analysis and experimental evidence the behavior of fluids under static and dynamic conditions. Both compressible and non-compressible fluids are considered. Although water is the special concern of the hydraulic engineer, he is tied to all the professions involving fluid motion, and contributes to and benefits from their scientific pursuits.

The hydraulic engineer applies his scientific knowledge of fluid, soil, and solid mechanics to the channelization of streams and rivers for irrigation; drainage; municipal water and sewage systems; the design of harbor facilities, including structures for the prevention of destructive wave action and beach erosion; and the design of dams for hydroelectric power production, municipal, industrial and agricultural water supplies, flood control, navigation, and recreation. Pumping machinery and hydraulic turbines are designed by hydraulic engineers to secure maximum efficiencies and to meet varying needs, from the smallest quantities at very low heads or lifts, to the huge pumps being planned for the movement of water across the Tehachapi Mountains as part of the California Water Plan.

Manpower requirements in the field of water resources management will be great. Solutions to water resource problems are so multi-faceted that an inter-disciplinary approach is needed, extending far beyond what is normally considered as civil engineering, yet remaining under the control of civil engineers. The management team must include men who have specialized in economics, statistics, political science, systems analysis and management. Chemical and industrial engineers will be functional members of the team, with particular emphasis on the needs of industry for water of specific quality and the processes for achieving this quality. Waste water treatment will become an essential phase of industrial processing, as it already is in many industries, in order that water quality may be maintained for downstream users. Many chemical engineering unit operations and processes will need to be developed and employed in water renovation for the future.

Sanitary engineering, the particular phase of water resources in which I am interested, has as its primary objectives the provision of safe and adequate water supplies for municipalities and industries; the collection, treatment and disposal of municipal sewage and industrial waste waters; the control of pollution of the air, land, and water environment; and other areas involving the application of scientific and engineering principles to problems dealing with the health of the public. A broad scientific background is needed for a man in this field, since the principles he must apply include those of mathematics, biology, chemistry, and physics. He must also be an excellent engineer because he is responsible for the design of hydraulic structures in which water and waste waters are collected, transported, and processed. A good background in the social and political sciences is also of great value because he is closely associated with people and politics.

Adopting current U.S. forecasts of population and industrial growth, the urban population by 1980 will be approximately 200 million. Over 150 million people will be dependent upon surface water supplies, many of which will be downstream from other municipalities. With almost 200 million people connected to sewers, all of the waste will be treated; but distances between waste-water discharges and water-supply intakes will become closer, and many new types of pollutants will be introduced. This will create new problems, as it has been predicted that the average use in large river systems will probably be six times what it is today before the end of the century. The most advanced sewage treatment processes will be needed to overcome this.

There is, first, the water renovation process. Renovated water can be an excellent replenisher of depleted groundwater, can serve to create fresh water barriers against the infiltration of sea water, and can prevent the present practices of mining aquifers that have been accumulating water for thousands of years. There is much sanitary engineering work ahead in this field to develop more efficient and economical processes that will assure the removal of all tastes, odors, organic contaminants, bacteria, and viruses.

Air pollution control is one of the great problems facing sanitary engineers in urban areas today. Exhausts from motor vehicles and from industrial plants, smoke from homes and from municipal dumps, and many other sources are contributing to the ever-increasing quantity of pollutants being discharged into the atmosphere. The U.S. Public Health Service has estimated that the economic damage from air pollution in the United States ranges from eight to eleven billion dollars per year. This includes damages to property values, agricultural products, corrosion of materials and structures, extra lighting costs, and reduction in transportation effectiveness on highways and at airports. Of greater significance is the effect on human health. Dramatic incidents have occurred in this country and abroad where people have been killed during severe epidemics of air pollution. The Public Health Service believes that circumstantial evidence may soon show that such serious chronic diseases as asthma, bronchitis, emphysema, and lung cancer are caused or accentuated by polluted atmospheres in urban areas.

City planning is another phase of civil engineering that is attractive to many in the profession. Here the engineer must know something about architecture and landscape design, since he is involved in the coordination of engineering with these two other professions in the comprehensive planning of new communities and the redevelopment of existing cities. A thorough knowledge of law, political science, and social science is also necessary.

Another division of the American Society of Civil Engineers that is of great interest to many young men is air transport. This involves the administration, economics, planning, design, construction, operation, and maintenance of civil and military airports, and requires cooperation with other scientific and engineering professions. Such agencies as the Port of New York Authority employ hundreds of civil engineers in this type of work. Other cities, counties, states, and the federal government employ thousands of civil engineers for the same purpose. As the population explosion continues, and as the desire for rapid means of transportation expands, airport terminal facilities will have to grow. This condition prevails all over the world. As aircraft become heavier, as landing speeds get higher and takeoff distances greater, airport runways must be lengthened and strengthened, and clearance paths must be increased in order to provide the safety and economy necessary for efficient transport operation. Furthermore, the aerospace age also requires much civil engineering in the design of facilities for the testing and launching of rockets and missiles, and in the control of living environment factors such as water supply and waste water disposal in space vehicles. There is no end of work for the civil engineer in this field.

A civil engineer, like a lawyer or a doctor, may practice his profession as an individual, making his services available to clients on a personal basis; or a number of engineers may form a partnership to undertake group practice. There are a thousand firms in this country with employees ranging in number from a few to hundreds. For instance, the author's firm is comprised of nine partners, with approximately 400 employees, many of whom are registered professional engineers.

Consulting firms perform highly varied work in the United States and overseas for commerce, industry, and for governmental agencies at all levels. The staffs of these firms may include civil engineers with specialized education and training in many aspects of the profession, as well as architects, mechanical, electrical, and chemical engineers, scientists, technical writers, draftsmen, cost estimators, construction and specification engineers, and supporting personnel. The services that are available to clients include: investigations, reports, feasibility studies, utility valuations and utility tariff studies, engineering economic analyses, master planning, research and experimental work, site selection and development, and the design, supervision of construction, and operation of civil engineering systems.

As an example of overseas consulting work, two projects (1963) of Metcalf & Eddy may be of interest. We are engaged in a comprehensive study of the water supply, sewerage, and drainage problems of metropolitan Calcutta, where the teeming populations are short of water and where cholera and other intestinal diseases may be carried by water supplies and sewage discharges. The World Health Organization and the United Nations are assisting the local jurisdiction in financing the study that, by the planning, design, and construction of adequate sanitary engineering facilities and systems, is aimed at stopping the transmission of disease and the creation of a healthful environment.

In Rangoon our engineering staff is making a comprehensive analysis of the water supply and distribution system for the city of Rangoon. When I visited there in 1962, I was the guest of one of my former MIT students, who is now City Engineer in charge of water supply for the Rangoon Corporation. He drove me all over the area and showed me some of the problems that must be corrected in order to control the spread of intestinal diseases.

Water in Rangoon is supplied to each of two major distribution areas for a few hours each day. Between these periods of water service the distribution reservoir must be refilled; but when the water is available, individual consumers are permitted to pump from the mains to fill water tanks in buildings. This creates a negative pressure in certain areas and even empties the mains. To add to the problem, service connections are made with rigid galvanized iron pipes to handle a corrosive water. As a result, leakage and breakage of service pipes are prevalent. Sewers are not available in most areas, so septic tanks and drainage systems are utilized, resulting in a highly contaminated groundwater at the level of the empty and leaking distribution mains. Thus, the populace must boil the water before drinking. In a fuel-short economy this becomes an expensive secondary method of water purification. It is obvious why the World Health Organization has as one of the objectives of its global water program the engineering of water systems to furnish water under pressure twenty-four hours a day.

The largest number of civil engineers are engaged on public works projects for various agencies of government, at the city, county, state, and national level. Excellent career opportunities exist in many of these agencies. For instance, in the federal government, civil engineers are employed by the Department of the Interior in the design and operation of the great water re-

source systems of the Bureau of Reclamation, which has designed
some of the greatest dams in the world, such as Hoover Dam on
the Colorado River, Grand Coulee Dam on the Columbia River,
and hundreds of others. The U.S. Geological Survey has many
hydrologists and groundwater specialists among its civil engineering personnel. The Department of Defense employs thousands
of civil engineers for the design of military and civil works.
The Department of Agriculture, through its Soil Conservation
Service, designs or supervises the design of thousands of small
dams on watersheds all over the country. The U.S. Public Health
Service attracts sanitary engineers to its water supply, pollution
control, and environmental sanitation programs. The Department of Commerce has many civil engineers in its Bureau of
Public Roads establishing highway design criteria, conducting
research and development on pavements, and supervising the
activities of federal assistance programs in interstate highway
systems.

State public works agencies employ thousands of civil engineers,
particularly on highway and bridge design. These are the key men
in our great network of highways and freeways. Planning, economics, soil mechanics, geology, materials science, photogram-
metry, computers, mathematical models of traffic simulation,
design, construction, and maintenance are all represented in highway engineering. Other state engineers are concerned with the
control of water resources, stream pollution, and public health.
Municipal and county governments offer the same possibilities
in city engineering and public works departments.

Transportation and utility companies employ civil engineers
in various capacities. Railroads offer interesting careers, starting
with maintenance of way and going up the ladder to construction
responsibility on new bridges, terminals, shortening routes over
mountains by tunnel construction, and improving grades and
alignment for higher speeds. Eventually, the engineer has an
opportunity to get into the operation of the system as train-
master, superintendent of a division, and then into various
managerial positions. The president of the New York Central
System, Alfred E. Perlman, came up this way. After graduating

in civil engineering from MIT in 1923, he obtained experience with various western railroads and in 1936 became chief engineer of the Denver and Rio Grande Western Railroad, where so many civil engineering problems existed on the mountainous routes between Denver and Salt Lake City. Later he became general manager and then executive vice president. His engineering and managerial abilities were recognized by the Board of Directors of the New York Central where he was made president at the age of 52. Many other railroad executives are, or have been, civil engineers.

Utility companies, such as the Pacific Gas & Electric Company in San Francisco, employ large numbers of civil engineers for the construction of dams, hydroelectric power plants, electric power transmission systems, generating stations, and power distribution facilities. Many civil engineers have risen to high positions in the electric power industry because there is always room at the top for a man who knows the details of the system and the many problems which arise in its construction, maintenance, and operation. Students with a talent for management are particularly encouraged to seek employment with the power utilities. The largest municipal utility in the country is the Department of Water and Power of the City of Los Angeles. Its general manager, Samuel G. Nelson, is a civil engineer who graduated from Cornell University in 1926. He advanced up the career ladder from the construction of dams, pipelines, and power generating stations, through the position of chief engineer of water works, to become the top man in 1961.

Producers of construction materials, such as steel mills, cement companies, and gravel and crushed stone plants, require men with a wide variety of backgrounds in civil engineering. The many advances in the knowledge of materials through scientific research have created demands for closer control over the production and use of construction materials to meet the needs of designers of civil engineering projects.

Practically all industries need civil engineers for the design and construction of new factories. Huge industrial complexes, such as those in the chemical, metallurgical, pulp and paper, electrical, machinery, and the space age industries, are designed and built by civil engineers.

Manufacturers of construction equipment present interesting opportunities for civil engineers to exercise ingenuity and resourcefulness. Such items as earth-moving equipment and machinery for mixing, placing, and finishing concrete on highways and in buildings have been greatly changed during the past two decades to accomplish rapidity of construction with greater quality control. Civil engineers employed by manufacturers must know the construction business from practical experience with contractors, must be able to speak their language, and to know their great demands for economy. Since the construction equipment industry in this country serves the whole world, cognizance must be taken of the problems in the underdeveloped nations as well as in this country, in order that the needs of the construction industry may be correlated with local resources of manpower, materials, and availability of repair facilities. We have a long way to go in helping other countries to achieve economy in construction. The civil engineer going overseas must be sympathetic with local conditions, must strive to help the people, and not offend them by emphasizing that our way is the only way.

Engineering schools offer many opportunities for young civil engineers, particularly those interested in research as well as teaching. Colleges are increasing in numbers every year, and civil engineering departments are always looking for good men who have a liking for the teaching of young people and the desire to work at the forefront of technology. Civil engineering education is an ever-changing field, keeping up with modern developments in science and technology, and the staff of university faculties have an admirable opportunity to engage in this type of work.

It is important for the civil engineering teacher to have some contact with the practical phases of civil engineering, just as a professor of medicine must have patients on which to practice and law professors should keep their hands in practical legal work. Thus, the teacher has an opportunity to engage in consulting work of a high order, where his services are made available to industry, government, and to other consulting engineers.

The rewards of the engineering teacher are greatest in terms of human relations. In my own case, I have found that the management of research laboratories, partaking in university activities, the seeking of funds to support staff and students in their graduate work, the daily contact with students from all over the world, and the chance to influence their careers have been great experiences for me. On a recent trip around the world for the International Atomic Energy Agency, I was met by former students at the airports in Beirut, Bombay, Rangoon, Bangkok, Tokyo, and Honolulu. Each one of these had a responsible position in the field of civil engineering in his state or country, and was using some of the material which he learned in our classes to improve the environment of his people. What greater satisfaction can one ask of life than to observe the success of friends such as these?

An area which should be of particular interest to our profession is public service. Civil engineers are well qualified to take part in the political arena since much of their experience is with governmental agencies and many problems of the people are of a civil engineering nature. Many a political battle in the West has been won on the platform of water for arid lands and thirsty cities. That, plus the promise of good government, won the election for George D. Clyde as governor of Utah. He had been the head of many water resource activities in Utah and for the federal government. A long-time member of the American Society of Civil Engineers, he was recently elected an honorary member, the highest award of the Society. John A. Volpe, another distinguished civil engineer and a highly successful contractor, recently served as governor of Massachusetts. An outstanding civil engineer with a high position in the federal government is James K. Carr, Undersecretary of the Department of the Interior, and a man long active in water resource engineering in California and in Washington, D.C. These are only a few examples of the many civil engineers who have been elected or appointed to high offices in government.

The rewards in civil engineering are far greater than can be measured in monetary terms; the civil engineer feels that he has built something of lasting benefit to mankind when his work is finished. At the San Francisco end of the Golden Gate Bridge there is a statue of Joseph B. Strauss. Underneath is a plaque on which he is identified as "The Man Who Built the Bridge," followed by a statement which epitomizes the work of civil engineers: "Here at the Golden Gate is the eternal rainbow that he conceived and set to form, a promise indeed that the race of man shall endure unto the ages."

8 _Aeronautical and Astronautical Engineering_

BY GEORGE S. SCHAIRER

VICE PRESIDENT, RESEARCH AND DEVELOPMENT

The Boeing Company

GEORGE S. SCHAIRER

Born: 1913, Wilkinsburg, Pennsylvania
Swarthmore College: B.S., 1934; Hon. D.Eng., 1958
Massachusetts Institute of Technology: M.S., 1935

Bendix Aviation Corporation, 1935–37
Consolidated Vultee Aircraft Corporation, 1937–39
The Boeing Company:
 Chief Aerodynamicist, 1939–46
 Staff Engineer, Aerodynamics & Power Plant, 1946–51
 Chief of Technical Staff, 1951–56
 Assistant Chief Engineer, 1956–57
 Director of Research, 1957–59
 Vice President, Research & Development, 1959–

Member: USAF, Scientific Advisory Group, 1944–45
 USAF, Scientific Advisory Board, 1954–58
 NACA Committee on Aeronautics, 1946–58
 NACA Committee on Power Plants, 1950–52
 NASA Committee on Aircraft Operating Problems, 1959–60
 Dept. of Defense Panel on Aeronautics, Steering Group, 1955–60
 Operations Evaluation Group, USN, 1960–
 President's Scientific Advisory Committee
 Panel on Scientific & Technical Manpower, 1962–
 American Helicopter Society
 American Astronautical Society
 Sigma Xi
 Sigma Tau
Chairman: NACA Subcommittee on Propellers, 1948–49
Fellow: Hudson Institute, 1962–
Technical Director & Fellow: American Institute of Aeronautics & Astronautics

Institute of Aeronautical Sciences Sylvanus Albert Reed Award, 1949
American Society of Mechanical Engineers Spirit of St. Louis Award, 1959

THE WORD aeronautical denotes vehicles that navigate within the earth's atmosphere (aero–air, nautical–navigate). Astronautical denotes vehicles that navigate in space. Within the engineering profession, we shorten the words aeronautical and astronautical engineer to aerospace engineer. For the remainder of this chapter I will write about aerospace systems and aerospace engineers, both for the sake of brevity and to avoid a tongue twister.

What are these aeronautical and astronautical, or aerospace, systems that the aerospace engineer designs, builds, buys, and operates? In the early days, an aeronautical "system" consisted of little more than an airplane, a funnel to pour gasoline into the tank, the mechanic's tools, and a wind sock at the end of a grass field. Today the word system denotes that we are working on not just an airplane, and not just a rocket, but also the ground support equipment, communications equipment, navigation equipment, and so on.

My first encounters with aviation were in the early 1920's when I saw surplus World War I Jenny's and DH-4's being flown by barnstormers. This led me to an interest in making model airplanes, both flying models and scale models. A great many of today's aerospace engineers started their interest in aviation with the building of model airplanes. Such an initiation into the aerospace business is just as interesting and rewarding today as it was then.

In 1927 the Spirit of St. Louis was designed and built in two months and flown across the Atlantic only one month later by Charles A. Lindbergh. This airplane and this flight, as well as the personality of Lindbergh, captured the imagination of the world and signaled the start of a tremendous boom in aviation. The rapid development of the commercial passenger-carrying transport airplanes and airlines started at this time. Some of the better-remembered airplanes are the Ford Trimotor, the Boeing 247, Douglas DC-3, DC-4, DC-6, DC-7, Lockheed Constellation, Boeing Stratoliner, and Stratocruiser, all of which led to the great airplanes of today.

I was fortunate to participate in the aerodynamic design and development of many of these transport aircraft of yesterday and today. As an aerodynamicist (an engineer who specializes in fluid flow problems), I worked on the detail design of control surfaces of the Stratoliner in 1939. My job was to bring the control forces required of the pilot within his strength capability and to eliminate from these control forces any surprises such as having the rudder suddenly go hard over. My part in the design of the Stratocruiser (1945) involved not only the balancing of the control surfaces but also the choice of the shapes of the wings and flaps, the engine installation, and the aerodynamic design of the propeller. Attention to propeller design was exceedingly important in all the years before the advent of the jet engine, and many aerospace engineers spent long hours in the development and understanding of propellers.

However, as early as 1943, engineers at Boeing were taking an active interest in the possibility of building a jet airliner, but it was not until 1948 that we had the necessary ingredients of an economical jet engine and a working knowledge of sweepback. By this time, though, we could put together an economical and competitive jet commercial passenger-carrying transport airplane, which has come to be known as the 707. My role was to supervise the synthesis of the aerodynamic design. One important design problem was finding a way to put the sweptback wing under the passenger floor and to mount the landing gear from the wing. Prior to this, all large sweptwing airplanes had the wing on top of the body and the landing gear mounted in bicycle fashion on the bottom. The airlines did not like this arrangement and provided the impetus to search for the now standard low-wing and tricycle gear arrangement. Today aerospace engineers are search-

ing in a similar fashion for the fundamental physical relationships of the main components of the supersonic transport.

Some of the earliest aerospace systems were flying boats. Since
large cleared areas for the operation of land planes were scarce
in many parts of the world, and since many air operations were
over water and engine failures were common, there was much
interest in operation from water with flying boats.

In 1919 the NC-4, a large flying boat, was flown across the
Atlantic by the U.S. Navy, and flying boats were used extensively
in World War II. My first acquaintance with flight testing and airplane performance came on the PBY airplane, which first flew in
1936 and is still very common wherever flying boats are needed. I
helped analyze flight tests to determine how the airplane could
be flown to get the maximum possible range. This experience
considerably sharpened my interest in airplanes designed to fly
a very long range and carry a large payload economically, as is
required by intercontinental commercial transports and intercontinental bombers.

Flying boats have gone out of fashion because of the development during World War II of reliable engines and good landing
fields all over the world. All those who worked on the design of
flying boats have substantial nostalgic interest in them because
they were a tremendous challenge to design and partly because
the developmental activities around the water were most interesting in themselves. I spent many interesting days developing flying
boat hull shapes that would not porpoise (a large pitching oscillation on the water). In the case of the 314 Flying Clipper, we
constructed a one-tenth size flying model that demonstrated the
same porpoising characteristics when towed on the water. A
large number of changes were then made on the model to find
a cure. A very simple change of the main step was discovered that,
when applied to the full-scale airplane, completely eliminated the
very dangerous porpoising characteristic. This type of activity is
typical of what makes aerospace engineers dedicated to their
work.

Although man's interest in aviation started with the desire to
emulate the birds, his first practical air navigation device was a

balloon, which has no counterpart in nature. Balloons are not very common today, but they hold great fascination for those few aerospace engineers who are dedicated to working on them. The very high altitude balloons that carry telescopes and instruments to the outer reaches of our atmosphere are very important scientific tools. There was a period during which dirigibles (rigid balloons with motors) were considered the aerospace system with the biggest future. A number of dirigibles were built in Germany, England, and the United States. Tremendous ingenuity went into the development of these dirigibles, and certainly much of our understanding of lightweight structures came from their development. However, dirigibles proved to be slow, cumbersome, and prone to accidents. Only a few of these dirigibles were scrapped; most of them came to an untimely end. I well remember seeing the Shenandoah several hours before it crashed in September, 1925, and the Akron on its last flight before crashing in the Atlantic in 1933.

Much of the evolution of large airplanes came about in the course of developing the military bombers which have gone through a long series. Some of the better-known large bombers are the B-17, B-24, and B-29 of World War II, the B-47 and B-52 sweptwing jet bombers, and the B-58 and B-70 supersonic bombers. These bombers are extremely complicated machines with autopilots, radar and visual bombing systems, electrically controlled gun turrets; and we are fully justified in calling them systems rather than airplanes. Since mistakes were expensive and time consuming and since these large airplanes took a long time to build, it was worthwhile to do a very sophisticated and thorough job of engineering on all phases of these weapons before they flew. The systems engineering applied to these bombers was the training and proving ground for many of the engineering and management procedures used today on complicated military and civilian systems.

Concurrent with this series of bombers was a long sequence of Air Force and Navy fighters and attack bombers. Some of the better known of these were the P-1, P-12, and F-4B fighter biplanes, the P-40, P-38, P-47, P-51, F-4U, F-4F of World War II, and the F-80, F-86, F-100, F-102, F-104, and F-4H jet fighters. These aircraft, being smaller, were cheaper and quicker to build than the big bombers, and hence they explored new power plants, speed regions, and so on, from two to five years ahead of the big bombers. The engineering of these small aircraft gave many opportunities, both pioneering and exploratory, and a good deal of the engineering was done by cut-and-try on the aircraft itself, rather than through the use of models and laboratory techniques as was common in the larger airplanes. Those who were fortunate to work on both types of projects had a wide range of engineering experiences.

Following World War II a number of air defense missiles were designed, tested, and put into service use. Some of the better known of these missiles are the Nike, the Bomarc, the Sidewinder, and the Falcon. The engineering involved was a tremendous challenge since there was no pilot to go along and maintain control.

The flight management of these defense missiles is largely accomplished through the use of radars, radios, and tremendously complicated command and control electronics systems. Thus the aerospace engineer has found himself very deep in the electronic business. He may not always make these radars and radios, but he must understand how they work, what they can do, and be fully up to date on the latest developments in the electronics, navigation, gyroscope, and control businesses.

The development of the atomic bomb brought about a tremendous revolution in aerospace systems. First of all, the bomb was sufficiently light, and so very destructive, that it made sense to develop the B-36 and B-52 long-range intercontinental bombers to carry a small payload over very long distances. The demands of the airplane designer caused the bomb designer to find lighter ways to make bigger bombs so that the bomber could be more effective. Many aerospace engineers participated directly in various phases of the development of the atomic bomb. The author assisted in the design of the stabilizing fins of some of the early bombs. By use of the latest supersonic airplane knowledge, the bombs were made to fall straight and accurately. There was substantial interdisciplinary work done by bomb designers and ballistic missile designers to bring about the intercontinental ballistic missiles. The nuclear physicists who were designing the nuclear weapons worked side by side with the aerospace engineers who designed the missiles.

One of the big revolutions in aerospace systems was the development of large-sized ballistic missiles. Skyrockets and similar small rocket missiles have been used for thousands of years. Small rocket-type missiles were used in large quantities in World War II, but the large long-range ballistic missile was not developed until late in that war. The Germans introduced the V-2 missile that weighed 28,500 pounds and could deliver 2,000 pounds of warhead 200 miles with an accuracy of several miles. Following World War II ballistic missiles were subject to intensive development, and the Atlas, Titan, and Minuteman intercontinental ballistic missiles came into being in this country. They could deliver hydrogen bombs anywhere in the world with great accuracy. The aerospace engineer had to learn how to keep them from getting too hot in the atmosphere, how to make them very light, and how to accomplish split-second timing in their control while maintaining their reliability at a high level. The development of these missiles has been one of the biggest challenges to the aerospace engineer in the last decade. He has found himself digging holes in the ground and studying seismic effects. He has found himself deep in the command and control business, and making use of the most refined knowledge available in the servomechanisms field. Also, engineers working on the Polaris submarine missile system have found themselves involved in submarine design as well as the underwater characteristics of the missile.

The development of large rocket engines and ballistic missiles opened up the possibility of going into space. Most satellites are boosted into earth orbit by modified ballistic missiles, and the challenge of the satellite is to make systems that will operate reliably for very long periods of time in circumstances that are sometimes very hostile. Some of the biggest projects of the 1960's will be the space boosters and space payloads by which space will be explored and military missions accomplished. This challenge of space is tremendously interesting to today's aerospace engineer, and he is thinking about going to the moon, Mars, and Venus. Although it is popular to describe these things as activities of scientists, the actual design, construction, firing, and flying of space missions are accomplished by aerospace engineers.

Probably the most numerous aircraft designed and built by aerospace engineers are the small private aircraft and trainers. For many years these aircraft were biplanes such as the Fleet, Waco F, and Stearman trainers. In 1929, while in high school, I made a scale model of the Fleet trainer. The Fleet was a well-designed airplane, and I became very familiar with it in the course of making the model. I remember looking at certain details of the airplane and wondering how one could possibly do a better job of its design, but in time I was able to think of different designs that might possibly have been better. This was one of my first experiences with a principal task of engineers: to improve a design of any airplane wherever possible. Engineers are dedicated to finding the most economical, the most reliable, the most available, in short, the best way, of doing each new task that comes to hand. This is the source of the fantastic progress that has been made from the original Wright brothers' airplane to the modern airliners and military missiles and aircraft of today.

In 1932 I took flight training in a Waco F and subsequently flew a number of other light aircraft. This is a very worthwhile experience for an aerospace engineer, one that I highly recommend. For an example, while I was taking graduate work in aeronautical engineering at MIT, one of my professors pointed out the large cross-coupling effects of flight controls, particularly the rudder. The rudder can be used to make an airplane roll as well as yaw and its untimely use can cause spins. I well remember renting a light airplane and, with plenty of altitude, applying full rudder to learn whether the professor was right. He was—and the resulting motion was quite spectacular.

Many of the very earliest attempts at flight were made with lifting propeller devices that would be called helicopters today. The early work of Berliner, Bréguet, Cierva, Sikorsky, and others has grown into the modern helicopters. These aircraft place a high reliance on the structural integrity of many rotating parts, with the result that helicopter engineers have become specialists at structural integrity and vibrations; the safety of modern helicopters is a tribute to these engineers.

The helicopter has found a large market in uses that require hovering, vertical takeoffs, vertical landings at zero air speed, and some rearward and sidewise flight capability. Little attention has been paid to high forward speeds. The challenge for the helicopter engineer today includes all the problems of the past plus the desire to fly long ranges economically and at high speeds. In attempting to do this the helicopter will be competing against the direct lift jet aircraft that are just now coming into being. These jet lift aircraft find it easy to fly fast and economically, but have their problems at zero speed with a dirt-digging jet blast and a high fuel consumption. The VTOL (vertical takeoff and landing) engineer faces the problem of the evolution of new types of aircraft that have the advantages of the helicopter at low speeds and those of the airplane at high speeds. This is a challenge for the next generation of aerospace engineers.

In the design and operation of aerospace systems, the aerospace engineer has the very important job of conceiving the basic design of the system. He must choose the size of the wings, the size of the engine, the arrangement as to where the engines are mounted, where the landing gear is mounted, how the missile is put together in stages, the type of rockets, solid or liquid, the electronic performance of the radars and radios, the aerodynamic performance of the total vehicle in terms of range, speed, payload, one-engine-out performance, and all the things which define the aerospace vehicle and its capabilities.

The real challenge to the engineer involved in conceptual design work is to start with the end use and required performance and evolve an article that will supply the customer with this end use capability at the lowest cost, greatest reliability, and so on. This is usually done in a very competitive atmosphere with other manufacturers attempting to get the contract to develop the product for the specified end use. The winning of these design competitions, which are based almost entirely on conceptual paper designs, is very vital to the aerospace industry.

Despite the importance of the conceptual work, it involves less than ten per cent of the jobs in aerospace engineering. Most aerospace engineers are devoted to the numerous tasks of detail design, testing, and management involved in bringing the conceptual designs into being in a workable, reliable, fully developed product. While working on the conceptual design of the 707, we were able, with the aid of some very simple model tests, to decide that we could offer a means for reversing the thrust of the jet engines so that they could assist in braking an airplane during its landing roll. The real job came when the airlines agreed to buy this reverse thrust device, and it was then necessary to choose the actual method by which the thrust would be reversed, to design the detail parts, have them made, to test them on an actual engine, first in a test stand and later on a moving airplane, and as the result of many changes get the workable reverse thrust devices that are now found on every 707 airplane. While testing these reverse thrusters, many problems were encountered, such as pieces of metal that cracked or bent in the hot engine gasses, leakage around valves that decreased engine performance, and such unforeseen problems as those which occurred when the reversed jet of one engine entered the intake of an adjacent engine. It was easy to decide that we could have reverse thrust, but getting it was something else. Most of the creative work went into the actual design of the final parts.

The aerospace engineer is most successful and finds his job most interesting when he is in a position where he can get some feedback of the success or failure of his designs. "Feedback" means a flow of information from end results to an earlier stage in a process. He can then emphasize the successful designs and correct the deficient ones. This is true whether it be the design of a reverse thrust device, a riveted joint, or an aerodynamic item such as a wing flap. Probably the most successful aircraft are those that have the most feedback during their design. Many airplanes in the past were built to designs that were frozen (could not be changed) before the aerodynamics engineer could build a wind tunnel model, test it, and determine the suitability of the design. Progress is slow under such circumstances, and there are many expensive errors to be corrected. An airplane designed today without going through this feedback process could not possibly be competitive.

This habit of test, evaluation, and change applies to all parts of an airplane and is characteristic of much of the effort of successful engineers. Of course much of the evaluation is done with mathematics and computers rather than by models or full-scale testing.

The successful aerospace engineer is always ready to use the inventions of others as well as his own. An engineer has the challenge of finding the best way to do a job, whether it is the way he did it yesterday, a new invention he makes today, or a method invented or used by some competing engineer. Success is measured by the results of the product and not by the identity of the inventor. In the aerospace business we face a condition known as the NIH problem. NIH stands for "not invented here." Many engineers dislike any idea invented by somebody else and hence limit the success of their work by using only those devices they can invent themselves. This is not good engineering. Similarly, the successful aerospace engineer is able to direct the work of others and get a team of people to do many times more than he could do himself. It is always a terrific shock to the young aerospace engineer when he is given his first assistant to supervise. This is his introduction to management and to teamwork, which accomplishes more than can possibly be done by individuals working separately.

I have already said that one of the challenges for the aerospace engineer is to choose a detail design that will best meet the stated requirements, but I would like to discuss this further.

Most engineering textbooks are devoted to determining the characteristics of a physical article that has already been described, and this process is called analysis. In contrast, creative aerospace engineering requires starting with the end result and finding a design that is optimum and that, when analyzed, can be shown to meet the requirements. This is called synthesis and represents the principal task of designing engineers. Aerospace engineering involves some of the most interesting and challenging opportunities in all of the engineering world, not only to synthesize designs but also to develop methods for synthesis. This comes about because of the high premium placed upon light weight and great reliability in airplanes and missiles. The majority of aerospace engineers are involved in synthesizing, analyzing, testing, and re-synthesizing the design of many items.

The challenge and the adventure that the aerospace engineer meets in his daily work are two of the reasons that so many talented engineers go into this work. There is an absolute minimum of repetition. The aerospace engineer finds himself always in a position in which he must use the latest technical knowledge in nearly all disciplines to build a product that does not resemble anything that has ever been built before. Jet engines have replaced reciprocating engines, rockets have replaced airplanes, fast airplanes have replaced slow airplanes, and short field length airplanes are replacing long field length airplanes. Thirty years ago the development of aircraft that could carry passengers across the North Atlantic and the Pacific was the challenge. Today a comparable challenge is to go to the moon. Tomorrow the challenge will be to go to Mars and Venus. Most aerospace engineers devote their lives to new challenges, and those who are consolidating the response to old challenges find opportunity and outlet for their energies in such things as the development of bus-type transportation at low fares across the North Atlantic.

Aerospace engineering is accomplished by large companies, very small companies, private individuals, professors in universities, civil service employees of the government, and by military officers. There are very challenging opportunities for the individual in each area; it is not necessary to work for a big company or the government in order to make important contributions. This challenge of interesting and adventuresome work awaits the aerospace engineer, and there is no foreseeable let-up in the demand for his services. He works on the forefront of knowledge and plays a major role in determining the course of future world events.

_9_ _Rocket Propulsion_

BY WERNHER VON BRAUN
DIRECTOR
George C. Marshall Space Flight Center

WERNHER VON BRAUN

Born: 1912, Wirsitz, Germany

Institutes of Technology, Berlin and Zurich: B.S., 1932
University of Berlin: Ph.D., 1934
Honorary Doctor of Science: University of Alabama, 1958; St. Louis
University, 1958; University of Pittsburgh, 1958; Canisius College,
1959; Clark University, 1959; Technical University, Berlin, 1963
Honorary Doctor of Laws: University of Chattanooga 1958; Pennsylvania
Military College, 1959; Adelphi College, 1959; William Jewel College,
1963
Honorary Doctor's Degree: National University of Cordoba, Argentina

Liquid-fueled rocket development, German Ordnance Department, 1932
Technical Director, Liquid-fueled Rocket & Guided Missile Center, Peen-
emuende, Germany, 1937–45
Project Director, Research & Development Service (Sub-Office Rocket),
U.S. Army Ordnance Corps, Fort Bliss, Texas, 1945–50
Chief, Guided Missile Development Division, Redstone Arsenal, 1952–56
Director, Development Operations Division, ABMA, 1956–60
Director, George C. Marshall Space Flight Center, National Aeronautics
and Space Administration, Huntsville, Alabama, 1960–

American Institute of Aeronautics and Astronautics
Fellow: American Astronautical Society
Honorary Fellow: British Interplanetary Society
The Norwegian Interplanetary Society
The German Rocket Society

Astronautics Award, American Rocket Society, 1955
Department of Defense Distinguished Civilian Service Award, 1957
Department of the Army Decoration for Exceptional Civilian Service, 1957
U.S. Chamber of Commerce Award for Great Living Americans, 1958
The Dr. Robert H. Goddard Memorial Trophy, 1958
Distinguished Federal Civilian Service Award, 1959
Notre Dame Patriotism Award, 1959
Gold Medal Award, British Interplanetary Society, Washington, 1961
Hermann Oberth Award, American Rocket Society, Huntsville, 1961
Order of Merit for Research and Invention, Paris, 1962
Elliott Cresson Award, Franklin Institute, Philadelphia, 1962
American Citizen Award, 11th Annual German-American Day Festival,
North Bergen, N.J., 1963

Author: Books, articles, and monographs on space exploration

Rocket PROPULSION—a fascinating field of engineering—did not exist as a career field when I was a boy.

Although basic principles of rocket propulsion have been known for centuries, only recently has it become a highly useful tool of man. It evolved slowly from the crudely fashioned "arrows of flaming fire" that the ancient Chinese used as implements of battle and the sparkling fireworks displays that have been used for years to entertain and amaze. Modern technology revived and nourished the ancient art of rocketry, and this field has come rapidly of age within our lifetime.

In the first third of this century, interest was limited to a few lone-wolf scientists who were often labeled "crackpots." One such "crackpot," Dr. Robert H. Goddard, is now credited with being the first to fly a liquid rocket, complete with a "regeneratively cooled" combustion system and a simple guidance system to keep it on course. Dr. Goddard, a truly great man, was a professor of physics at Clark University in Worcester, Massachusetts. His rockets, which were first flown in 1926, may have been rather crude by present-day standards, but they blazed the trail and incorporated many features used in our modern rockets and space vehicles.

The first years of development of modern rockets were cloaked in military secrecy. It was World War II that brought rockets to public attention, as thousands were fired by opposing sides, on land and sea. The largest and most advanced rocket, by far, was the German V-2. Although the V-2 was a weapon of war, it was born through a dream of a group of scientists inspired by the writings of Professor Hermann Oberth. He first suggested that a

119

practical rocket could be built that could propel man into space to explore the universe. Professor Oberth, who is still living in Germany, was a great inspiration to me and to many of my associates in our early struggles to build rockets that would reach high altitudes.

When World War II came, our inspiration was pressed into service to develop a family of military missiles, among them the V-2. The V-2 was a truly remarkable machine for its time. It embodied many of the principles we still use in the field of rocket propulsion, although some twenty years have passed since its development began. In those early days of rocketry leading up to development of the V-2, we were foolhardy and took chances, chances we would never take today.

When I was 12 years of age, I had become fascinated by the incredible speed records established by Max Valier and Fritz von Opel. So I tried my first practical rocket experiment. It resembled one tried in 1500 by a Chinese named Wan Hoo. This visionary Oriental foresaw the use of rocketry in going to the moon. And he wanted to be the first to do it.

Using the technology then available, Wan Hoo fastened a huge kite to a sedan chair on which he had strapped forty-seven solid-propellant rockets. Bravely he sat in the sedan chair while coolies held torches to the rocket fuzes. Wan Hoo disappeared in a burst of flame and smoke.

Although I had not heard of Wan Hoo's fateful experiment, my approach was similar. I chose a coaster wagon instead of a sedan chair. Selecting half a dozen of the biggest skyrockets I could find, I strapped them to the wagon. Since there were no coolies to apply the torch, and since I lacked Wan Hoo's courage and determination, my wagon was unmanned, and I lighted the rockets myself.

It performed beyond my wildest dreams. The wagon careened crazily about, trailing a tail of fire like a comet. When the rockets burned out, ending their sparkling performance with a magnificent thunderclap, the wagon rolled majestically to a halt.

The police, who arrived late for the beginning of my experiment but in time for the grand finale, were unappreciative. They quickly took me into custody. Fortunately, no one was injured and I was released to the Minister of Agriculture (my father).

I was attending the French Gymnasium school in Berlin, but was not a star pupil. A fellow student and I had a far more absorbing project than our school books. We were building an automobile in my father's garage.

My grades improved after my father transferred me to a boarding school, the Hermann Lietz School in ancient Ettersburg Castle near Weimar. There we worked in the afternoons in groups to develop technical skills, to build things. And before bedtime I was permitted to examine the stars for an hour or two with a small telescope my mother had given me as a confirmation gift. I was 14 when I became seriously interested in space and astronomy.

One day in 1925, I saw in an astronomy magazine an ad about a book called *The Rocket to the Interplanetary Spaces,* by Hermann Oberth. I wrote for it at once. To become an engineer and to build such rockets—that would be a challenge worth living for, I figured.

When the book arrived, I opened it breathlessly. To my consternation, I couldn't understand a word. Its pages were a baffling conglomeration of mathematical symbols and formulas. Rushing to my math teacher, I cried, "How can I understand what this man is saying?" To my dismay, he told me to study math and physics. But in the glamorous prospect of a life devoted to space travel, these subjects took on new meaning for me. Determined to master them, I buried myself in their mysteries, and after a few years I even succeeded in graduating a year ahead of my class.

As soon as I graduated from school, Willy Ley, already a prolific popular writer on space and rocketry, introduced me to Professor Oberth. The professor was working to prove his contention that liquid fuels instead of solids were the best approach to rocket power for space vehicles. In my spare time, after working eight hours a day as a mechanic's apprentice in a Berlin machine factory, I joined Klaus Riedel and Rudolf Nebel, two other members of the German Society for Space Travel, as Professor Oberth's assistants.

Our equipment was elementary, and our ignition system was perilous. Klaus Riedel would toss a flaming gasoline-soaked rag over the gas-spitting motor, and then duck for cover before Oberth opened the fuel valves and it started with a roar. We were temporary guests on the proving grounds of the Chemical and Technical Institute, the German equivalent of the U.S. Bureau of Standards.

Iu August, 1930, Professor Oberth's little rocket engine succeeded in producing a thrust of 7 kilograms for 90 seconds, burning gasoline and liquid oxygen. An official of the Institute certified the demonstration. The liquid-fueled rocket motor was thus recognized for the first time in Germany as a respectable member of the family of internal-combustion engines. This was a tremendous forward step. But because he had to eat and support a large family, Professor Oberth was forced to return shortly thereafter to his teaching job in Romania.

Our zeal for space travel was undaunted, but with Oberth's departure our status as guests of the Chemical and Technical Institute expired. Looking around for a place where we could continue the work we had been doing under Professor Oberth's direction, Nebel soon found an abandoned ammunition storage depot near a suburb of Berlin. Eloquent as he was, he persuaded the city fathers to grant us a lease on it—free and for an indefinite period. Weeds and underbrush were taking over the 300-acre site. We selected one of the blockhouses for our laboratory, and hung out our shingle, *Raketenflugplatz Berlin* (Berlin Rocket Field).

We had no financial backers. Rudolf Nebel did an amazing job of scrounging free materials, which we swapped for skilled labor, such as tin bending or welding. Klaus Riedel sketched out a design for a "Minimum Rocket," and we started to build it. The motor was located in the nose, not for any scientific reason, but simply because Nebel had scrounged a truckload of aluminum tubing that could be used only if the motor dragged the tanks by the fuel lines.

In June of 1931, I interrupted my studies at the Institute of Technology of Berlin by a semester at the Federal Institute of Technology in Zurich, Switzerland. I returned in October of the same year, however, for the first public firing of Klaus Riedel's minimum rocket. Several local industrialists had been persuaded by Nebel to pay one mark to witness the demonstration. When the moment of truth came, the rocket moved halfway up the launcher tracks, then settled peacefully back on the pad. We were embarrassed, but we did not return the admission fees!

The trouble with our rocket was found to be unreliable pressurization of the fuel tanks. This was corrected, and within a few weeks successful launchings became commonplace. The rocket reached an altitude of about 1,000 feet.

A small parachute carried in the tail section would float it back to earth. Klaus Riedel would dash across the field in an old car, jump out, and sometimes catch the rocket before it struck the ground. After such a lucky "hand recovery," we could fire the rocket again immediately.

While I attended all these exciting activities on a two-hour-a-day-plus-every-weekend basis, I continued my formal engineering studies.

In the spring of 1932, I was graduated from the Berlin Institute of Technology with a bachelor's degree in aeronautical engineering. During semester vacation in 1931 and 1932, I had also taken gliding lessons. In 1933, I took up motor flying and received my first private pilot's license that summer.

My early exposure to rocketry convinced me that the exploration of space would require far more than applications of the current engineering technology. Wanting to learn more about physics, chemistry, and astronomy, I entered the University of Berlin for graduate study. I was graduated with a Ph.D. in physics in 1934.

My thesis, reflecting my absorbing interest, was on liquid rocket propulsion. While solid-propellant rockets had been in use for centuries, liquid propulsion was new. Only miniature motors had been built and tested, although they used the same liquid oxygen and watered alcohol propellant combination later used in large ballistic missiles. I wanted to attempt to measure and analyze in detail some of the puzzling phenomena that take place in a rocket engine, such as injection of fuels, atomization, combustion, and expansion of gases. Such scientifically oriented experimentation had never been conducted anywhere. But it would be costly, of course, and entirely beyond my personal financial means, which were nil. Under these circumstances I considered myself fortunate when the research department of the German Army Ordnance Corps, under a university grant program, took over the sponsorship of my thesis and permitted me to conduct my highly dangerous experiments at the Kummersdorf Army Proving Ground.

After my graduation, I became a civilian employee of the Army and continued the work I had begun as an Army-sponsored university student.

Thus, I began a career in rocketry that has stretched over three decades. There have been ups and downs, feasts and famines, and stop-and-go progress. But through the years there has always been a singleness of purpose, a certain consistency, that has guided my efforts and those of my teammates. And while for many years, and on two continents, the more immediate task (and the only one for which support was available) was to build rockets as weapons of war, our long-range objective has remained unchanged to this very day—the continuous evolution of space flight.

Fantastic progress in the manned and unmanned exploration of space has been made since October 4, 1957, when the Russians launched Sputnik I.

Ten years ago most rocket engineers would have agreed that one could build a launch vehicle and orbit an earth satellite within five to seven years after being given the nod. We actually launched Explorer I, the free world's first earth satellite, 83 days after having been given the go-ahead, by putting together a rather crude jury rig consisting of a modified Redstone missile with solid propellant upper stage. Ten years ago even the greatest optimists estimated that an expedition to Mars could be ready to take off no sooner than about 2050. We are now talking of a manned expedition to Mars by the mid-1980's!

What speeded up the schedule? Pieces of knowledge and

hardware emerging from many apparently unrelated fields of science and technology became available, and they permitted solutions of problems hitherto beyond the engineer's reach. The transistor, the electronic digital computer, the frictionless gyroscope, or even new materials such as fiberglass or titanium, may be quoted as examples. The most important single contribution to our sudden breakthrough into outer space, however, came undoubtedly from the amazing advances made in rocket propulsion. These came about in the United States because the public developed a deep interest in defense and space, and its representatives in Congress were willing to appropriate public funds for rocketry. Large sums of money have been spent during the past two decades on the research, development, and production of a variety of rocket propulsion systems, both solid and liquid. Each has been designed to perform a specific mission, and most of them have been extremely successful.

Rocket propulsion has revolutionized the principles and techniques of modern warfare. It has become the swiftest and most invulnerable method of delivering explosives on selected targets—whether it be a pinpoint target at short range, a larger target halfway around the globe, or even a hostile object speeding toward us through the upper atmosphere—or through space.

Of vital importance to the enrichment of man's destiny, rather than his destruction, the rocket is the only propulsion system that can be used for exploring space. The National Aeronautics and Space Administration is using a variety of rockets to send scientific instruments and man himself on extensive journeys in search of greater knowledge of this endless environment.

We originally lagged behind the Russians in the size of our rockets. Much sooner than we did, the Soviets set out to develop a huge rocket propulsion system in their military intercontinental ballistic missile program. High thrust and huge amounts of propellants were necessary because of the heavy weight of their early nuclear warheads. Leading in the field of nuclear weapons, the United States had reduced the weight of its atomic warheads while increasing their destructive power. When, much later than the Soviets, we finally initiated our own intercontinental ballistic missile program, far less powerful rockets were needed to hurl them over the same distances. This situation, more than anything else, led to our acute embarrassment when the Soviets began using their enormous military rockets for space projects and we could only respond with far less powerful ones.

We are now developing much larger rocket propulsion systems that will develop the tremendous thrust necessary for extensive manned space exploration and heavy deep-space probes. Soon we will no longer be restricted to performing our space missions largely by modifying underpowered rocket systems that were originally designed and built for military purposes.

The first powerful launch vehicles to be designed specifically for space are the members of the Saturn family. The Saturn rockets are being developed by a large government-industry team consisting of NASA's Marshall Space Flight Center at Huntsville and its contractors across the nation.

Our first approach toward meeting the pressing need for greater thrust was to form a cluster of proven rocket engines. Eight liquid oxygen/kerosene engines, based on a Rocketdyne engine proved in the Jupiter, Thor, and Atlas missiles, were combined in the first stage of the Saturn I. The eight engines produced a total thrust of 1.5 million pounds. At first, the simultaneous operation of so many rocket engines was looked upon as quite a challenging task we had set for ourselves—but it worked. We are now developing a larger kerosene/oxygen engine, a single one of which is capable of producing a thrust of 1.5 million pounds, and we'll cluster it again to multiply our space power. We are also designing and developing engines that burn liquid hydrogen and liquid oxygen to give us greater specific impulse than the kerosene/oxygen propellant combination.

But let's turn now to some of the more basic questions you may have about this career field.

Just what is rocket propulsion, and why do we need it for space exploration?

To gain a better insight into these questions, let's first shrink the earth down to the size of an apple. If we shrink the remainder of the solar system by the same proportion, we find that the moon is a small orb about half the size of a ping-pong ball, circling the earth about once a month at a distance of about six feet. On this scale, the sun is a gigantic ball of fire twenty-two feet in diameter, located about half a mile away from the apple. And the atmosphere of our earth is equal in thickness to the skin of the apple.

For thousands of years man has been confined in his wanderings to this very thin layer of atmosphere surrounding our earth. To survive outside its warming, protective cloak would be impossible. Man's delicately balanced body can withstand only a small percentage of the maximum variation of temperature that is encountered in space. We can work effectively, with complete disregard to the weather, in an exceedingly small range of from 60 to 85 degrees Fahrenheit. And we often complain if the temperature varies even slightly above or below the comfort level between 68 to 72 degrees. When man enters space he must take with him a homemade capsule of his natural environment, consisting of a fresh supply of oxygen, plus thermal protection and cooling. Our space traveler must also be protected against excessive vibration and shock, radiation, and speeding meteoroids.

Wherever he goes in the solar system, he will be subject to the gravitational pull of planetary bodies, and the sun itself. Newton's law of gravitation says that the gravitational force of one object on another is directly proportional to the mass of the two objects and inversely proportional to the square of the distance between the two objects. The tremendous mass of our earth, which is more than a billion times a billion tons, creates a powerful force on any object that is near it. For example, the earth tugs away constantly at an average-sized man on its surface with a force of about 175 pounds. To overcome this pull and remove him completely from the earth's gravitational field, a man must be hurled away from the earth at an enormous speed, at "escape velocity," as space men call it. He cannot be accelerated too suddenly, however, for his body would not stand the crushing force of extra "G's." The Saturn V will leave the launch pad slowly, but just under 12 minutes after blast-off, the three astronauts will be speeding around the world at 17,500 miles per hour, and a few minutes later they will have attained the escape velocity of about 25,000 miles per hour.

When men first ventured from the earth's surface in gliders and powered aircraft, they were still within the atmosphere, which held them aloft. As long as there was a working fluid to "bite into," they could use propellors to lift themselves high within the atmospheric "skin." Jet aircraft engines were developed for faster speed and higher altitudes. These, too, depended upon the atmosphere, breathing it in and using its oxygen to burn the fuel. In space there is no atmosphere to support man or his craft.

How can man propel himself in space? This brings us to another of Newton's laws: For every action, there is an equal and opposite reaction. If we fire a rifle, the kick we receive from the butt of the rifle is caused by the reaction on the rifle of the gas pressure that is propelling the bullet forward. (The reaction is not caused by the push of the bullet against the atmosphere of the earth.)

I have often used an inflated balloon to demonstrate this reaction. The elasticity of the balloon forces the air through the opening, causing the balloon to move in the opposite direction. I discontinued this demonstration after using it at a banquet table recently. The balloon careened wildly about and ended its flight with a splash in the soup bowl of the chairman's wife.

In a chemical rocket, two "propellants," a fuel and an oxidizer, are burned in a combustion chamber. High temperature gases are produced. These are expanded through a nozzle to create a thrust in the opposite direction. This is easily understood when we think of each of the billions of tiny gas molecules as a bullet speeding out of a rifle barrel. The billions of little recoil "kicks" produce the rocket's steady thrust. It is also important to remember that, unlike the jet engine, the rocket engine does not depend on the atmosphere for its oxygen, but carries its own supply along. The rocket engine then works independently of the earth's atmosphere, and can provide the tremendous thrust necessary to lift man and his life-sustaining capsule free of earth's gravity.

Doesn't this sound simple? If so, you may wonder if there is really enough to the field of rocket propulsion to set it aside distinctly and separately as a field of engineering.

It is true that the basic principles of rocketry are simple, and we have some fairly simple rockets in our arsenal. For example, the solid propellant rocket has a high-strength casing that contains some solid material, composed of fuel and oxidizer. A simple device ignites the propellant, and it burns much like a Fourth-of-July Roman candle. These simple, rugged propulsion systems are now being built to extremely large sizes, although their specific propellant performance is modest compared with that of some of our modern liquid propellant combinations.

There is also a fairly simple type of liquid propulsion system. Fuel and an oxidizer are pressurized in separate tanks, injected into a combustion chamber where they ignite upon contact, and burn to create combustion gases that are expanded through a nozzle.

The basic elements and principles of operation of liquid and solid propulsion systems are fairly simple. It is the harnessing of these basic principles, the development of devices needed to control performance and to attain the highest degree of efficiency, that makes the job of a rocket engineer both difficult and challenging.

We have been working for years with what we call conventional fuels, such as alcohol and kerosene, but we are far from exhausting the possibilities of chemical propulsion, both liquid and solid. We are just beginning, in fact, to flight test some of the more exotic fuels, such as liquid hydrogen. Hydrogen provides about 40 per cent more specific impulse, more thrust per pound, than kerosene. It is a "cryogenic" fuel, boiling at −423 degrees Fahrenheit, and consequently difficult to handle. We are studying the use of other cryogenic propellants such as liquefied fluorine, to produce even higher impulse.

Besides pure chemical propulsion, two other forms that will assist man in his exploration of space are nuclear "blowdown" propulsion and nuclear electrical propulsion.

In the commonest form of nuclear propulsion, the blowdown

rocket, liquid hydrogen is pumped through the white-hot core of a perforated nuclear reactor and expanded through a nozzle much as in a chemical rocket. Since chemical combustion does not take place, an oxidizer is not required, and a single propellant is sufficient. A pound of propellant in a nuclear rocket produces more than twice the energy of the most powerful chemical propellant combinations. Hence, the nuclear blowdown rocket is very efficient, but it is somewhat hindered by its heavy reactor and shielding and the dangerous radiation it emits. For these reasons, the nuclear blowdown rocket is more suitable for upper stages and deep-space propulsion than for take-off from the ground.

Electrical propulsion is based on the same law of action and reaction, but the particles that are expelled from the rocket nozzle to produce forward thrust are the minute charged atomic particles known as ions. These ions are accelerated to a tremendous velocity by electric fields, which, in turn, must be produced with heavy nuclear-powered turbogenerators. Although the thrust or forward force that can be achieved by this type of propulsion is small, it takes very little "fuel" to produce it. The thrust per unit weight of propellant of an electrically propelled nuclear space ship would be downright phenomenal. This form of propulsion will someday be extremely useful in long voyages through space.

Both nuclear blowdown and nuclear electrical propulsion are in the early stages of development and are not yet used in operational vehicles, as chemical systems are. It is these fields, however, that show significant promise for man's true exploration of space.

If there are so many disciplines involved in the field of rocket propulsion, and no standard curriculum, how does a student who wants to enter this field know what courses to take?

This depends upon the particular discipline in which the student of rocketry is interested. If it's the field of rocket propulsion as a whole, a degree in almost any of the fields of engineering, science, and mathematics is appropriate. Here are some of the specialist areas, along with some possible courses of study:

Rocket Power Plant Design. The design of chemical rocket power plants involves the fields of chemical and mechanical engineering and an even more specialized field, gas dynamics. If we are dealing with solid propellant engines, the fields of chemistry and chemical engineering enter heavily into the formulation of propellant compositions that give the proper burning rate, impulse, and physical properties, and the design of nozzle materials which will withstand high temperatures without auxiliary cooling.

Mechanical engineering is also important because lightweight combustion chambers must be designed to hold the high pressure gases. In liquid propulsion systems the fields of mechanical engineering, hydraulics, pumps, turbines, pneumatics, fluid flow, and thermodynamics play large roles, since the liquid power plant is actually a small, lightweight, efficient combustion engine for producing the high temperature gases required for propulsion.

Propellant Research. Before a propellant is selected for a particular rocket application, a workable composition has to be developed that not only can be burned, but also handled, and that is compatible with the rocket's construction materials. This field involves detailed research in the fields of organic and inorganic chemistry, metallurgy and cryogenics. Advanced degrees are almost invariably required in this area because of the complexity and number of combinations and compositions of propellants that can be made available.

Structural Engineering. A rocket propulsion system is usually an integral part of a larger system, such as a space vehicle, a military missile, or an aircraft. As such, it must lend itself to its environment as well as contribute to the strength of the over-all system. This requirement leads us into the field of structural engineering, which includes studies of the stresses, strains, vibrations, and dynamic characteristics of the rocket propulsion system with its related vehicle. Structural engineering is normally studied as part of over-all curricula on civil, mechanical, or aeronautical engineering.

Gas Dynamics and Physics. Since a rocket is basically a hot-gas generator, study of the properties of fluids and gases is extremely important for the accomplished rocket propulsion engineer. He must know the behavior of various types of gases under varying degrees of temperature and pressure, and he must be able to calculate the balance of their composition as well as their thermal, erosive, and corrosive effects on surrounding materials.

The field of thermodynamics, usually a part of the mechanical engineering curriculum, enables the engineer to build a rocket that will be able to produce, and that will itself withstand, the effects of the propulsive gases.

Electronics. The field of electronics is becoming increasingly important in connection with rocket propulsion, as well as with other fields. Rocket systems need means of ignition, control, guidance, telemetry, tracking, and communications. The fields of electrical engineering and electronics engineering offer huge opportunities in themselves in support of the rocket propulsion engineer, and in hundreds of other fields.

Aeroballistics. Since rocket propulsion systems usually propel some vehicle, either through the atmosphere or through space, the behavior of the system in this environment must be considered in its design. Most colleges and universities now offer a field of study called "Aerospace engineering," which covers the fields of aeronautical and astronautical engineering across the board. Although these curricula specialize in aerodynamics, astrophysics, flight mechanics, and ballistics, the fields of propulsion and other related subjects are covered.

Mathematics. Although mathematics is needed heavily in all of the fields mentioned above, there is also an opportunity to specialize in the field of mathematics applied to the field of rocket propulsion. Many problems are so complex in the rocket field today that high-speed computers are needed to solve them. High-speed mathematical computation is also required to follow a vehicle's course and to correct it within fractions of a second. Computers, however, can't do anything unless they are first told how to do it. It is the mathematician who must interpret the engineer's problem and put it into machine language before the computer can automatically process it to derive an answer. This involves every phase of mathematics, from complex variables, to differential equations, to statistical computations.

There are many other fields in which a person can specialize within the field of rocket propulsion. Specialization in such a rapidly moving field, however, is often a result of experience in conjunction with education, rather than education alone. But a bachelor's, master's, or even a doctor's degree is almost invariably required as a base upon which to build before a person can become qualified to contribute significant engineering achievements to the field of rocket propulsion.

While we are talking about rocket propulsion, we don't want to overlook the fact that it is only one facet of the vast field of rocketry. There are other equal challenging facets, such as guidance and control, communications, celestial mechanics, materials, nuclear physics, structural engineering, static and flight testing, and many others. All are important in the development of a complete space vehicle system.

A space launch vehicle or missile weapons system is developed on a carefully prepared time schedule. Each part of the system —units, assemblies and sub-assemblies—must be designed, tested, and delivered by contractors and subcontractors at a certain date to dovetail in the fabrication and testing of a complete system. More than 3,500 NASA employees are concentrating their efforts on the Saturn V project. They are supported in their job by a much larger team made up by some of the leading industrial complexes in the country, since more than ninety per cent of the research and development effort is performed by contractors. Integrating their efforts is one of the toughest challenges facing technical management today. Before the first contract was let, before a single item of hardware existed, the date of the first launch was set—five years in the future!

Even within the area of propulsion you will find a diversification and complexity that calls for the highest order of teamwork for the success of a project. You will rarely find a person labeled exclusively as a rocket propulsion engineer. Instead, you will find scientists and engineers who are specialists in chemistry, mathematics, and physics, in structures, materials, aeroballistics, celestial mechanics—and management.

You may now be wondering: If pioneers have contributed so much, and if there are now tens of thousands of people working as specialists in rocket propulsion, is there room for an individual who wants to contribute toward further advances? Will rocket propulsion not pass from a research and development phase to routine production?

I think the fact that there are so many highly qualified specialists in the field merely emphasizes the fact that there are still many tough problems to be solved. Research never ends. Every answer we find raises a dozen new questions. We can never reach perfection, even though we are always trying. There is a great need for individuals with imagination, initiative, and perseverance to explore even newer and more advanced techniques in rocket propulsion and in all the other areas of rocketry.

Let me illustrate it this way: If I grab up a handful of straws of various length and hold them erect, they could symbolize the numerous problems and unexplored areas in rocket propulsion. The straw that sticks up the highest would represent the most serious and urgent problem, the one we must tackle first. If we pluck out the tallest straw when that problem is solved, another straw becomes the tallest in the bundle. And so on.

A technical education is important—if not mandatory—these days in the field of rocket propulsion. But other forms of education are also required. These educational pursuits are associated with the field of technical management. We have seen already that in view of the size and complexity of the systems we are developing, it is no longer possible for a single, small, closely-knit team to do the job of developing a complete rocket system. The complex nature of the space and propulsion business today dictates that many organizations be involved. Since organizations are composed of people, a large part of the technical job of developing a workable system involves dealing with people. All types and levels of management people are needed.

One of the toughest challenges in Project Apollo—our national space-flight program geared to a manned lunar landing—is effective management. It is the job of directing, coordinating, and supervising the efforts of all the people involved. Project Mercury, just completed, cost less than half a billion dollars. Project Apollo will cost an estimated twenty billion dollars, and involves a total force of about 200,000 scientists, engineers, craftsmen, technicians, and supporting workmen across the nation.

The technical manager needs not only to know how the system works and how to design and develop it; he must also have the poise, finesse, diplomacy, and salesmanship to motivate people and keep them working together toward a common goal. In my dealings with other technical people for the past thirty years I have endeavored to practice several management principles that I will let you in on, and that may help you:

1. *Every individual must be given an opportunity to make a contribution and to express his views.* In my experience I have found that you can learn something from every person if you allow him to contribute. No manager should take the attitude that "Papa knows best." Papa simply doesn't always know what is best because he usually doesn't have all the facts. He gets the best answer to a problem if he asks the man who is to do the job.

Individuals appreciate recognition, and if they are adequately recognized they have a tremendous urge to contribute more. When I say "recognition," I don't necessarily mean a pay raise, a rug on the floor, or a reserved parking space. Although these things are important recognition and prestige factors, I mean *personal* recognition from the people he works for and with. It is unbelievable what an appreciative word, glance, handshake, or intimate conversation can do to keep a person's spirit filled with the proper inspiration to get the job done—and done well.

You must give each member of the team an opportunity to be recognized and you must attempt to derive the maximum contribution from each individual on the team.

2. *An "integrated" solution can be found to every problem.* The primary role of a technical manager is to bring together the various aspects or elements that are concerned with a prob-

lem, and then to formulate an "integrated" solution or decision. First, of course, all available facts must be at hand. Many decisions are invalidated in a short time because the manager failed to assemble all the facts.

With the facts at hand, many problems lead to two or three possible solutions which appear incompatible. Often, particularly if the emotions of individuals enter into the discussion, there are two opposing sides that disagree violently with each other. In this case there are three ways to solve the problem: (a) an arbitrary decision in which one side is satisfied and the other is not; (b) a compromise in which either side is only partially satisfied and (c) an integrated solution in which both sides are satisfied.

You will note that the first method listed above is probably the easiest way to solve a problem. That is, it takes the least effort on the part of the manager. But it also achieves the least desirable results: an unsatisfied party. Under our first ground rule we should not completely ignore or frustrate this input. The last method listed is probably the most difficult to achieve but obviously has the most desirable end results.

3. *Another important principle to follow is "aggressive management."* In the press of everyday problems we often fall into the trap of exclusive "managing by exception." In this situation we delve into only those limited areas that are brought to our attention by problems, and our daily actions resemble the operation of a fire brigade. In many cases these areas are detailed in nature and do not necessarily represent the total, over-all picture of how a large technological development program is progressing. It is necessary to find time each day to do some "aggressive management," that is, to ferret out the problems by inquisition, to summarize the situation by review, and to take positive action in anticipation of problems. In other words, it is sometimes far more effective to remove a fire hazard than to fight a fire.

The above three principles are only a few of the many things an engineer or scientist dealing with more than one discipline or one group of people learns through experience. It is possible, however, to gain some insight into these problems during your period of engineering education, and you can do this by several means. First, it is desirable to sprinkle your technical studies with studies such as economics, psychology, politics, and the fine arts. You will be surprised how much these subjects actually enter into the work of an engineer, scientist, or technician in the field of rocket propulsion.

Further to gain the ability to deal with people and to co-ordinate their activities, participation in extra-curricular activities is desirable. Being a leader in a technical field requires some of the same attributes needed for being a leader in a science club, school newspaper, or football team. This type of activity helps to develop many of the characteristics needed to coordinate activities where more than one element is involved. In our complex world the skills of leadership, management, and the ability to deal with people are becoming a necessity just as is the requirement for higher education.

Too many people spend their lives working at an occupation which they consider drudgery, saving themselves from complete stagnation with an absorbing hobby that is an outlet for their creative energies. Rocket propulsion is a vocation that will challenge the originality of the most energetic person, and is as fascinating as any hobby, as well.

You may still be wondering: "But with so many people working in these fields, and so many ideas being generated, how can our country possibly sift out the most valuable ones?"

When I attended a meeting of the International Astronautical Federation a few years ago, I posed the same problem to a Russian scientist.

"One of my problems in getting anything done," I said, "is the time it takes to evaluate the flood of suggestions from individual engineers and scientists, as well as industrial organizations, on new designs, programs, or schemes NASA should support. Many of these proposals are brilliant, represent lots of detailed thinking and planning, and can't be dismissed lightly. Moreover, I find it increasingly difficult to invent a new gadget nowadays, because the chances are that some enterprising young man in Los Angeles has already formed a small company and is manufacturing it."

"I wish I had the same problem," the Soviet scientist replied.

"In the Soviet Union," he continued, "there is a strong tendency on the part of the engineers to stick to well-proved solutions. It usually takes a directive from upstairs to set up a group of people to probe into new untried fields."

Maybe this little exchange on a seemingly unpolitical subject carries quite a message about the relative merits of free enterprise versus planned economy systems.

Of course we, too, can't support *all* the new ideas—only the best ones. However, this hard but irrefutable fact of life introduces competition in rocket propulsion on the American scene, just as it does in other engineering fields. And competition, a mechanism to keep everybody on his toes, is one of the best attributes of our form of government and our economic system.

The future of rocket propulsion is inseparably entwined with national defense and space. Programs will be determined by the national need, public recognition of that need, and willingness to support it. It would be unwise to drop our defenses until the outlook for world peace is more certain. And the challenge of space seems to me irresistible. NASA has built up considerable momentum for investigations on a broad front. Stop-and-go, "grasshopper" progress would be wasteful of resources, and not in the best interests of the country. At the recommendation of President Kennedy, and the whole-hearted support of President Johnson and Congress, NASA is pursuing a hard-driving U.S. effort in space. I feel certain that the American people will accept nothing less than a sustained, determined effort for years to come.

The culmination of a rocketeer's work comes in the launch. And no matter how many I am privileged to witness, it is always a thrilling sight. The tension which builds up during the long hours of checkout and countdown becomes exhilaration when the engines roar into life, the hold-down arms are released, and the rocket climbs upward from the launch pad. Its flaming exhaust can be followed higher and higher into the sky, until it disappears from sight.

The launching is not the end, however. Rocketry is not an end within itself, but a means. A rocket's role is to carry scientific instruments or man himself into space. It is a workhorse on which man's curiosity may ride in search of greater understanding of the universe.

The propulsion engineer who helps to develop it has the satisfying reward of knowing that he has contributed to the advancement of all mankind.

10 *Nuclear Engineering*

Engineering

BY MANSON BENEDICT

DEPARTMENT OF NUCLEAR ENGINEERING

Massachusetts Institute of Technology

MANSON BENEDICT

Born: 1907, Lake Linden, Michigan

Cornell University: B. Chem., 1928
Massachusetts Institute of Technology: M.S., 1932; Ph.D., 1935

Harvard University:
   National Research Fellow in Chemistry, 1935–36
   Research Associate in Geophysics, 1936–37
Massachusetts Institute of Technology:
   Professor of Nuclear Engineering, 1951–
   Head, Department of Nuclear Engineering, 1958–

National Aniline and Chemical Co.: Research Chemist, 1929–30; 1937–38
M. W. Kellogg Co.: Research Chemist, 1938–43
Kellex Corp.: In charge of process design of Oak Ridge Gaseous Diffusion Plant, 1943–46
Hydrocarbon Research, Inc.: Director of Process Development, 1946–51
National Research Corporation: Scientific Advisor, 1951–57; Director, 1963–
U.S. Atomic Energy Commission:
   Reactor Safeguard Committee member, 1947–52
   Chief, Operations Analysis Staff, 1951–58
   General Advisory Committee: member, 1958–; Chairman, 1962–64

American Nuclear Society: Fellow, Director, 1959–; Vice President, 1961–62; President, 1962–63

Member: National Academy of Sciences
   American Academy of Arts and Science
   American Chemical Society
   American Institute of Chemical Engineers

NUCLEAR ENGINEERING is one of the newest and most challenging of the engineering professions. Today's nuclear engineer is heir to recent scientific discoveries that enable him to derive tremendous practical benefits from two consequences of nuclear reactions that not long ago were regarded as physically impossible, transmutation of the elements and conversion of mass to energy.

The first of the long succession of discoveries that ultimately made nuclear engineering possible was Becquerel's finding, in 1896, that uranium ores spontaneously gave off radiation. Subsequently, the researches of the Curies led to the discovery of radium and an understanding of radioactivity. They found that radioactive decay of uranium initiated a whole series of further spontaneous nuclear reactions. The over-all process consisted in the transmutation of uranium into lead and helium, and the release of a great deal of energy.

But even though these discoveries of spontaneous decay of uranium and radium shattered the former belief that atoms were immutable and indivisible, no one at the turn of the century knew how to speed up the process or where the released energy came from.

Discovery of the source of the energy came rather quickly, in 1905, with Einstein's inspired postulate of the equivalence of mass and energy through the now famous equation $E = mc^2$. The energy given off in the radioactive decay of uranium could be explained by the loss in mass that occurred when uranium changed into lead and helium.

The puzzle of how to extract energy from uranium at will,

instead of being dependent on its slow release through natural radioactivity, challenged scientists and engineers for many years. The fascination of this problem has never been better expressed than in the prophetic words of the professor in H. G. Wells' novel, *The World Set Free—A History of Mankind*, written in 1914: "We stand today towards radioactivity exactly as our ancestor stood toward fire before he had learned to make it. . . . This is the dawn of a new day in human living. . . . The energy we need for our very existence, and . . . which Nature supplies us still so grudgingly, is in reality locked up in inconceivable quantities all about us. We cannot pick that lock at present, but we will."

It took thirty years to pick that lock. Rutherford took the first step, in 1917, when he found that irradiation of nitrogen with high-speed helium atoms transmuted a few of the colliding nuclei into oxygen and hydrogen. Although the discovery showed that artificial transmutation was possible, the process smashed the lock instead of picking it. Far more energy was put into the process than was recovered, and yields were minute. But it was a step in the right direction. In 1932, Chadwick, working in Rutherford's laboratory, found that similar irradiation of beryllium with high-speed helium atoms produced a new and highly reactive particle, the neutron. The neutron proved to be the key that would open the lock of the nucleus.

In the early 1930's a series of brilliant investigations by Fermi showed that almost every known element would react with neutrons and become radioactive, and in radioactive decay would be transmuted into the element of next higher atomic number. Uranium was of special interest to Fermi, because it had the highest atomic number of any element then known. In irradiating uranium with neutrons, he hoped to produce a new element of still higher atomic number. He was disappointed when he was unable to identify the expected new element among the radioactive products of the irradiation. Although Fermi had actually split the uranium nucleus, he failed to realize it. In 1938, Hahn and Strassman showed that the much smaller atom, barium, was one of the radioactive products of neutron irradiation of uranium.

Hahn and Meitner then deduced that neutron irradiation split the uranium nucleus, with release of three million times the energy given off in combustion of the same mass of coal, with simultaneous production of more neutrons than were consumed in initiating fission. Scientists and engineers realized that the fission reaction could be kept going by the neutrons produced in fission, without having to be supplied by another process. Fission of uranium could be carried out in a self-sustaining chain reaction. The lock of the nucleus could be opened at will.

The imminence of the Second World War caused this great discovery to be used first for military rather than for peaceful purposes. In the tremendous industrial enterprises of the Manhattan Project, which led to the development of nuclear weapons, nuclear engineering was born. Despite their immediate military objective, many of the engineering achievements of the Manhattan Project laid the groundwork for today's peaceful applications of nuclear energy.

The first of these achievements was the design and construction of the world's first self-sustaining nuclear reactor. In a squash court under the stands at Stagg Field on the University of Chicago campus, Fermi, Zinn, and their colleagues found that when a large pile of graphite and uranium was stacked in a carefully contrived array, the mass "went critical" and the uranium underwent nuclear fission steadily and at a controllable rate. The nuclear age was born on December 2, 1942.

Before they achieved success with this first nuclear reactor, Fermi and other scientists had been obliged to learn the rate at which neutrons reacted with many nuclei, including the two isotopes of natural uranium—abundant uranium 238 and scarce uranium 235. They found that fission occurred primarily with the scarce isotope uranium 235, and that the abundant isotope uranium 238 absorbed neutrons without producing many fissions. To create a self-sustaining chain reaction, it would be necessary either to separate large amounts of these two isotopes, a task of unprecedented difficulty, or to use many tons of exceptionally pure natural, unseparated uranium metal stacked with specially purified graphite in a lattice of strictly specified dimensions.

Natural uranium was used at Stagg Field. Production of the requisite large amounts of purer uranium metal and graphite than had ever been made before were notable engineering feats. Even more of an engineering triumph was the success of the highly original design methods devised by Fermi to predict the behavior of neutrons in the pile of uranium and graphite. The concepts and methods introduced by Fermi are still used by nuclear engineers in designing today's nuclear reactors.

After the Stagg Field reactors proved successful, Fermi, Wigner, and their colleagues joined forces with engineers of the duPont organization in one of the most novel and successful engineering projects the world has ever seen, the plutonium production plant at Hanford on the Columbia River in Washington. Scientists had found that the neutrons absorbed by uranium 238 produced a new artificial element, plutonium, which, like uranium 235, underwent fission readily with neutrons, and could be used in nuclear weapons. To make this new element in useful amounts the Hanford engineers designed reactors that would release nuclear energy at the rate of billions of watts, compared with the few hundred watts put out by the Stagg Field reactor. In addition, they devised a process for separating plutonium, an element never seen before, from unreacted uranium and its fiercely radioactive fission products. The enormous Hanford re actors, silently transmuting uranium into plutonium while liberat· ing enough heat to warm the mighty Columbia River, and the concrete-shielded plutonium separation plant, so radioactive that it can be viewed only through periscopes and operated only with remotely actuated manipulators, are eloquent witnesses to the novelty and magnitude of this engineering wonder.

A third nuclear engineering achievement of the Manhattan Project was the successful separation of uranium 235, at Oak Ridge. This separation was first accomplished in enormous mass spectrographs, which picked out uranium 235 literally atom by atom, making use of the slightly smaller distance traveled in electric and magnetic fields by the lighter uranium 235 atoms compared with the heavier uranium 238. This process used so much electrical equipment that it was necessary to borrow silver from the U.S. Treasury to build the plant. This electro-magnetic separation process was soon replaced by the less ex-pensive but equally impressive gaseous diffusion process. In this process, the Manhattan Project engineers took advantage of the laboratory finding that uranium 235 was enriched relative to uranium 238 by a few tenths of a per cent when uranium hexa-fluoride, a highly reactive gas, was pumped through fine-pored metallic membranes. They obtained nearly pure uranium 235 in large quantity by pumping uranium hexafluoride through thousands of stages of membranes, each scaled up to millions of times the capacity of the original laboratory equipment. The magnitude of the gaseous diffusion plants is indicated by their consumption of almost ten per cent of all the electric power in the United States, during their peak operating period.

When the Atomic Energy Commission took over these plants from the Manhattan Project in 1947, it was clear that useful power could be produced from the fission of uranium, but it had not yet been done. The Hanford reactors operated at too low a temperature to serve as heat sources for a steam power plant and were too large and expensive for the amount of heat they produced, because of their dependence on natural uranium. Nuclear engineers realized that the route to follow in getting power more economically from uranium was to raise the tempera-ture at which heat was produced and to use uranium enriched in the 235 isotope from Oak Ridge in place of natural uranium.

These steps would doubtless have been taken in due time, but the development of peaceful nuclear power was greatly advanced by another dramatic military application of nuclear power, the nuclear submarine. Uranium 235 was potentially an ideal fuel for a submarine. As no oxygen is consumed in nuclear fission, a nuclear submarine could remain submerged for days. And the energy latent in a few pounds of uranium 235 would enable a submarine to cruise for months without refueling. The Navy and the Atomic Energy Commission therefore gave high priority to development of a nuclear submarine, and a team of nuclear engineers headed by Admiral Rickover succeeded bril-liantly with this development. By using nearly pure uranium 235 they were able to eliminate graphite and make the reactor much more compact than Hanford's; by putting the water coolant under pressure and raising its temperature, they were able to generate steam to power a submarine's turbines. To prevent corrosion of uranium fuel by high-temperature water, without losing neutrons through absorption in steel, it was necessary for nuclear metallurgists to develop a new class of alloys based on the little-known element zirconium. The first reactor of this type was built into a land-based prototype of a nuclear submarine, which first generated electric power from nuclear fission in Idaho in 1953. The second reactor of this type powered the Nautilus, the world's first nuclear submarine, whose pioneering voyages are known the world over. More than fifty similar reactors have subsequently been built for submarines and surface naval vessels.

The dramatic success of the Nautilus provided convincing evidence of the technical feasibility of using the energy of the nucleus for electric power generation, but it left unanswered the question whether nuclear electricity could be generated at low enough cost to be of commercial interest. In the United States this question is being answered with a resounding yes, through a series of orderly engineering advances. First, the Atomic Energy Commission authorized the team of nuclear engineers that produced the power plant for the Nautilus, again led by Admiral Rickover, to design and build a nuclear reactor to produce steam for an electric generating station of the Duquesne Light Co., at Shippingport, Pennsylvania. In 1957 this plant came on the line, and has been producing 60 megawatts of electric power ever since. Although costs in the Shippingport plant were still high, it proved conclusively that a pressurized water reactor could be used as a dependable heat source in a commercial power station. An important innovation of the Shippingport plant was its use of refractory uranium dioxide as nuclear fuel in place of relatively low-melting uranium metal.

With the example of Shippingport's dependable operation, development of economical nuclear power moved into normal commercial channels. Electric equipment manufacturers offered nuclear power plants for sale, and, in partnership with engineering firms and power companies, began a concerted effort at reducing the cost of nuclear power. The 160 megawatt nuclear power plant built by Westinghouse and Stone and Webster for the Yankee Atomic Electric Co., in western Massachusetts, went into operation in 1960, and the 208 megawatt Dresden nuclear power station built by General Electric and Bechtel for the Commonwealth Edison Co. near Chicago came on the line at about the same time. The Yankee plant uses a power cycle similar to that of the Nautilus and Shippingport reactors, in which pressurized water from the reactor is used to generate steam for the turbine in a separate boiler. The Dresden plant uses a simpler power cycle, in which water is boiled right in the reactor, and steam from the reactor is passed directly to the turbine. The uranium used in each plant is richer in uranium 235 than natural uranium, but is not the fully enriched uranium used in the Nautilus and is therefore less expensive. Each plant produces electricity for around ten mills per kilowatt hour, much less than the cost of power from Shippingport, but still somewhat greater than the seven mill cost of electricity from conventional plants burning coal or oil in these parts of the country.

The experience gained from Shippingport, Yankee, and Dresden has shown nuclear engineers how to cut nuclear power costs still further. They have learned how to build bigger plants with lower unit costs and how to eliminate non-essential elements designed into the early plants because of lack of experience. By early 1964 electric power companies in the United States had placed orders for six more nuclear power stations in sizes ranging from 315 to 550 megawatts, and with projected costs based on fixed-price contracts in the range of 4 to 6.5 mills per kilowatt hour. When these plants come into operation, in 1968, the U.S. will have around 4600 megawatts of installed nuclear electric generating capacity, about 5% of the total generating capacity of the country. By the year 2000 the Atomic Energy Commission predicts that one half of the electricity produced in the United States will be derived from nuclear fission.

At these costs, nuclear power will be economically competitive with power from either coal or oil in those regions of the United States remote from coal mines or oil fields and in foreign countries without conventional low-cost fuels, such as Sweden, Spain, Japan, and India. If the predicted growth of nuclear power is to take place, the cost of nuclear power must be reduced still further, so that the regions of the world in which nuclear energy is the cheapest source of electricity will become ever wider. A young man entering the nuclear engineering profession today can contribute to cost reductions in many ways: by understanding the performance of today's reactors to learn how to design tomorrow's better; by learning how to use less expensive components and materials without jeopardizing reliability or safety; by finding how to extend the life of nuclear fuels, so that more heat can be obtained from a given amount of uranium; and by learning how to operate water-cooled reactors at still higher temperatures, so that more electricity can be produced from a given amount of heat.

Although water-cooled reactors are the type most widely used in the United States, other types that may ultimately lead to lower cost power are being developed by the Atomic Energy Commission and its research contractors. Reactors cooled by liquid sodium, helium gas, or a high-boiling hydrocarbon are potentially capable of operating at higher temperatures and converting nuclear heat to electricity more efficiently than water-cooled reactors. But until experience has been gained with these coolants comparable to that obtained with water at Hanford and Shippingport, the full potential of these types of reactor will not be known. A young man entering the nuclear engineering profession today has a fine opportunity to participate in the development of these novel types of reactors, or to conceive of even more advanced reactor systems.

Another extension of nuclear submarine technology awaiting exploitation by nuclear engineers is development of economic nuclear power plants for merchant ship propulsion. Successful operation of the nuclear merchant ship Savannah has demonstrated the feasibility of the concept, but nuclear engineers have much to do before nuclear ship propulsion is a commercial success. The type of reactor best suited to ship propulsion must be determined, and great engineering skill must be exercised in adapting the nuclear power plant to shipboard use. The power plant must be made more efficient and its costs reduced without loss of reliability. The increases in speed potentially attainable with nuclear propulsion and the increased cargo carrying capacity obtained by eliminating storage space needed for conventional fuels provide great incentives for this development.

Another assignment to challenge nuclear engineers is the development of economical breeder reactors, which can obtain nuclear energy from abundant uranium 238 or thorium as well as from the scarce isotope uranium 235, which is the principal energy source in today's water-cooled reactors. If such breeder reactors could be developed, the available resources of nuclear fuel would be extended so greatly that the world's needs for electric power could be supplied for millions of years. From the long-range point of view, development of breeder reactors is the most significant nuclear engineering problem in the world today.

To obtain nuclear energy from uranium 238, it is necessary to convert it first to plutonium, by reacting uranium 238 with neutrons. By using a mixture of plutonium and uranium 238 as fuel in a properly designed reactor, it is theoretically possible to convert enough uranium 238 into plutonium to replace the plutonium as fast as it is consumed. Such a breeder reactor, however, must be very different from today's water-cooled systems. Use of plutonium in place of uranium 235 as fissionable material introduces many new problems. To obtain a sufficient yield of neutrons from plutonium, it is necessary to induce fission with high-speed neutrons instead of the low-speed neutrons that make up most of the neutron population in water-cooled reactors. Consequently, plutonium breeder reactors must be of the sodium-cooled or gas-cooled type.

A breeder reactor fueled with thorium operates through the intermediate formation of uranium 233, produced by reacting neutrons with thorium. Uranium 233 is fissionable, like plutonium, but to use uranium 233 effectively in breeding, still a different type of reactor, such as a reactor cooled by heavy water, is needed.

To solve the technical problems of these various types of breeder reactors and to determine which can produce power at lowest cost is a task that will occupy nuclear engineers for many years to come.

Many other uses of nuclear reactors await exploitation by nuclear engineers. Since man uses at least as much energy in the form of heat as in the form of electricity, it is important to determine in what situations nuclear heat can compete with heat from coal, oil, or gas. One possible application of nuclear heat now coming into prominence is the production of fresh water from the ocean. The full development of many dry regions of the world, such as southern California and the Middle East, is handicapped by the lack of low-cost water. If nuclear engineers can provide cheap and abundant water from the ocean, they will literally "make the desert blossom as the rose."

A unique property of nuclear fuel, already exploited in the nuclear submarine, is its compactness. Since so much energy can be obtained from so little mass, nuclear reactors have unique value wherever energy is needed in remote locations, where the great cost of transporting conventional fuels would be prohibitive. Nuclear engineers can participate in development of compact nuclear reactors as energy sources for power stations in the Arctic and Antarctic, in remote mountain regions, on the bottom of the ocean, in space craft, and on the surface of the moon. The ability of nuclear power plants to function without oxygen makes them practically essential for undersea, space, and lunar applications.

Another exciting use of nuclear energy in space is as a heat source for rocket engines. With compact U-235 as fuel and liquid hydrogen as propellant, it is hoped that much greater thrust-to-weight ratios can be obtained than in chemically fueled rockets. Such nuclear propelled rockets are essential if we are ever to take large payloads to other planets. In the Rover project of the Atomic Energy Commission and the National Aeronautics and Space Administration, nuclear engineers are trying to solve the many problems of this type of rocket engine. Among these problems are development of a nuclear fuel that will resist chemical attack by hot hydrogen and design of a structure that will withstand stresses induced by the enormous temperature changes between the deep cold of liquid hydrogen and the fierce heat of nuclear fission.

The widespread use of nuclear reactors has made radioisotopes much cheaper and more readily available than when the only source was radium and the few other natural radioactive elements. Radioisotopes are now obtained both from the fission products remaining after nuclear fuel has been burned, and from absorption of reactor-produced neutrons in elements to be made radioactive, such as cobalt. Nuclear engineers now produce millions of curies of both types of radioisotope, which are the equivalent of millions of grams of radium. Nuclear engineers are also concerned with developing new uses for these versatile and valuable substances.

In trace quantities, radioisotopes are used to follow living processes, such as the uptake of fertilizer by a plant or the assimilation of food or a drug by a human patient. They are used to follow materials in a chemical process, such as determining whether sulfur in cast iron comes from the coke or the iron ore. They determine how materials move in nature—underground waters, ocean currents, or the circulation of the atmosphere. Nuclear engineers select the best radioisotope for a particular experiment, devise instruments sensitive enough to detect radioisotopes at the low levels that must often be used to avoid health or safety hazards, and carry out and interpret the experiment.

In large quantities, radioisotopes have rapidly increasing industrial and research uses. Nuclear engineers are designing electric generators without moving parts, in which heat from an electron-emitting radioisotope, such as strontium 90, is converted directly into electricity by thermocouples or thermionic devices. Such radioisotope power sources of up to several hundred watts capacity are being used in unattended weather stations, harbor channel markers, underwater sonar generators and power packages for satellites. Gamma-emitting radioisotopes such as cobalt 60 are used in medical therapy, sterilizing pharmaceutical products, killing insects, and preserving food. The design of efficient gamma irradiating equipment coupled with radioisotope production facilities in a reactor is an important field for nuclear engineers.

Nuclear engineers take part in the design, construction, and operation of high-energy particle accelerators. These are used for research in nuclear science and engineering, as neutron generators, as radiation sources for industrial processes such as curing of plastics, and as a source of ions for fusion experiments.

One of the most challenging and difficult fields for nuclear engineers is research on the fusion reaction. In the fusion reaction high-speed heavy hydrogen ions combine to form helium ions and neutrons, and liberate even more energy per unit mass of reactants than does uranium in fission. Because of this high energy output and the abundance of heavy hydrogen in nature, the fusion reaction is potentially of tremendous value. A practical, controlled fusion reactor would provide the world with still another energy resource of unlimited abundance.

But no practical fusion reactor for releasing energy in a steady, controlled manner has yet been developed. What makes this development so difficult is the fact that a controlled fusion reaction must be carried out in a fully ionized plasma, heated to a temperature of millions of degrees, and confined by a strong magnetic field. As much is still to be learned about such thermonuclear plasmas, research on their properties is of great interest to nuclear engineers. Other problems challenging nuclear engineers are development of a practical reactor for producing and confining a thermonuclear plasma and design of efficient and economic means for recovering the energy and neutrons produced in the fusion reaction.

From all this it is apparent that a young man entering the nuclear engineering profession has a choice of many exciting and important fields. In addition, he may choose among almost as many different types of activity as of fields in which to work. He may select a position involving research, development, design, manufacture, operation, or management. A few examples will illustrate the nature of each type of activity.

Research may be either theoretical or experimental. To illustrate each type of research, we may consider how nuclear engineers are endeavoring to learn how to confine the hot plasma needed for a successful fusion reactor. Although the basic laws governing the motion of individual ions in electric and magnetic fields are completely known, the collective behavior of many ions interacting with each other and with their confining fields has many puzzling aspects. The theoretically-minded research engineer must apply the most advanced mathematical techniques to understand the collective behavior of ions in a plasma and to devise schemes for stable confinement of the ions. He then has the task of designing and building an apparatus to test the proposed scheme, and of determining how long ions can be contained by it.

The breeder reactor field will provide us with an illustration of the types of work done by nuclear engineers in research, development, design, manufacture, and operation. At the beginning of a breeder reactor project, the research engineer would have the job of measuring the nuclear properties needed for accurate design and of confirming the applicability of nuclear reactor theory to the type of reactor of interest. To do this he would build a critical assembly of plutonium and the other materials to be used in the proposed reactor. With this he would learn whether the critical mass and distribution of neutrons predicted by theory was confirmed.

The development engineer's job is to use the predictions of nuclear reactor theory and the results of the research man's experiments to evaluate the promise of different reactor designs and to decide what developmental test experiments should be carried out. He might, for example, decide to make up a new form or composition of nuclear fuel and test its performance in a reactor. The end product of this development engineer's work would be demonstration of the feasibility of a particular type of breeder reactor.

The design engineer becomes the key man when the decision is made to build a breeder reactor. From the objectives set for the reactor, the information supplied by the research man and the capabilities and limitations of the proposed type demonstrated by the development engineer, he works out a detailed design of a reactor that will do its job reliably and at minimum cost. The design engineer draws on many kinds of engineering knowledge. To name a few, he must combine information about reactor physics, properties of materials, flow of fluids, transfer of heat, attenuation of radiation and behavior of structures to obtain an optimum design. He must examine many alternative combinations of design variables, and is aided by modern high-speed computers in evaluating these alternatives. But for his final decisions he must rely on his personal engineering judgment.

When the reactor is to be built, the manufacturing team takes over. These men procure the necessary materials, supervise fabrication of the parts, often from such exotic materials as plutonium and zirconium, to exacting specifications, direct assembly of the parts into the complete reactor, and check out its performance as far as possible in the manufacturer's shop.

In the construction phase, the reactor and other parts of the breeder power plant are brought together at the plant site. Here the nuclear engineer has the job of erecting the components of the plant, often both massive and delicate, of seeing that the assembled systems are clean and tight, and of meeting the many special requirements imposed by nuclear processes. These include safe handling of fissionable and radioactive materials and field fabrication of unusual materials such as dense concrete or beryllium.

The operating nuclear engineer steps in when the plant construction is completed. His jobs are many. He must first check out the plant to be sure it has been built in accordance with specifications, that all parts are on hand and operative, and that non-nuclear performance tests are met. Then comes the ticklish job of loading nuclear fuel. As loading proceeds, the operating engineer must check continually to be sure that the designers' predictions of critical mass and control system strength are being confirmed. An error at this point might lead to an uncontrolled nuclear excursion and destruction of the reactor. After the fuel is fully loaded, the reactor is gradually brought to full power, while the performance of the control system and power plant are checked at each increase in power. Finally, when the plant is operating at full power, its performance must be kept under continuous observation, to anticipate trouble before it occurs. The operating engineer keeps track of changes in fuel composition occurring during operation, to decide when to move fuel in the reactor or replace spent fuel with fresh. The operator of a nuclear power plant has even more serious responsibility than the operator of a conventional power system because of the large amount of extra fuel present in a nuclear plant, which, if improperly used, could cause heavy damage to the reactor.

Coordination and direction of the efforts of all of the preceding members of a nuclear team is the responsibility of management. Managerial opportunities are open to experienced nuclear engineers both in private organizations and in government agencies. The Federal Atomic Energy Act gives the Atomic Energy Commission wide responsibility both for promoting nuclear developments and for regulating nuclear enterprises to ensure that efficient use is made of nuclear fuels and that radioisotopes and fissionable material are handled safely. Thus, a nuclear engineer interested in a managerial position has opportunities both in a private concern similar to those in other fields and unique opportunities with the government in helping the Atomic Energy Commission carry out its missions under the law. To be successful in either type of organization, it is especially important for the engineer to have a thorough grasp of the technical side of nuclear engineering, plus the managerial capabilities needed for success in any large and complex enterprise.

Because of the novel character of work in nuclear engineering, a young man wishing to do well in this field will require a longer period of college education than in some of the more conventional branches of engineering. A minimum of five years of college is essential.

College education for nuclear engineering should start with solid, intensive preparation in the following subjects: mathematics, through advanced calculus; physics, both classical and modern, and for men interested in fusion, advanced work in electromagnetic theory; chemistry; and engineering fundamentals, including applied mechanics, fluid flow, thermodynamics, and heat transfer. An undergraduate program leading to the bachelor's degree in applied physics or engineering science usually includes all of these subjects. In many schools an undergraduate program leading to the bachelor's degree in physics or civil, chemical, electrical, mechanical, or nuclear engineering alternatively provides adequate education in these fundamentals. After these have been mastered, the student should have at least one year of more specialized work in nuclear subjects, at the graduate level. Every student of nuclear engineering should participate in advanced research, as nothing else will teach him so well how new knowledge is gained and technical advances made. Research with one of the devices of current importance in the nuclear field—a fission reactor, an accelerator, or a plasma experiment—provides especially valuable experience.

Education through the doctor's degree is practically essential for a young man who expects to make a career of advanced research or teaching. It is less necessary for the practicing engineer, where on-the-job training can provide equivalent supplementary education.

Throughout his college education, the nuclear engineer should place more stress on fundamental information than on specific details, and should learn how to solve new problems rather than merely how old ones were solved. Nuclear engineering is evolving and changing so rapidly and so unpredictably that a young man can be sure that the details of what he learns in college will be far less useful to him than learning how to keep on learning.

I would like to conclude by stressing the bright future a nuclear engineer may look forward to. The nuclear power field is expanding rapidly. Professional opportunities are numerous and varied. Positions are open with the Atomic Energy Commission, national laboratories, universities, research institutes, and private companies. A young man entering the field can work almost anywhere in the world, from the poles to the equator or in more civilized spots between. He can work on fission or on fusion, in pure research or on practical applications. His services will be in demand and he will be well paid. He may, if he chooses, contribute to the solution of one of the world's most important problems, the development of economic means for utilizing the unlimited store of energy in the atomic nucleus. Most important of all, he will have the keen satisfaction that comes from working on challenging technical problems and using his professional skills to the fullest extent.

11 _The Design of the Whole—Systems Engineering_

BY SIMON RAMO

PRESIDENT

The Bunker-Ramo Corporation

SIMON RAMO

Born: 1913, Salt Lake City, Utah

California Institute of Technology: Ph.D., 1936

The Bunker-Ramo Corporation: President, 1964–
Thompson Ramo Wooldridge Inc.: Vice Chairman of the Board, 1961–
Member Board of Directors, 1958–
The Ramo-Wooldridge Corporation: Executive Vice President, 1953–58;
Scientific Director, U.S. Air Force Ballistic Missile Program (Atlas,
Titan, Thor), 1954–58
Hughes Aircraft Company: Vice President and Director of Operations,
1946–53
General Electric Company: Electronics Laboratory, Physics Section, Head,
1934–46

Panels for President's Advisory Committee, 1959–
Committee on Science and Technology, Chamber of Commerce of the
United States, 1960–
Space Museum, Advisory Committee, 1961–
Air Force Systems Command, Board of Visitors, 1961–
University of California at Los Angeles, Institute of Geophysics, Advisory
Council, 1962–
Harvard University School of Engineering and Applied Physics, Visitor's
Committee, 1964–
President of California Institute Associates; Trustee of California State
Colleges, Case Institute of Technology, and California Institute of
Technology
Research Associate, California Institute of Technology, 1946–, and Re-
gents Lecturer, University of California at Los Angeles, 1961

Author of scientific texts, including *Peacetime Uses of Outer Space* and
Handbook of Automation, Computation, and Control

Holder of twenty-five patents in microwaves, electron optics, guided
missiles, and automatic controls.

I F ONE is to understand the profession of engineering, if he is to know what engineering is all about, he must understand both its technical and non-technical aspects so that he can see the profession as a whole. The kind of engineering that most readily discloses both these facets is systems engineering, the design of the whole.

Systems engineering is concerned with the creation of the entire answer to some real-life problem, an answer based on science and technology. It is appropriately defined, therefore, as the design of the whole as distinct from the design of the separate parts. We all are accustomed to the word systems in such engineering projects as an electric power system, a transportation system, an intercontinental ballistic missile system, a telephone system. The word systems—or system—implies that there is an array of devices (in fact, most often both devices and people) that form an interconnected assembly or network, the whole of which has a job to perform and must be designed as an integrated harmonious ensemble.

The systems engineer has to attack this whole problem. His work must go from the recognition of the need to the creation of the complete complex of men and machines to fulfill that need. The systems engineer must find ways to go from the requirements of the user—the company, the government, the individual who is asking for the solution—to the over-all answer. He goes by way of known scientific laws, by using available designs and existing apparatus, or by creating new apparatus, and at the same time using whatever resources are necessary for

163

furnishing trained manpower. He matches all this, of course, with the all important economic and organizational factors.

He must break down the total job into its parts for the various specialists to work out. He must specify and control what they do so that it all will fit together in an engineering sense, in regard to both timing and economic balance. Out of its many facets must be created a program of steady accomplishment.

To understand this further, let us suppose that you are an engineer and that you have the job that I had for several years of being the chief engineer on the nation's intercontinental ballistic missile program. The project was full of problems. From the outset, we had to consider that the re-entry into the atmosphere might be virtually impossible to solve. Some scientists made calculations that indicated that there was just no conceivable way, within the understanding of the laws of nature, to get rid of the heat on re-entry, and that no material could ever be invented that could stand it. They spoke of the need for making the nose cone out of "unobtainium." Others pointed out that if we were to guide a ballistic missile halfway around the world to a target and hit it with military accuracy, so that the whole project would make sense, we would need to know the velocity of light to one more significant figure. If so, this would require putting some pure scientists to work to measure this basic constant of nature more accurately than it had ever been measured before. If they succeeded, those scientists would deserve a Nobel prize. These two little examples, re-entry and guidance accuracy, illustrate how pure research science figured in the whole drama in the opening act.

There were other problems that one might consider closer to "ordinary" engineering but that involved questions of great, and therefore speculative, advance. For instance, we needed to have a lighter structure, by a factor of about ten times that of any airplane or smaller rocket that we had previously designed. We needed to have complex electronic parts and other instruments that would stand up under accelerations and vibrations ten times that of any we had previously experienced.

We needed to design a flying vehicle that would be stable in flight, even though it went through an amazing set of changes in its environment, all in a few hundred seconds. First, in getting off the ground, full of fuel, the missile would be so heavy that the engines would barely lift it off slowly. It would thus have none of the stability that an airplane can be made to have as a result of the aerodynamic forces. It would be somewhat like balancing a glass full of water on the end of your finger. Then, picking up speed, it would quickly go from subsonic speed in thick air to supersonic speed in very thin air, and finally into space where the atmospheric effects are essentially nil. During all this time, it would be changing shape and weight, throwing away large pieces, changing its weight distribution as it burned fuel, and all the while it would have to be steered on an accurately controlled trajectory with a very careful control of the exact velocity with which it finished off its powered flight—if we wanted it to fall on a designated spot several thousand miles away.

We needed to know more about the earth, how it is shaped, how its gravity forces are distributed, than was known. We needed to know more about the effect of the water vapor in clouds, and the atmosphere in general, on the propagation of electromagnetic waves used for guidance.

Clearly, then, as a systems engineer I knew that the project required the participation of that class of engineer who knows science the way the best experimental research scientist and theoretical physicist know it. In other words, some of our engineers had to be individuals who might call themselves scientists, not engineers, but who had to be engineers on our project because their interest was not only to extend knowledge of science, but to apply that science as soon as it came off the laboratory "production" line.

There was good "old-fashioned" engineering, too—like making the rocket engines swivel the right amount with the least weight and equipment, like insuring that thousands of new parts would all work reliably at the same time, without making literally tens of thousands of these parts and laboriously going through the problem of debugging every one in turn while years and years and thousands of test flights went by. We had to devise ways to simulate the operation of the whole system so that we could try out various designs.

Besides this technical, or scientific, part of systems engineering, there was the non-technical question of need. Was the ICBM really needed? The question obviously is a part of the whole, yet clearly it is a non-scientific one having to do with political foreign-policy considerations. Our country, during this period, laid great emphasis on the concept of "deterrency." Our plan was to deter an aggressor nation from striking us by making it clear that he would receive such penalizing and inevitable retaliation, by means that would survive even his most vigorous surprise blow, that it would be suicidal for him to contemplate such an attack. Such considerations lie in great part outside the problems of engineering the ICBM, yet they are not entirely separate. A systems engineer could hardly go about trying to lay out a good system, a development program, and a set of designs for all the apparatus and manpower to bring the system into being, without being able to relate his science and engineering to the requirement and policy and environment and point of view of the user, the customer, the society for which the solution is intended.

How much can the nation afford for an intercontinental ballistic missile system? Why is it a better solution than manned aircraft? You do not answer such questions by some engineering numbers alone. Is the industry necessary to produce ICBM's all ready to go, or does it have to be created? Do we have enough engineers and scientists, or, for that matter, do we have enough of certain critical materials? How are we to decide which companies will be given the task of building various parts? Should it go out equally to the various states of the union, on a political basis? Is it possible to have a competition and give it to the lowest bidder when really, in the case of some components of the system, the chief engineer and his associates are not certain yet in their own minds whether it can be done at all? How much time can we allow? Is it better to spend more money in a crash program to get it earlier or, in an effort to save money, take longer in deciding how to do it? How sure can we be about what a potential enemy will be doing in the interim? How do we go about preparing all the manpower to do each part of the job, if the design is not yet complete? Do we have to test the missiles over several thousand miles? If we do, how shall we find out what has happened out there unless, as turned out to be the case, there are islands available to instrument the test range? But these islands belong to other nations. What shall be our policies on secrecy and security? Certainly these multiple questions are not matters of science; they indicate the non-technological, the non-scientific, part of systems engineering.

The ICBM example brings out the fact that the systems engineer has to be much closer to these problems that are political, that have to do with government or business, that involve resources and goals, than does an engineer who is a specialist in any one technical branch alone.

Systems engineering—the invention, the design, and the integration of the whole ensemble—is actually an old and ever-present part of practical engineering. Any device, no matter how simple, represents to some extent a systems engineering kind of problem. This applies to a chair as well as to a transportation system, to a hand tool as well as to an anti-ballistic missile system. There is always the need to break down the over-all problem into its component parts and to specify the requirements on each of those parts. There is always the problem of relating the parts to the whole, and the whole to the outside world that will be the user and that will expect a useful result. Why, then, since this field of systems engineering is an old one, is it of such growing importance? Why is there such a tremendous interest in systems engineering that did not exist a few decades ago?

The systems with which we are now concerned are far more complex and more difficult to engineer, and a typical new system depends on immediate application of the newest discoveries of basic science. Furthermore, the relationships between the engineering considerations and the economic, military, governmental, and even sociological considerations have become increasingly important. In these times, in which technology is altering our world so rapidly and in which government and industry must continually adjust to these changes, it is quite natural that systems engineering has become of widespread interest in circles that previously had little or no concern with it.

It will be helpful now to return to the technical parts of systems engineering, and to compare its over-all disciplines with those employed in the detailed and specialized engineering design of the components within the system.

We have already seen that a systems engineering team must include individuals who have broad backgrounds in fundamental science. The team must also include graduates from all the specialties that make up engineering—chemistry, metallurgy, gyroscopy, computers, vibration, aerodynamics, propulsion, guidance. This is not to suggest that a systems engineer has to be an all-around expert in everything. No one can be that. But a fraction of the specialists of each branch of engineering must broaden themselves so that they have an appreciation of the other branches, and, at the same time, they must become particularly adept at the matter of interactions. They must learn how to handle problems that are interdisciplinary in nature.

Let us illustrate these interactions and interdisciplinary problems by continuing with the intercontinental ballistic missile example. If you ask the propulsion engineer to provide the thrust to bring the rocket engine up to the necessary speed, it is not enough to tell him the magnitude and duration of thrust required and assign him a weight allowance, and then let him, working in isolation, go after the design. You must also consider that there is an interaction between the rocket thrust and the guidance accuracy. If we are not too fussy about the accuracy, then a large variation of thrust of the engine, varying from the figure we specified, can be tolerated. This makes it easier for the propulsion engineer to deliver his hardware in less time, for less cost, and with greater reliability. If, on the other hand, we allow the thrust value to be too sloppy, then the guidance engineer must complicate his apparatus to alter the trajectory continuously so as to compensate for the variable thrust and still make possible hitting the target. If we make life easier for the electronics engineer, who is trying to control the direction of the missile by sending signals into it to control its devices, then we may have to ask that the propulsion engineer produce a thrust so precisely predictable and constant that he finds it impossible.

Similarly, if we ask the group of engineers working on re-entry—these consist of experts in materials, aerodynamics, thermo-dynamics, chemistry, and stress analysis—to cut down the effect of unknown wind drift over the target to an absolute minimum, to make it easier to bring the nose cone in on the target accurately, then they are required to increase the weight of the heat shield in order to achieve fast re-entry without burning up. On the other hand, if we allow the nose cone designers too much leeway on re-entry speed, asking for the lightest heat protection, then we will find it more difficult to guide the nose cone to the required accuracy. If we give all these "subsystem" designers more liberal weight allowances, they can design with greater reliability and better performance, but then the missile may be too heavy to get off the ground. Again, if we choose certain exotic fuels, we get better performance, but we may make it dangerous for men to be around the rocket, or we may not be able to have the rocket ready to go on a moment's notice.

The systems engineer must find ways to set up all these variations—perhaps to use large computers in the process because there are so many combinations and permutations to consider—and to find optimum relationships so that he gets the best results. For this purpose, of course, a group of systems engineers must have enough knowledge of all the disciplines to be able to work with the specialists in each discipline, to give each of them challenging proposals and introduce a great deal of give and take until the best possible compromise is reached.

The systems engineer is particularly busy with the "multi-parameter" problem, and his job hardly can be put down in a nice, simple statement. He usually has too many factors bearing on the best answer to be able to write down easy mathematical equations. As a matter of fact, this is one reason why it is hard to study systems engineering realistically in college. It does not lend itself to short problems that you can take home for home-work. Every problem seems to have many variables, and the result is difficult to attack theoretically. Furthermore, the many equations to write about every aspect of the job can themselves become terribly complicated. Thus, a systems engineer must become very ingenious in finding great simplifications and ap-proximations. Like the pure research scientist who is dealing with the universe and all its multiple facets, he tries to find over-riding general laws. The systems engineer makes much use of mathematical models that are approximately true descriptions of his problem. He becomes good at approximation.

The systems engineer is repeatedly confronted with the chicken-and-egg situation. He can't settle one part of a problem until he knows the other, and vice versa. This sounds hopeless at first, does it not? Often he just specifies some parts by crude approximations (maybe first guesses), and then he assumes that certain factors are relatively unimportant and that others are most important. Then he tries to test all this by setting up the other parameters and introducing the facts to the computer. The com-puter knocks out results while the systems engineer gives the computer different possibilities, seeking to improve his theories and his decisions until he gets a pretty good match of the various facets of the design.

The multiparameter problem is truly tough because even if the sole task of the systems engineer were to analyze and predict the performance of a system whose configuration and subsystems and components were already set, the mathematical equations necessary to describe the operation of the over-all system would be hopelessly unwieldy to solve by hand. Such situations can be handled only with the aid of large-scale computers.

Large digital computers have become common only during the past several years. With their high speed and large computational capacity, thousands of engineering computations can be per-formed in a reasonable time. This makes it practical not only to explore a wide range of values for the main parameters of the system, its subsystems, and its components, but also to study a variety of competing systems having basically different configurations. In fact, one could say that systems engineering in the truly modern sense really became possible only after the advent of the large digital computer.

Digital computers, however, cannot be used conveniently or efficiently to obtain answers to all problems. In some cases even they cannot solve the equations in any reasonable time. In other cases the problems are not understood well enough for satisfactory mathematical formulation. In these circumstances, we can often turn to analog, real-time, simulation devices to act as a model that will predict the behavior of the systems. No engineering computing center is well equipped without such simulation or modeling devices. The ultimate in systems analysis techniques, reserved for the outstandingly difficult problems, is the connection of computers, simulators, and an actual portion of the system, the whole becoming a simulator on a grand scale.

Generally, the systems engineer's first problem is to invent several suitable configurations to consider. These may differ substantially in their choice of subsystems and components and in their interconnections, and yet all appear to have some reasonable chance of providing the required performance. As a consequence, the systems engineer typically must analyze not just one, but several possible approaches. Furthermore, for each basic approach, he must vary the parameters within the general idea of the particular configuration in order to find the combination that is most advantageous.

After comparing the various approaches, there may still be more than one configuration that remains in the running. There is hardly ever a single number that flatly rates one system against another. One may be more reliable but more expensive. Another may be less desirable technically, but more acceptable because it requires fewer changes in existing systems and procedures. A third, while in principle the best, will take an additional year to bring into being. The list of criteria can be both long and lacking in clarity. But one way or another, a decision must be arrived at. Hopefully, it will be prompt, and, also hopefully, it will be taken with a full appreciation of the technical, as well as the non-technical, parameters involved.

Systems engineering, more than any special branch of engineering, is concerned with another troublesome problem of the real world of applying science. I shall call this the problem of "unwanted modes." When you connect together a lot of components in a telephone system, a power system, an automation system in a factory, a reservation-making system for the airlines, an air defense system, or even an over-all automobile, it is not enough to assure that you have chosen a good ensemble of parts and a good design for each part. It isn't enough to insure that you have the right compromises of all the factors, and that the parts all relate well to each other, match up, and integrate into an ensemble that gives you the result you are seeking. You also must be sure it does not have some modes of operation you didn't ask for and didn't anticipate. It usually happens that when energy passes through various components of a system and changes form, or if information is transmitted around a network, some funny things can result that you may not have considered.

For instance, a receiver in a telephone system is left off the hook. You didn't plan it that way, but that's the way it may work, so it is necessary to list all such possibilities in the system's performance to make certain it is not impaired. You plan a heating system with a thermostatic control that is supposed to stay at 70°—and indeed it does, by oscillating between 80° and 60°, which you had not expected. It is hardly ever comfortable, but it averages 70° on the nose, just as specified.

"Feedback," in which some of the output comes back around to the input, can make the whole system oscillate unstably. For instance, a missile is about to miss the target, and the guidance system recognizes this, just as the design calls for it to do. The guidance signal urges a quick motion to the left. As the missile moves to the left, responding beautifully, it overshoots just a little (which we may not have anticipated fully), whereupon the guidance system frantically calls for it to turn back to the right. The missile control surfaces respond by moving all out to the right, so that the greater the excursions, the greater and more desperate becomes the signal that asks for the correction, with the result that the missile is wildly oscillating between two extremes. On the average, it may hit the target only in the silly sense that half of all missiles fall too far to the right and the other half too far to the left—a useless device that nevertheless performs "well" by some really worthless average performance specifications. These matters of stability, oscillations, overshooting, inadvertent peculiar modes of operation, must all be examined because the systems engineer must think of everything, and he must find organized ways to be sure he has gone through all the possible relationships in the design.

The systems engineer is especially aware of something that is true in all of nature, and that is the indefiniteness of it. We should recognize that no problem ever comes up, except perhaps in the textbook in school, with infinite precision. To start with, the initial specifications for a systems engineering problem must be stated in terms of probability if they are going to be truly realistic. We may wish to design a system, for example, that will shoot down enemy bombers if they come to attack us. But we have to specify what we are shooting against in terms of probabilities and not exactitudes. As a result, we have to be satisfied with describing the objectives of our proposed system in terms of a given probability of shooting down a certain fraction of enemy bombers that we have already specified as having certain probabilities of certain speeds, numbers, altitudes, and so on.

Even if we did not have to live with the probabilities of the external conditions, the performance of our system would still have to be described in terms of probabilities. For instance, every part in the system can be described only approximately. Each electronic tube, each gear, each switch, each transformer has some range within which it deviates from its optimum value (to say nothing of the occasional error that is bound to slip in). We accept this spread in faithfulness from one end of the system to the other and allow for it as best we can because to do otherwise is to ask for the impossible. To specify performance so rigidly that the spread is no longer important is to add greatly to the costs and probably delay the program, and for large, complex systems it would be strictly impossible.

The fact that we have a huge number of components in modern

systems will of itself often require that we specify conditions of performance and of design by probable values rather than by precise ones. This is something like saying that in a Gallup poll for a national election we must be satisfied to talk about the probable general reaction without trying to predict or measure the precise response of every individual in the population. We do not have to have fifty million components before this concept begins to be important. We simply have to have enough so that it becomes impractical to measure with sufficient precision the workings of each of the individual parts.

The probability problem is worth dwelling on in other respects. Most systems depend upon information transfer throughout the system, be they intercontinental ballistic missile systems, electronic banking systems, or world-wide communication systems. All components of a system capable of transmitting, handling, or storing information also have the characteristic that they produce some noise. They can never be completely quiet. Every electron tube always has electrons moving about in response to the natural interactions among the electrons and atoms caused by the local temperature of the tube. These moving electrons continously contribute to the tube output along with any signals that are being carried. A system for information transfer must be able to out-shout this natural noise, just as a home radio should be designed so that the background static is not too annoying to the ear that is trying to concentrate on the music being transmitted. This kind of noise, from the systems engineering standpoint, is only one example of the causes of errors that are produced by unwanted, as well as wanted, signals being pushed through the system from one end to the other. While it is obviously desirable to have a high "signal-to-noise" ratio, we must also recognize that there are practical limits to how high this ratio can go. A part of the systems design problem is to insure that the ratio is high enough to achieve the specified probability of success in transmitting the signal without error.

As we mentioned earlier, human beings are often parts of the system. They have their own possibilities of performing their duties with errors. They, also, can introduce "noise," unwanted responses that take their place in the system along with the proper responses.

Among his other responsibilities, the systems engineer usually has a very tough job of testing. A big, expensive system cannot be built and then taken apart and rebuilt in a trial-and-error attempt to make it work. In any engineering problem, the nicest approach is always to understand everything so well that you just lay out the best design on paper, build it that way, and it works. But if the problem is complicated and new, if it involves a huge number of components, if some of the scientific phenomena are still being worked out, if the cost and even the geographical spread of the whole ensemble is fantastically large, then the systems engineer is faced with a dilemma. He cannot afford to build the whole thing to experiment with it, to try it out and come to understand its behavior; nor can he afford to rely on paper designs alone, because he cannot be that confident of all his information. Accordingly, he has to be ingenious in organizing his test program. He must set up parts of the problem on strong theoretical basis where he is confident that he has the science and the detailed information. He must choose some experiments to pin down a key issue. He must perform some tests of a confirming nature with the actual hardware, and then he must simulate the operation of the rest of the system through a cheaper, adjustable model, as previously indicated. He must fix it so that the parts that remain when he builds the whole, the parts that will still need adjusting and debugging and reworking, are a satisfactorily small enough portion that both his cost and time schedule can be met. The same kind of individual who delights in devising an ingenious experiment to track down some illusive aspect of the laws of nature will find similar satisfactions in devising ways to assure that a complicated system will work.

It is easier now to understand why the systems engineer uses large-size simulators and computers. In fact, we "flew" the equivalent of thousands of missiles on our computers as part of the process of shaking down the design. We tested parts of the missile system separately. We devised various ways of bringing the parts together so as to check out the interactions of one part on the other before building the complete missile. We "shot" some hardware down. We held complete missiles on a stand, not allowing them to fly, while giving them the equivalent of a short flight. We introduced many channels of telemetry onto our missiles as they flew, recording what happened throughout the missile. We devised a flight-test program of a few flights that shook down the remainder of the unanswered questions, and we did this not only by instrumenting the missile at every unknown point, but by choosing tasks for the missiles to do during the flight that were different from what they would ordinarily be called on to do. As a result, a few flights (a dozen or so) were enough to complete the data-gathering, settle the design, and confirm that we had a successful intercontinental ballistic missile system. Without this kind of systems engineering and without the benefit of the computers and simulators and the special "static" tests, we would have needed so many test flights that an intercontinental ballistic missile system would have been utterly impossible even to contemplate.

How do you prepare yourself for systems engineering? It may sound at first as though the designing of the whole requires that the systems engineer be a superman, and it is a little difficult to prepare yourself to be a superman. But, really, the systems engineer, to a first approximation, merely embodies characteristics that make for success in any kind of engineering. Preparing in the background science and avoiding specialization in the early years of college is probably a good idea, no matter what branch of engineering a person might be interested in eventually.

It has been my experience that some of the best systems engineers are merely graduates from some specialized branch who have learned to be good engineers, and then gradually have become interested in the broader problems. They have become more curious than the average engineer, or scientist, in the interaction of the various disciplines, electronics, nucleonics, space, and so on. Also, they may have become tired, perhaps, of their specialized field, and have begun to be interested in similarities and differences among the various branches. They expose themselves to at least a little understanding of some of the other branches, and in time they become expert at the various tricks of the trade such as handling the problems of trade-offs and interactions. They get accustomed to the idea of the indefiniteness that is typical of systems engineering. They learn that there is more than one answer to a problem and that it is sometimes difficult to pick out which approach is best.

It should be said, too, that a good systems engineer is a scientist or engineer who finds himself interested in the non-technical aspects of a program and finally begins to be pretty good at working with these interactions.

Systems engineering, to be useful in designs of structures and mechanisms, has to be a great deal more than the science that is behind it and a great deal more than the working out of formulations from that science. While systems engineering has always meant applying science to achieving an integrated answer to a real, total problem, this creative effort today operates in a new environment, one in which technological effort is revolutionizing society. Now, more than ever, systems engineering effort must be in proper match with social, industrial, economic, governmental, and psychological needs. So complex is the list of considerations that no one will become the best systems engineer merely by learning the technical facets.

The well-rounded education of the engineer today is not met by injecting some courses in the humanities into the over-all curriculum of science and engineering. Too often such courses in the humanities have been organized to "broaden" the young engineer as a man, to make him a happier and more useful citizen. It is true that his personal adjustment to life may be improved by study of these non-technical subjects, but besides this study there is needed an acceptance of the idea that non-technical courses of the right kind are necessary to complete his *engineering* education.

The broad engineering education he needs should give him some understanding of the world outside of engineering, and a knowledge that an over-all, real-life engineering job is not complete unless his solution matches and fits this outside non-technological world. It is necessary that he be broadly educated in society as well as in science, not as a luxury in personal development but as a part of his professional preparation, so that his professional activity will be truly competent.

12 *Metallurgy and Materials*

BY OSCAR T. MARZKE

VICE PRESIDENT, FUNDAMENTAL RESEARCH

United States Steel Corporation

OSCAR T. MARZKE

Born: 1907, Lansing, Michigan

Michigan State University: B.S., 1929
Massachusetts Institute of Technology: D.Sc., 1932

American Steel and Wire (Worcester, Massachusetts):
  Research Laboratory, 1933–34
  Assistant Director, Research Laboratory, 1934–38
  Assistant District Metallurgist, 1938–40
  Works Metallurgist, North Works, 1940–42
  Works Metallurgist, Waukegan Works, 1942–46
U.S. Naval Research Laboratory:
  Superintendent Metallurgy Division, 1946–54
  Associate Director of Research, 1954–55
  Director of Research, 1956–57
Office of Naval Research:
  Head, Metallurgy Branch, 1951–53
United States Steel Corporation (Pittsburgh):
  Vice President, Fundamental Research, 1957–

National Academy of Sciences:
  Materials Advisory Board, Navy Liaison Member, 1952–57; Member,
    1960–64
  Highway Research Board, Executive Committee, 1962–
American Institute of Mining, Metallurgical and Petroleum Engineers:
  Chairman, Institute of Metals Division, 1959
  Board of Directors, Metallurgical Society, 1963–
Iron and Steel Institute (British)
Institute for Metals (British)
Research Society of America
Washington Academy of Sciences

Member: National Science Foundation, Advisory Panel for the Engineer-
    ing Sciences, 1959–61
  Visiting Committee, Department of Metallurgy, Massachusetts Institute
    of Technology, 1958–62
  Advisory Committee, School of Metallurgical Engineering, University
    of Pennsylvania, 1958–62
  Advisory Committee, Department of Metallurgical Engineering, Car-
    negie Institute of Technology, 1962
  Advisory Committee, Metallurgy Division, National Bureau of Stand-
    ards, 1962–
  American Society for Metals, Documentation Committee, 1963–

IT WAS a very long time ago, even before written history, when that early dim fellow first made copper, inadvertently, at his fire on a hearth of a copper mineral. Almost the whole history of civilization lies between that day and today. The story of man and metals is long and infinitely diverse; it is part of the history of household arts, agriculture, hunting, warfare, the decorative arts, printing, commerce; and it is a most important part of the history of the long-continuing industrial revolution. Throughout the long years it has always been clear that he who made metals was of the greatest importance to society."

The above quotation is taken from the 1960 Henry Marion Howe Lecture of Professor R. F. Mehl, one of this country's most distinguished metallurgists. It puts any discussion of metallurgy and of those who have chosen it as their profession—the metallurgists—into good perspective.

What are metallurgists? What do they do? Most people would probably say they must do something with metals. While this is certainly true, it is not a very helpful answer; it does not say very much about one of the world's oldest professions, one that obviously goes back to the Bronze Age, and yet one that today is looked upon to solve many of the problems upon which so many of the current important technical developments—atomic power, missiles, space vehicles, electronic devices—are dependent.

If you should ask metallurgists what they do, you might become quite confused, for you would probably receive many different answers. The reason is that metallurgy covers a broad range of activities. It spreads over the whole spectrum of research and technology, from basic research to test and evaluation; and it touches and frequently uses just about every field of science and engineering. One metallurgist may be working on the chemistry of complex minerals in order to get information that would be useful for developing a method for separating a metal from an ore. Another may be studying the electronic properties of a new alloy, or the mechanism of solidification, or the design of a plant to produce a million tons of steel a year. Another may be working on the production of a few grams of a highly purified compound for an electronic application, on quality or process control, on applications for a newly developed alloy, or with the sales department to solve a customer's problem.

As a metallurgist, you may be in research, in production, in sales. You may be associated with a business organization, an academic institution, or may be working for yourself. You may be called a scientist or an engineer. You may work in a laboratory, in a plant, or in an air-conditioned office. You may work by yourself or with a group. While you may only have to turn out reports, you may also have to sell your ideas to skeptical people. You may become an executive and have to handle all sorts of problems and people. You will, however, have one thing in common with all other metallurgists, and that is an interest in metals.

In view of the wide scope of these activities, it is not surprising that metallurgists have graduated as chemists, physicists, chemical engineers, mechanical engineers, and so on, as well as metallurgists. It is often recognized and frequently said that today's complex problems can be solved only by bringing many scientific or technical disciplines to bear on them, and this is certainly true of metallurgy, for it has been an interdisciplinary activity for many years. Yet it offers many areas of specialization and may be entered via several academic routes.

Perhaps it also offers something else. The metallurgist is continually faced with complex problems that have several variables, some of which are not—at present anyway—subject to exact or quantitative treatment. He develops special skills to handle them. Such complex systems are, of course, widespread; we encounter them frequently in our daily lives. Training and experience as a metallurgist develop abilities that are helpful for constructive participation in many other activities.

My introduction to metallurgy occurred during my senior year in college while working for a degree in chemical engineering. One of the few elective courses was one in metallurgy. Since the equipment used for the production of chemicals is largely metallic, this looked like a good supplementary course. Here I was introduced to such things as the heat treatment of steel. The variations in properties, and the accompanying changes in structure resulting from different heat treating schedules, fascinated me. The structure just mentioned really should be called microstructure, since it was necessary to use a miscroscope and look at the structures with a magnification of 100X or greater. Many were beautiful and, I thought, could well be exhibited as pieces of modern art. I became so interested that I decided to do graduate work in metallurgy.

Upon finishing graduate school, I took a job with a wire manufacturer who made a great variety of products from steel, copper and aluminum. At that time there was limited technical information on many of the processes and products. Some had been developed through trial and error over a period of many years and had been passed on from father to son. Then making of wire was much more of an art than a science. My job was to add a little more science so that a consistently better product and a better yield could be obtained. It required, in addition to laboratory work, transferring the findings into practice. This was challenging, sometimes frustrating, but generally rewarding.

What are the opportunities for metallurgists today and what are the current problems of greatest interest and importance? Suppose we start by mentioning those of outer space. Here there are two major metallurgical problems, that of high strength-to-weight ratio and that of resistance to high temperature. The first is associated with the structure or frame of the rocket or launching vehicle; the second with the rocket engine, nose cone, or re-entry body.

A high strength-to-weight ratio material is necessary in order to carry the maximum payload, for the heavier the weight of the structure, the smaller the payload. But the structural material, in addition to having high strength-to-weight ratio, must also have sufficient ductility so that it can withstand handling prior to launch and buffeting during flight. Unfortunately, an increase in strength is generally accompanied by a decrease in ductility. Thus there has been, and still is, a large effort on the part of metal producers, missile manufacturers, government laboratories, and other groups to improve ductility at high strength levels. Considerable laboratory evidence has been obtained to indicate that greater ductility may be possible, but these laboratory findings must be verified or confirmed and then methods worked out so that they can be used in production. This latter may well turn out to be the most difficult problem of all, for entirely new methods of manufacture, new tools, and new controls may have to be developed. Moreover, many of the presently encouraging leads may have to be abandoned, for they may be impossible or very difficult to apply, or may give much less improvement than anticipated.

The second problem is that of developing materials to withstand very high temperatures for relatively short times. While a partially satisfactory solution for present applications has been obtained through an ingenious combination of materials and design, designers would like better materials so as to permit greater efficiency of operation, simpler design, and easier fabrication. Here, refractory metals, those having very high melting points, such as tungsten and molybdenum, ceramics, metal-ceramics, combinations, and other types of composites, are being investigated. These materials must not only retain strength but must also be able to withstand the corrosive environments in which they are frequently used.

The ability to withstand high temperatures is also a prime requirement for the structure and skin of the supersonic aircraft —Mach 2-3—that are now under discussion. The skin temperatures of planes operating at a speed of Mach-3 will reach several hundred degrees. Materials used must not only retain their strength at these temperatures, but also must not oxidize or corrode appreciably during the exposure for the thousands of hours that such aircraft will be operated. Here, also, it is not necessary to use a single, homogeneous material. A composite made from several different materials may very well be the best solution. This has led to studies of all sorts of combinations of materials—plastics, ceramics, metals—in many different forms, such as powders, fibers, and sheets. But with such materials there is not only the problem of making the components and then the composite but also of forming and joining the composite. The latter may well be the most difficult thing to do.

There are also major metallurgical problems in under-the-sea activities. The Navy wants submarines to go deeper and deeper. Here again, higher strength-to-weight materials are required. And again, the old problem of brittleness at high strength levels comes up, for submarines must be able to withstand not only the pressure due to the water depth, but also the effects from weapons and the possible accidental damage encountered in normal operation. The hulls have, of course, to be fabricated, and this involves forming and joining, with all the many difficulties that are encountered in doing so with high strength materials.

The newer types of power systems—nuclear, thermoelectric, magnetohydrodynamic, fusion—about which you hear and read so much these days, require extremely high operating temperatures. (Even the efficiency of conventional power systems improves with increased temperature.) Again, the materials for these systems must have not only the necessary strength at the high operating temperatures, but also the ability to stand up more or less indefinitely at these temperatures and frequently in a reactive environment. Cyril Stanley Smith, a distinguished metallurgist who was in charge of the metallurgical work at the Los Alamos Laboratory during the development of the atomic bomb, described the metallurgist's role in these new developments very well when he stated during a round-table discussion on the atomic bomb back in February of 1946: "Anything conceived by a physicist sooner or later turns out to involve a metallurgical problem."

One can safely say that there is now, and probably always will be, an increasing demand for materials that can be used at higher and higher temperatures, that have higher strength-to-weight ratios, that have greater ductility at high strength levels, that have better oxidation and corrosion resistance. Metallurgists will always have plenty to do.

Perhaps a little more detail on how we stand on some of these problems would be of interest. Significant improvements can, of course, be best made if we know the basic mechanisms that govern and control them. During the past few years, our knowledge and understanding of what controls strength and ductility have greatly increased. This has resulted from both theoretical and experimental work. (The atoms in metals, as you undoubtedly know, are arranged in a regular pattern. Deviation from regularity —caused by introduction of atoms of other elements, by missing atoms, or by misalignment—is the most important factor governing strength and ductility.) We can account qualitatively, at least, for the wide gap that exists between the theoretical strength of a metal and that which is usually found. In the case of iron, which has a theoretical strength of about 2,000,000 pounds per square inch, very small whiskers of high purity have been produced that approach this value. Yet similar high purity iron in massive form has a strength of less than 10,000 psi. This great difference is due to the large number of imperfections in the massive iron, imperfections that we would like to know how to remove, introduce and control. Today we can actually observe the action of some of the important defects by looking through thin sections of metal with an electron microscope. Such microscopes can magnify over 100,000X.

Nature, however, does not give up its secrets of metals any more easily than it does on most other things. There are problems that have been under investigation for over a quarter of a century without resulting in a completely satisfactory answer. One of these is the brittle, catastrophic failure of large welded structures. The seriousness of this problem was brought out forcefully during World War II when some of the hastily constructed ocean-going vessels suffered severe damage, sometimes even broke completely in two, during rough seas or cold weather. Today we know how to specify and produce steels that, along with better design and methods of construction, can eliminate this type of failure. But we still do not know exactly why certain heats of steel, of essentially the same composition and method of manufacture, are more susceptible to this type of failure than others. There is considerable evidence that some impurities in very small quantities may be the culprits. This, along with an interest to know what the properties of really pure iron are, has led to a sizable effort to produce pure iron. This is another challenging problem, one that involves not only new methods of preparation but also new ones for analysis.

Today the primary interest in high purity materials stems from the effect of small, controlled amounts of impurities on the electrical, magnetic, and electronic properties of several materials, particularly the semi-conductors. Because of their experience in producing high purity materials, metallurgists are collaborating with solid-state physicists and electrical and electronic engineers in the development of the many remarkable solid-state devices, such as the transistors, that are now so well known. Such devices are possible because metallurgists developed techniques for producing very high purity single crystals and for introducing into them impurities on the order of a few parts per million. The current rate of development of such devices indicates that here there will be many further opportunities for metallurgists.

We are not as far advanced in our knowledge and understanding of the basic mechanisms of oxidation and corrosion as we are in those of strength and ductility. This is most unfortunate, for it is estimated that our annual bill for corrosion in the United States exceeds five billion dollars. New tools and new approaches have been introduced or suggested recently that should be very helpful in our attack on these problems. One of the new tools is a microscope that permits observations of individual atom sites. With this instrument one can study the movement of atoms, their reaction with other atoms, their impurities, and the growth of reaction products.

Metallurgists are, of course, concerned with problems of production as well as those of properties. Here the principal objective is usually to improve quality or to lower cost. New knowledge, new types of equipment, new materials of construction offer continued opportunities for process improvement. In the steel industry, for example, the blast furnace practice has been modified within the last few years so that without increasing the size of furnace, the rate of production is almost doubled. And the availability of pure oxygen in large quantities at low cost prompted the development of oxygen steelmaking furnaces that have a rate of production more than six-fold that of open-hearth furnaces, which have been and still are the principal means of production.

There is also a change under way in the casting of the molten steel. The traditional way has been to cast it into ingots of fixed size that may vary from a few pounds to many tons. Generally, some part of such ingots is unsuitable for further processing due to porosity or segregation, and this results in an appreciable loss. The loss could be minimized, of course, if casting could be done continuously. Some non-ferrous producers have been doing this successfully for many years, and the process has been generally considered to be limited to the handling of small tonnages, such as those characteristic of the non-ferrous producers. Recently, considerable interest in this process has been shown by the steel industry. The interest stems not only from the possibility of increased yield, but also of improved quality. Several such installations now casting steel are in Europe, and several are being constructed or planned for the United States.

Undoubtedly, problems will develop in the introduction of this method, and extensive study of the process will be required in order to develop practices that will permit attainment of maximum production along with optimum quality. Then, of course, there is the possibility of a truly continuous operation in which ores go in one end and solid metal comes out the other. This has intrigued metallurgists for some time, and several schemes have been proposed and some investigated. Such a process has many difficult problems, and much research and engineering ingenuity will be required before a completely satisfactory one will be developed.

In some of the earlier paragraphs I have used the word

materials in place of, or in addition to, metals. In many applications several different types of materials may be used, and the choice may largely be based on economics. For other purposes, perhaps only one material may be suitable, and this may not necessarily be a metal. But metals and other materials that are used for structural purposes have so many things in common that it is difficult, if not impossible, to divorce them. I would like to say a little more about other materials that are used in "competition" with metals for structural purposes—ceramics, glasses, plastics.

Because of the ability of ceramics to withstand high temperatures, the principal interest in them is for those high temperature applications where metals are not suitable. The biggest drawback of ceramics is lack of ductility. Much research is being done to improve resistance to both thermal and mechanical shock. While the possibility of obtaining appreciable ductility appears small, it may well be that sufficient improvement can be made so that these materials, coupled with design modification, may be successfully used.

Remarkable strides have been made in improving the toughness of glass. You may have one development in your own kitchens, namely, glass capable of being heated to a high temperature and then plunged into water, or of being dropped on the floor without breaking. Not so long ago, a sheet glass was announced so tough and flexible that it is being used in the rear windshield of a convertible automobile top. And everyone is familiar with the wide use of glass fibers in fishing rods, boats, and golf clubs. The fibers are combined with a plastic to form a composite structure. Composites are very promising materials for meeting some of the unusual requirements with which we are faced; they offer unlimited possibilities through combining various materials in different forms and ways. The study and development of composites is just beginning; the results are very encouraging.

The ancient prophets who foretold a time when "they shall beat their swords into plowshares and their spears into pruning hooks" spoke of a time not yet here, a vision of improved man not yet brought to reality. But improved plowshares, better swords, missiles instead of spears we can and do make. In the world of science there is progress, and acceleration of progress, and of opportunity. Possibly this age of progress and opportunity in science and all the industries and activities based thereon—just possibly, this age may be the necessary prelude to the centuries when even the cantankerous problems of humanity itself may become subject to solution. The long-range view of all scientific work is immense. The near view of metallurgy and materials is full of variety, and full of opportunity and challenge.

13 Energy and Energy Conversion

BY PHILIP SPORN

CHAIRMAN
SYSTEM DEVELOPMENT COMMITTEE
American Electric Power Co., Inc.

PHILIP SPORN

Born: Austria, 1896; naturalized U.S., 1907

Columbia University School of Engineering: E.E., 1917; Postgraduate work, 1917–18

Numerous honorary doctoral degrees from such schools as Stevens Institute of Technology, Illinois Institute of Technology, Polytechnic Institute of Brooklyn, Ohio State University, University of Grenoble (France), and Haifa Technion (Israel).

American Electric Power Company, 1920–
   Vice President and Chief Engineer, 1934
      President and Director—also of the 20 companies in the American Electric Power Company System, 1947–61
      Chairman, System Development Committee, Director and member Executive Committee, 1961–

Ohio Valley Electric Corporation, President and Director, 1952–
East Central Nuclear Group, Chairman Research and Development Committee, 1958–
Chairman, U.S. AEC Ad Hoc Advisory Committee on Cooperation Between Electric Power Industry and AEC, 1949–51
AEC Ad Hoc Advisory Committee on Reactor Policies and Programs, 1959
U.S. State Department Ad Hoc Advisory Committee on U.S. Policy Toward the International Atomic Energy Agency, 1962
U.S. Delegation Geneva Conference for Peaceful Uses of Atomic Energy, Member, 1955; Accredited Observer, 1958
Chairman, Sea Water Conversion Commission, Government of Israel, 1959–
Chairman, Executive Advisory Committee, Federal Power Commission, National Power Survey, 1962–
Member of advisory groups for several colleges and universities

Member, National Academy of Sciences
Fellow and Honorary Member, American Society of Mechanical Engineers, Institute of Electrical and Electronic Engineers
Fellow, American Society of Civil Engineers
Chevalier French Legion of Honor
Recipient numerous awards and honors from professional associations

Author: Books and numerous articles in field of energy, electric power generation, transmission, and utilization

Inventor: In the field of electric power generation and transmission

THE WORLD as we know it today would be inconceivable without the ubiquitous use of very large quantities of inanimate energy. This is likely to be even more so in the world of to-morrow.

There are currently four principal sources of primary energy: falling water, coal, oil, and gas. Rising increasingly large on the horizon is a fifth source: nuclear fuel, or atomic power. Minor primary energy sources, more or less exotic and negligible in their over-all economic value, are wind power, solar energy, and tidal power.

Electric energy is not a *primary* source of energy. It is a converted, highly refined form of energy. In the United States at the present time 20% of the total energy used is converted to the electric form. Electric energy is important in technologically and economically advanced societies, and, indeed, it has contributed significantly to the technological and economic progress in such societies.

The discovery, extraction, delivery, and application of the several forms of primary energy and the development of the technology for their conversion into electric energy have provided outlets for the investment of human and capital resources unmatched in their challenge. In particular, the problems associated with the exploitation of energy resources and energy conversion present exciting opportunities to engineers of character who are properly trained and possess imagination and dedication.

The great productivity and high standard of living and material welfare that have been achieved in our American society have been characterized by the application, in increasing quanti-

193

ties, of our large variety of abundant fossil fuels to activate almost all industrial processes and make our entire society mobile and dynamic. There can be no doubt, therefore, that the problems of energy and energy conversion are important and are fraught with an incalculable social and economic influence upon the future development and enhancement of our society and, therefore, merit a great deal of attention and study.

The development of energy use in the past can serve as a valuable guide to an understanding of energy use in the present and, even more importantly, to its potential future significance.

While man for thousands of years has had available to him the supplementary energy of tamed animals, by far the largest contributor of animate energy in man's history has been man himself. However, as an energy producer, man is extremely limited; and as long as he was dependent upon his own energy, supplemented by the contributions of his other animate servants, his progress in the production of food, clothing, and other goods was extremely limited.

Major strides in material progress and rising productivity began to appear with the development of mechanical energy, which ushered in the industrial revolution in England some two hundred years ago. Only then did it become possible for more than a relatively small segment of the population to aspire to and achieve standards of living above the bare subsistence level.

In the United States the commercial exploitation of mineral energy is roughly two hundred years old, the bicentennial of the first commercial production of coal in Virginia having been celebrated in 1959. However, coal was not consumed in significant quantities until about 1860. Thereafter it quickly began to substitute for wood as a railroad locomotive fuel and as a source of coke for the growing steel industry. In the fifty-year interval to 1910, energy use expanded more than seven-fold and coal increased to over 75% of the total energy use of the country. At about 1910, however, coal began to lose its relative position in the total energy supply, first to petroleum and later to natural gas. These fuels began to supply an increasing share of the total energy until at the present time they account for more than two-thirds.

The appearance of the automobile and the expanding automotive use of petroleum provided the major impetus to the growth in the petroleum share of total energy in the last half century. To this has been added the displacement of coal-fired heating by oil heating systems and, especially during the last two decades, the almost total conversion from coal-fired steam locomotive to the diesel-electric locomotive.

The expansion in natural gas use that has been going on over several decades received greater impetus with the development of welded seamless piping, which made possible the extensive long-distance pipeline network that has been constructed largely since the end of World War II. This has made possible inroads on coal and oil markets, most notably in the field of household heating.

Thus, during the past one hundred years the almost eighteen-fold growth in annual energy use from 90 million tons of "bituminous coal equivalent" (all energy converted to bituminous coal on the basis of equivalent energy or heat content) to over 1,700 million tons has been accompanied by significant changes in the relative importance of the several sources of energy. However, these changes have been evolutionary rather than revolutionary, with each new energy source gradually assuming its place in the structure of energy use.

Electric energy, because of its unique qualities—ease of transportation and distribution, complete flexibility, cleanliness and safety, most sensitive susceptibility to control, potential applicability to almost all energy-using processes, and its ability to be produced from every primary energy source—has had an especially significant impact on our society. In 1882, three years after Thomas Edison developed the carbon filament incandescent lamp, he placed in commercial operation the historic Pearl Street Station in the City of New York. One year later, in 1883, an insignificant share of the 280 million tons of coal equivalent used in the United States was converted to electric energy. By 1960, however, out of the total of some 1,700 million tons of bituminous coal equivalent used in the United States, the equivalent of 322 million tons, or close to 20%, was converted into electric energy by the electric utility industry, and the United States, with roughly 6% of the world's total population, accounted for close to 37% of the world's total electric generation.

The length of time over which the dynamic growth in the production and utilization of electric energy in the United States has been sustained, which over many decades has averaged about 7% per year compounded, is unique. No other energy industry, indeed no other industry, has been able to sustain such a high rate of growth over such an extended period. Even more significant is the fact that it now appears that this growth rate is likely to continue for the next two decades before any significant saturation factors can be anticipated even to begin to make their appearance.

Since electric energy is a converted form of energy, then to the extent that our society may be confronted by limitations on primary energy supplies, we may also be confronted by a corresponding possibility of limitation on electric energy production. However, because electric energy can be produced from any primary energy source, whether fossil fuel, nuclear, solar, wind, tidal, or any other primary source, and because it is uniquely capable of application to any energy-using process, electrification offers a particularly excellent route for the resolution of the problem of potential exhaustion of our mineral fuels.

This comes about from the arrival on the scene of nuclear fuel—the first new primary energy source in almost a hundred years. Its coming has markedly enhanced the prospect that through increasing electrification we will be able to compensate for the depletion of any or all of the other primary fuels.

The qualification is that so far the progress made in the application of nuclear energy has been limited almost entirely to the generation of electric energy, which means that, at present, nuclear fission can relieve the burden on our mineral fuels only to the extent that energy use is electrified. A hard fact here is that the largest consumer of energy at the present time in the United States is transportation, and transportation is based almost entirely on petroleum—with no immediate prospect of nuclear fission easing this burden on petroleum.

As indicated earlier, only about 20% of the total primary energy use in the United States is presently converted to the electric form. The extent to which nuclear energy can relieve the pressure on our fossil fuels is limited by the increase of this 20% in the coming decades. Keeping in mind the present limitations on nuclear fuels, and the historic course of development in energy use, one can attempt to assess the outlook for energy requirements, and also to appraise the technological and economic opportunities during the next several decades.

These decades are likely to be characterized by the following significant factors: a rapid world-wide increase in population; the emergence of a large number of newly independent nations, almost all of which are underdeveloped; a rapidly rising level of material expectation, especially in the underdeveloped areas; the expanding influence of science and technology; an intensification of the age-old yearning of man for a spiritually more rewarding life free from the burdens of heavy toil; and finally the now clearly formulated historic conflict between two different sets of political ideologies—Communism and Western democracy.

The conflicts stemming from these often violently interacting factors seem destined to continue for many more decades, and the character of their resolution will depend in large measure on the relative scientific, industrial, and technological strength of the two contending ideological groups. If the possibility of a large-scale nuclear war is excluded, it becomes clear that the maintenance of our national economy in a flourishing and expanding condition becomes inextricably intertwined with any program for assuring our survival. The ability to support over a long period of time an economy capable of providing for a fully effective military deterrent, while at the same time satisfying national and international aspirations for rising levels of welfare, requires the continued dynamic expansion of the American economy.

The requisite economic growth must come from greater productivity, which involves the extension and development of our technology to new heights. The development of our technology in turn necessarily involves the development and utilization of new resources and new materials which will require increasing quantities of energy. Thus energy resources will play, as time goes on, an even more important role in our economy than they do today.

Given these general assumptions, one can attempt to project the energy requirements of the country for 1980 and for the year 2000. Such projections are needed for at least two reasons.

First, since the future is the result of a continuous process by which it is reached from the present, we need to attempt to visualize the future if sound policy decisions are to be made in the present and over the entire period. The future, no matter how bright it may appear, can be realized only if society can pass through the next year, and then the next five, ten, fifteen, twenty years, successfully—politically, economically, ideologically.

The second reason for making these projections is to help reach sound decisions regarding the directions that future technological effort should take, especially in the field of atomic energy. There is a very bright future for atomic energy, but there are still ahead in this field very difficult technological and engineering-economic problems. I am completely confident that these problems can be solved with reasonable application of effort, but it will still take time. A sound judgment of the future of atomic power and its significance for our society cannot be drawn, nor policy with regard to atomic power in relationship to our other energy resources established, unless such projections beyond the next few years are made.

My projections, centering on the years 1980 and 2000 as convenient benchmarks, indicate that from 1960 to 1980 there will be a growth of almost 80% in total energy use, rising to the equivalent of 3,050 million tons of bituminous coal. During this same period electric energy generation will grow at almost twice the rate of total energy, increasing three-and-a-half-fold to 2,700 billion kwh. However, because of increasing efficiency in conversion, the share of total energy used for electric generation by 1980 will increase to only about 30%, or about 920 million tons.

In regard to nuclear power, we now believe that of all electric generation in 1980 nuclear power will account for about 300 billion kwh, or slightly more than 11%. It should be noted that this amount will represent only a little more than 3% of the total energy use in that year.

If nuclear power had no more place than this in our total energy requirements there would be little justification for all the effort and all the national activity being devoted to our atomic program. The justification for our nuclear programs is the belief that, as the country's future need for energy expands, atomic energy will, on an economic basis, be able to assume an increasing share of the burden that the other sources of energy may by then, as a result of resource depletion or difficulty of recovery, be unable to carry effectively.

This can be visualized more clearly by extending our view to the end of this century. Between 1980 and the year 2000 total energy consumption is expected to increase almost one-third to 4,000 million tons of bituminous coal equivalent. Electric generation, however, will grow more than two-fold to 6,000 billion kwh and account for about 40% of the total energy use.

Assuming these projected requirements, I estimate that by the year 2000 the role of nuclear power in the total electric generation will have changed sharply. In contrast with the 11% anticipated for 1980, it is likely that by the year 2000 nuclear power will account for almost 55% of the total electric energy. This will represent over 20% of the total energy use projected for that year. Nevertheless, even with this most optimistic estimate of the rate of development of nuclear power, some 45% of the total electric energy will be provided by other sources of fuel, mostly by coal.

If the expansion of nuclear power to a position of dominance in electric power generation is to be accomplished, it will have to overcome severe competitive pressure from the conventional fuel technology. This pressure will stem from a two-pronged challenge: a challenge to the oft-assumed inevitable trend of rising fossil fuel costs, particularly for coal, and a challenge to the concept of a static state in the technology of electric energy generation through the conversion of fossil fuels.

While I shall later want to return to the problem of fuel as a prelude to conversion, and to the problems of transmission as an indispensable item following conversion, the balance of this chapter will be devoted, in the main, to conversion itself.

The electric power industry has witnessed a series of developments over many decades of which most people, because of their low-level reaction to the non-spectacular and non-exotic, have not even been aware. These developments have been the product of slow, painstaking research and development that have been going on since the very inception of central station electric power over eighty years ago. This evolution has brought the original efficiency of conversion from about 5%, or less, to very close to 40% efficiency in today's most modern plants. Had this been a rapid achievement, one encompassed in a period of three to five years, it certainly would have been recognized as a most spectacular achievement. But such progress does not come rapidly, and so this startling improvement in efficiency has been barely noticed because it has come about in small increments—a more or less steady improvement from year to year. This progress is still going on.

The process of converting any of the primary sources of energy, particularly coal, oil, gas, or nuclear fuel, involves a preliminary process of heat release that is today a highly advanced and sophisticated technology using most complicated processes, machines, and equipment. Yet in essence the process employs principles that are more than a century old. The generator that converts the mechanical energy to electric energy dates back to Faraday's discovery of electromagnetic induction in 1831. The steam turbine, the intermediate engine utilized to convert the thermal energy coming from the combustion of coal, oil, gas, or nuclear fission to mechanical energy, dates back almost two centuries to Newcomen and Watt.

Since the first commercial generation of electric energy in

1882, there has been over eighty years of uninterrupted progress in the development of the technology embodying these principles. This progressive development has increased the efficiency of conversion to the point that it is now possible to obtain eight times as much electric energy per unit of fuel as was possible at the end of the last century.

However, more exotic ways of converting primary energy into electric energy are now coming under increasingly intensive investigation. But these, too, are based on principles that in many cases go back more than a hundred years. As a result of the remarkable revival of interest in these principles in recent years, energy conversion as a basic area of research and development is in a more fluid and more exciting state today than ever before.

These energy conversion principles all involve the conversion of primary energy into electric energy without recourse to a heat engine such as a steam engine, steam turbine, diesel engine, or gas turbine. They have received a great deal of stimulus from the new knowledge and understanding of basic phenomena and the development of new processes and materials during the past decade.

Four avenues of research show particular promise of leading to advances in energy conversion that may affect large-scale electric energy generation of the future. These four routes are: thermionic generation, thermoelectric generation, fuel cells, and magnetohydrodynamic generation (MHD). Each of these highly intriguing prospects depends on different principles. All, however, have in common the prospect of direct conversion of primary energy into electric energy without resorting to an intermediate mechanical engine of some kind.

Thermionic generation is based on the phenomenon of electronic emission from the surface of an electron-conducting material owing to the thermal energy of the electrons within the material. The phenomenon was observed by Edison in the course of his work on the electric lamp in the 1870's and is known as the Edison effect.

Thermoelectric generation owes its basic discovery to Seebeck in 1822. Seebeck discovered that in a circuit of two different metals, if the two junctions were maintained at different temperatures, a voltage was developed in the circuit. By pure accident Seebeck achieved thermal efficiencies with his thermocouple that were comparable with the then contemporary steam engines. However, as steam engines improved in efficiency the thermocouple was relegated to the background and eventually became nothing more than a temperature-measuring device.

The fuel cell has been known for some 120 years, although not by that name. Sir William Grove constructed a gaseous voltage battery and generated an electric current from the combination (oxidation) of hydrogen with oxygen in 1839. This is the reverse of the electrolysis of water and its dissociation into hydrogen and oxygen upon the passage of a current through it. The theoretical efficiency of a fuel cell is 100% and this, in theory at least, offers the prospect that the fuel cell could enter the field of mass generation of electric energy, if the cell could be developed to utilize a fuel that can be made available in a competitive cost range for mass energy generation.

Considerable progress has been made in recent years in all three of the above technologies, but in no case has there been any indication of reasonable hope that any of the three can be developed into a competitive energy converter on a commercial scale in the near future.

Magnetohydrodynamics (MHD), the fourth of these new avenues of approach to energy conversion, while showing thus far no greater progress than any of the other three methods described above, appears to offer much more exciting possibilities for development that will lead to new achievements in generation of electric energy. Faraday's discovery of electromagnetic induction brought to light the fundamental fact that when a conductor and a magnetic field move with respect to each other, an electric voltage is induced in the conductor. When a load is connected in the form of a lamp, appliance, or motor to the terminals of the conductor, an electric current will flow through it. Faraday's basic law did not tie the conductor to any special form—a loop of wire, for example. The conductor could just as well be a fluid—a gas or a liquid. The basic idea of using a conducting fluid with a magnetic field constitutes the phenomenon of magnetohydrodynamics.

Faraday himself attempted to experiment with the River Thames as the conductor and the earth's natural magnetic field as the magnet. This experiment was unsuccessful in that Faraday was not able to measure any electric output, but it was highly successful in exemplifying an idea for later men to ponder.

In the 1950's, intense interest in the properties of high-temperature gases was stimulated by the efforts to solve the problem of the re-entry of ballistic missiles into the earth's atmosphere and by attempts to achieve magnetic containment of high-temperature plasmas for thermonuclear fusion. A great increase in our knowledge and understanding of the properties of gases at high temperatures and pressures resulted from this work. This increased knowledge in turn made possible an attempt, on a much broader base, to achieve power generation by a moving gas. These efforts culminated in 1959 in the successful production of electric energy at the rate of 10 kw by flowing arc-heated argon seeded with potassium through a magnetic field, the potassium in this case being utilized to provide extra conductivity. Subsequently this work was carried to the point where, for short periods, energy up to 1,500 kw has actually been produced by the MHD process. A great deal more work is now going on and much remains to be done.

Nevertheless, MHD offers the promise of a great simplification of the electric generation process and the possible achievement of very high thermal efficiency—as much as a 33% improvement over the best present figure of 40%. Because of this exciting promise, a considerable amount of work is going on today all over the world, looking toward the development of MHD to commercial practicality.

The development of these advanced energy conversion systems and the problems associated with the discovery, extraction, transportation, and utilization of a greatly expanded requirement for energy, confront the engineers and technologists with almost unlimited intriguing challenges to their skills, ingenuity, imagination, and enterprise. Their excitement can perhaps be more definitely evoked by a slightly more detailed discussion of the problems in the field of electric energy conversion with which this author is most intimately familiar.

To begin with, the supply of primary fuel for conversion to electric energy will present a wide range of difficult technical-economic problems. It is anticipated that coal will be the energy source for most of the electric generation not provided by nuclear fuel in the year 2000. If coal does, in fact, provide 40% of the total energy for electric generation at that time, it will have to supply 600 million tons for this purpose, or almost 50% more than the current total coal production for all purposes in the United States. This is a conservative estimate based on the most optimistic assumptions regarding the speed of atomic development.

This immediately raises the question of whether this quantity of coal can be made available without a significant increase in costs. The prospect that this can be done is bright, but it cannot be left to chance. A great deal of engineering remains to be done. To assure that this large quantity of coal will be provided at low cost will involve much more extensive exploration and geological evaluation of our coal resources than has been carried out heretofore. It will require very extensive efforts in the development of mining equipment and systems that extend across the entire spectrum of mining technology. The further development of transportation technology will also be necessary if the delivered costs of coal at the point of use are to be held to a minimum.

The modes of transportation of coal are numerous. Not only can coal be hauled over the road in trucks, by rail and by river and ocean barges, but within recent years important forward strides have been made in the movement of coal by belt conveyor, by pipeline in the form of a slurry, and electrically, that is, by wire.

Each of these modes of transportation presents many difficult and fascinating problems that need to be solved if they are to make their maximum contribution toward the continuing availability of low-cost energy.

Although coal has constituted one of the principal elements in the industrial revolution and has been an important source of this country's growth to its present position of strength and affluence, it remains a fuel about which we know almost nothing chemically. We are particularly ignorant about its many impurities, not only the common forms like sulphur and iron, but such elements as sodium, potassium, chlorine, and their various compounds, and their interactions with steels and other materials under conditions of very high temperatures. These chemicals, inherent in coal until it is brought to combustion, create many difficult material problems from their interaction as well as other problems associated with their effects on the air and on the flora and fauna of the countryside when they are discharged into the atmosphere as the final products of combustion.

At the same time that coal will be presenting its challenge, the many difficult problems of utilizing nuclear fuel will also be calling for imaginative engineering solutions. As we have seen earlier, by the end of this century nuclear fuel is expected to be the principal source of primary energy for the generation of electric energy. Since the development of the first nuclear fission atomic pile in 1942, a great deal of work has been done all over the world to bring atomic power into the competitive arena as a commercial reality. Undoubtedly the most advanced work in this area has been done in the United States. Yet much more work remains to be done for nuclear power to attain the expected position of importance in the electric energy supply of the United States. There is still a great deal of work to be done in the development of advanced reactor systems, new reactor concepts, new methods of cooling reactors, new methods of fabricating and processing fuel to reduce its cost, and techniques for extending the life of the fuel in reactors. If nuclear fuel is to provide a significant addition to our total energy resources, it will be necessary to develop breeder reactors that convert nonfissionable material to larger quantities of fissionable material than they consume in the process, and this technology is still in its relative infancy.

One of the very important contributions to the technology of electric energy conversion within the past twenty-five years has been the development of large-size generating units. Currently there are under construction several units to go into operation within the next few years that will have generating capabilities of close to 1,000,000 kw. All the units at that rating are in a so-called cross-compound design where the energy initially resident in high-pressure steam is converted into mechanical energy in two units thermodynamically in series, the steam starting at the highest pressure in the first unit and then entering the second unit at a reduced pressure, perhaps one-twentieth of the initial pressure, where the balance of the energy is converted, and the remaining steam is rejected to the condensing system for reconversion into water to begin the cycle over again.

However, there are today under construction generating units that will produce over 600,000 kw, or more than 800,000 horsepower, on a single shaft. Thus all that power and energy is generated in a single electric armature. The prospect of further extensions of size of the single shaft machine, with its promise of still further reductions in capital costs and improvements in thermal efficiency, will challenge the capabilities of the most competent engineering talent.

Specifically, the problem of building a 1,000,000 kw turbo-alternator on a single shaft presents a host of difficult engineering and economic problems, including those of shafting and blading of turbine wheels, of cooling of the rotating and electric fields of such huge engines, and the problems of providing excitation, since an alternating current generator cannot furnish its own excitation.

The mere contemplation of such large units, and the still larger plants into which they will be incorporated, raises many problems of economic risk. A large 1,000,000 kw machine will represent an investment of about $125,000,000 and a single flaw in any one of the hundreds of its parts will immediately make it necessary to shut down the entire complex. Obviously if such technical developments are to be economically feasible they will necessitate new standards of reliability. This will involve new research efforts and a wide range of problems affecting the question of reliability, the causes of unreliability, and how reliability can be engineered into equipment. This itself is almost a new field of engineering, opening upon a substantive technology that greatly needs to be developed if the causes and nature of equipment failure and unreliability are to be understood and methods developed for materially minimizing them.

The conversion of primary energy into electric energy involves losses. This is another way of saying that an important question in the conversion process is its efficiency. It is too frequently assumed that the eight-fold increase to 40% conversion efficiency since the turn of the century has now reached a plateau.

A careful examination and evaluation of the problem indicates that this is not true at all. It is undoubtedly more difficult to improve upon the present 40% thermal efficiency of conversion than it was to improve on the 5% efficiency of sixty years ago, but the need for achieving higher efficiency is, if anything, greater today than it ever was. This is particularly true from the standpoint of conservation of energy resources. With an annual generation of 6,000 billion kwh projected for the year 2000, an average reduction in the energy required to generate a kilowatt hour of as little as 100 BTU will mean an annual saving of 23 million tons of coal a year. A saving of 1,000 BTU would reduce the demand on our fuel resources by 230 million tons of coal. There would appear to be no valid reason to despair of engineering research and development being capable of achieving new materials, such as high-quality steels, to make possible higher steam temperatures and pressures, new improvements in the construction of the mechanical thermal engines and of electric alternators to bring about a further advance in efficiency that would reduce the present best heat requirement of about 8,600 BTU to, say, 7,600 BTU per kwh. Indeed, this objective and its potential significance should challenge engineers and stimulate their imaginations.

The mere statement of the problem and the very simple—but staggering—arithmetic of its implications for our society should stimulate a dedicated effort to overcome the obstacles to further improvements in thermal efficiency. The successful development of MHD would, itself, represent a major achievement in this area. Although the successful technological and economic implementation of MHD is not yet at hand, it does appear to be a very real possibility well before the end of this century, perhaps as soon as the next decade.

But, even without MHD, seemingly small incremental improvements in thermal efficiency will, as in the past, continue to be cumulative and, at the magnitude of electric generation projected for the year 2000, will make major contributions to the national economy and to the national welfare.

It was pointed out earlier that one of the important advantageous characteristics of electric energy is its ability to be transported instantaneously. But as the quantities of electric energy continue to grow and, in some cases, the distances over which it must be moved increase, the need for higher transmission voltages to move these large quantities of energy economically becomes indispensable. At the present time 345,000-volt transmission is the highest in actual operation in the United States. But high-voltage transmission is in a very vigorous phase of development. Higher-voltage transmission lines of 500,000 volts are already under construction, and in Canada there is underway a project that will bring power in from some of the northern regions to the centers of Canadian population at a voltage of 735,000.

Within the next decade or decade and a half it may be found desirable in some parts of the United States to undertake the construction of transmission facilities at the 700/765-kv level. While this will present no major obstacles, a number of detailed technical problems remain to be solved. Two major research projects that will lead to their solution are now actively underway in the United States. It is already becoming quite clear that extra-high transmission voltages will not stop with 765 kv. There is every indication that before the end of this century one million volts, and possibly voltages at least 10% higher, are reasonable expectations.

But if this is to be accomplished, there are many technological unknowns that will have to be explored and problems resolved if these higher voltages are to be introduced with maximum efficiency and reliability.

For example, the basic system that was developed approximately fifty years ago for insulating high-voltage conductors from their metallic supporting structures performed extremely well for voltages as high as 132,000 and has continued, with some improvements, to perform the same kind of function for 345,000-volt lines and for the 500,000-volt lines that are now under construction. They will unquestionably also be extendable to the 765-kv lines of the future. However, there is clear indication that as lines are projected to the levels of 1 million or 1.1 million volts, the only system of insulation known today will cease to have technical and economic validity. Thus a practice that will by that time have served in the growth of a great industry for close to a hundred years will have become impractical and uneconomical for the voltages that the industry will by then demand. This opens up a new area of opportunity for important engineering effort in research, in development, in design, and in inventiveness.

There are also likely to be some special circumstances in which it may be possible usefully to apply direct-current transmission. But many difficult problems remain to be solved if direct-current transmission is to find extensive application. At the present time there is not available a direct-current switch to permit switching and tapping direct-current lines. Knowledge of how to integrate direct-current lines with existing alternating-current systems to permit parallel operation is also severely limited. These are among the many difficult engineering obstacles that must be overcome if direct-current transmission is to become a significant element in the future movement of electric energy.

This brief analysis of the outlook for our energy resources for the balance of the century, and the greatly foreshortened recitation of the technological problems and opportunities they reveal, can barely scratch the surface. Nevertheless, a number of important conclusions can be drawn.

It is quite clear that during this period the country will continue to rely primarily on its existing energy sources—those that have taken care of the needs of our country, and indeed of the world, for roughly the past hundred years. But these resources will have to be supplemented by new sources such as nuclear fuel, and they will have to be extended by improved technology for finding and extracting them and for using them more efficiently and more effectively. New concepts of transportation will have to be developed, as well as new ideas for conversion. New technologies of utilization will be necessary, especially to make possible the substitution of electric energy for the direct use of the primary fuels, if the opportunities for nuclear power to contribute to our energy needs are to be expanded. These needs will raise innumerable problems demanding solutions that can come only from the application of the most highly sophisticated analysis and engineering synthesis.

The solutions will be extremely important to the continued strength and material welfare of our free society. Thus the field of energy and energy conversion will offer unlimited opportunities to challenge the most vigorous, imaginative, and highly trained engineers. They will provide technologists and engineers with exciting opportunities to grow and develop and to derive the material and spiritual rewards that can come from contributing to the welfare of society.

The basic function of engineering is to discharge at a high level of responsibility the obligation to bring a nation's resources into optimum combination. This involves bringing together these resources—physical, human, and capital in the form of machines, equipment and complex systems—to improve and enhance the welfare of society. The problems of energy and energy conversion should—indeed must, if our society is to continue to flourish—elicit a challenging response from the best engineering talent that the nation has available. Those who undertake to apply their engineering skill and imagination to the problems of energy and energy conversion in the decades ahead will find their professional activities among the most rewarding and stimulating in our society.

14 *Electronics*

BY BERNARD M. OLIVER

VICE PRESIDENT

Hewlett-Packard Company

BERNARD M. OLIVER

Born: 1916, Santa Cruz, California

Stanford University: B.S. in EE., 1935
California Institute of Technology: M.S., 1936
Technische Hochschule, Darmstadt, 1937
California Institute of Technology, Ph.D., 1940

Bell Telephone Laboratories:
  TV Research, 1939–41
  Automatic tracking RADAR Development, 1941–45
  Television and Information Theory Research, 1945–52
Hewlett-Packard Company:
  Director of Research, 1952–57
  Vice President for Research and Development, 1957–

Institute of Electrical Engineers:
  Fellow, 1954
  Director-at-Large, 1958
  Vice President, 1962
  Past Chairman, San Francisco Section
WESCON: Past Member, Board of Directors
Palo Alto School Board: Member

Holder of over forty U.S. Patents and author of numerous articles and papers

On DECEMBER 14, 1962, at 11:15 A.M. a large parabolic antenna at Goldstone, California, was pointing at the planet Venus. At that moment the first successful interplanetary spacecraft, Mariner II, having approached within 22,000 miles of Venus, was scanning the surface as it passed by. At Goldstone, radio signals from Mariner's three-watt transmitter were being received, amplified, and recorded: signals that told us that Venus has almost no water, no magnetic field, no radiation belts, that the Venusian day is extremely long, and that the surface of the planet is hot enough to melt lead.

Had it not been for a delicate mid-course correction, Mariner II would have passed Venus on the opposite side at ten times the distance and would have told us little or nothing about the planet. One week after launch, electronic computers had digested the tracking data, computed the rendezvous error and what to do about it. Two days later instructions were radioed across one half million miles to the spacecraft, which stored them in its memory until it received a precisely timed command to carry them out. It then switched from solar to battery power and to gyro control of attitude. It withdrew its high gain antenna out of the way of its own rocket exhaust. It rolled over slightly so that its jets would turn it the specified 140 degrees in the right direction. Upon reaching the proper attitude, it fired its rocket motor for 27.8 seconds, thereby adding an essential 45 miles per hour to its orbital speed of 60,250 miles per hour. Retracing its steps, it picked up the sun and the earth on its sensors, restored sensor attitude control and solar cell power. With its high-gain antenna again pointed toward earth, it turned on its transmitter and, in a series of pulses confirming the above maneuver, saluted its commanders with a coded "Aye, aye, sir!"

Eighteen months later another spacecraft, Ranger VII, executed a similar maneuver to correct its aim toward Mare Nubium, the "sea" of clouds on the surface of the moon. It scored a bull's eye and during the last few minutes of its headlong plunge sent us over four thousand high quality pictures showing the surface of the moon in far greater detail than can be obtained with any telescope. In the last picture, only partially sent before impact occurred, craters only a yard in diameter can be seen.

A space program capable of producing Mariner II, or Ranger VII, would be impossible without a branch of applied science and engineering called electronics. So would many of the things we take for granted in our modern society. Television and long distance telephony are obvious examples. Ships sailing through fog, and airliners in flight, rely on radar and other electronic navigational aids. Your flight reservation is cleared electronically and so is the check you write. Electronics probes the earth for oil and the blood for disease. It listens to the rhythm of the heart and brain and to the noise of distant galaxies.

What is this electronics that so permeates our technology? What is its role? How did it all start? What makes something "electronic"? What new marvels has electronics in store? Does a career in electronics still hold promise, or has electronics come of age? Perhaps a little history will help us to answer these questions.

At the turn of the century the electric telephone was in trouble. Whereas the telegraph could span oceans and continents, the telephone could not. The signals grew weak with distance and after a few hundred miles were inaudible. A very large telephone line, more like a power line really, connected New York and Chicago. On hot days even this was useless. Over longer distances, human repeaters were sometimes used. An electromechanical repeater was tried but it introduced considerable distortion. Some good means of amplifying the signal en route was desperately needed and the search was on. In 1907 Lee De Forest discovered that a grid of wires could control the flow of electrons between the filament and plate of a vacuum tube, without itself drawing any appreciable current. With almost no input power, large output powers could be produced and instantly varied. De Forest's three electrode (triode) vacuum tube, or "audion," as he called it, became the long sought amplifier of electric signals. And though no one could have foreseen it in 1907, the age of electronics had just been born.

Very soon it was discovered that these new vacuum tubes would not only amplify, but, by returning part of their output to their input, could also be made to oscillate: to generate waves of almost any desired frequency. (In fact, great care was required to *prevent* these amplifiers from oscillating or behaving in unintended ways, and some of the "inventions" of those days stemmed more from accident than insight.) Then ways were found to impress a signal upon an oscillation to produce what is called a modulated wave. Such waves carry the signal in a different frequency range from the one it originally occupied. In this way many messages can be sent at once over a single telephone line, and many programs at once by radio. Each message occupies its own frequency range or "channel." These developments not only made low-cost long distance telephone a reality, they also paved the way for radio broadcasting.

The roar of the 1920's was partly the roar of radio. Starting as a curiosity, radio ended the decade as a major industry. It swept aside the phonograph industry only to revive it later, bigger and better than ever. In the late Twenties, electronic techniques of recording and reproducing sound were coupled to the movie camera and projector to produce the talking motion picture. But radio dominated the era. Hundreds of broadcast stations poured thousands of kilowatts into the air, to be caught by millions of receivers. Around these receivers America sat, open-eared and dreamy-eyed. De Forest's audion had begun to modify our society.

During the 1930's, radio and talking pictures flourished, and their success stimulated bold research to combine their appeal: to bring living pictures into the home. New electron tubes, the iconoscope, the orthicon, and the kinescope were invented to convert pictures into electrical signals and vice versa, and the decade closed with experimental television of almost modern quality a demonstrated fact. World War II put commercial TV on ice; its impact was not felt until the late 1940's, but it had arrived ten years earlier.

While the decades between World Wars I and II saw vacuum tubes put to use in radio direction finders, altimeters and other navigation aids, and in a few industrial applications, electronics before 1940 was overwhelmingly involved with communication and entertainment. In fact, the term "electronics" had not yet come into general use. The engineers who were graduated in 1940 and who were to develop radars and computers and servomechanisms and sonar and traveling-wave tubes and radio telescopes were not yet called electronics engineers. We were electrical engineers who had taken the "communications" or "radio engineering" options at college. We were all hopeful for the future of our chosen field, but none of us expected it to develop so many branches or to grow to the ten-billion-dollar industry we know today.

World War II accelerated enormously the growth of radio into electronics. The young technology was searched for answers to the urgent problems of defense and attack, and inventions began to pour forth. In the late 1930's the klystron and cavity magnetron were invented. Both of these tubes generated high power radio waves at far higher frequencies than formerly was possible. The magnetron in particular was capable of hundreds of kilowatts of power in the so-called microwave range, provided the power was demanded in short pulses of only a few millionths of a second duration. But this sort of electromagnetic thunderclap was exactly what was needed to scan the skies for approaching aircraft or the surface of the seas for ships. Furthermore, because of their short wavelength, these high-frequency waves could be focused into intense search beams capable of producing detectable reflections from objects tens and even hundreds of miles away. On December 7, 1941, RADAR (Radio Detection And Ranging) equipment at Pearl Harbor gave clear warning of the impending Japanese attack, but nobody trusted the equipment enough to believe the awful truth, so the mute warning went unheeded. Months later, radar was sinking unseen ships and turning the tide of the war in the Pacific.

In radar, the higher the radio frequency, the sharper the beam, and the better the ability to separate different targets in angle. Similarly, the shorter the pulse, the better the ability to separate targets in range. So the search for better radars led to ever higher frequencies, higher powers, and shorter pulses. Communications engineers, used to handling continuous waves of a few microwatts at a few megacycles, began to speak of microsecond pulses at megawatt power levels and kilomegacycle frequencies. Overnight the art had changed.

New pulse detectors were invented to tell when the antenna was off target in angle or when the range indication was wrong. Then the signals from these detectors were amplified and used to drive motors that steered the radar back on target. These automatic tracking radars can follow a target despite its best evasive actions. The combination of error detector, amplifier, and a motor whose rotation reduces the error is called a servomechanism. Communications engineers recognized in these servomechanisms the principle of the feedback amplifier developed years earlier to permit stable low-distortion long distance telephone circuits. Suddenly the elegant theory of feedback amplifier design found application in a new field, and servomechanisms reached new heights of performance. Automatic tracking radars began to track high-speed planes miles away with errors of only a few feet.

Having located the present position of the target, electronics was next asked to predict its future position. More servomechanisms were used to transform the radar data into actual flight coordinates and project the flight path to a future point where the guns were aimed. These gun-laying computers were among the first electronic analog computers. Attempts to improve their performance led to advances in the mathematical theory of data smoothing and prediction. Radar-directed gunfire soon became so effective that the Luftwaffe had to stop bombing England and the expected German invasion never materialized.

Meanwhile other communication engineers, working on submarine detection and other naval warfare problems, were developing SONAR, the acoustic equivalent of radar. Still others were developing magnetic mines, and proximity fuses, which made a near miss as good as a hit. Everywhere the vacuum tube was being pressed into new applications.

Prior to the war most communication employed what is called amplitude modulation in which the amplitude (or strength) of a radio frequency is varied in accordance with the signal to be sent. With amplitude modulation, the amplifiers and all circuits handling the signal must be very linear. That is, the output at all times must be directly proportional to the input (and not the square of the input, for example). Otherwise new frequencies are produced and distortion results. The signal cannot be allowed to become too large or it overloads the circuits, producing non-linear response and distortion. Nor can it become too weak or the needed amplification adds disturbing noise. Communication engineers became quite expert at handling with care their delicate signal cargo, at keeping it clean and free of harmful changes of shape as it flashed thousands of miles through hundreds of amplifiers.

Shortly before World War II a new form of modulation was introduced in which the frequency rather than the amplitude of the radio frequency is varied in accordance with the signal. Although suggested a decade earlier and abandoned because it required a wider channel, frequency modulation, or FM, came into vogue because it offered greater freedom from noise and certain kinds of distortion. In a sense the signal was better packed for shipment.

With the advent of pulses in radar (and television), engineers began to devise ways by which pulses could be made to carry a signal. Systems were invented in which the pulse length, height, time of occurrence, or repetition rate was varied in accordance with the signal. Each of these systems had certain advantages, but the most powerful was pulse code modulation, or PCM. In pulse modulation methods, samples of the signal are taken at a high enough rate to define the signal unambiguously. Then, in PCM, each sample is coded into a group of pulses, a binary number, that uniquely and most closely represents the height of that sample. With PCM the receiver merely has to determine whether or not a pulse is there, not how big it is, nor how long. It can then generate a brand new pulse in response. No new noise is added, no distortion. In PCM the signal is truly crated for rough shipment.

PCM brought communication full circle, back to the techniques of Morse and the telegraph. Instead of sending the signal or a linear counterpart, one sends a coded description of the signal. Later, Claude Shannon, in a classical paper on the theory of communication, was to show how to use the redundancy in signals to shorten their descriptions. For the first time it became clear to engineers what "information" is and what the maximum capacities of channels are. Shannon gave us a yardstick by which to measure the performance of any communication system.

The experimental television systems developed before the war were synchronized, just as modern ones are, by complex trains of pulses. To maintain an exact number of scanning lines and proper interlace, pulse frequency dividing circuits were devised. Work on these, on nuclear radiation scalers, and on PCM circuits made it evident that electronic circuits could be made to count and to store numbers. Soon ways were found to add the stored numbers, to multiply and divide them and thereby to execute almost any sort of calculation. Not only could individual calculations be made but long sequences could be programmed automatically and the results printed out. Earlier automatic computers had used mechanical relays. When these were replaced with the vacuum tube, the enormous increase in computing speed made a whole hierarchy of new applications practical.

Although the electronic industry had greatly expanded during the war, the cease-fire brought no great decrease in employment. Some military support continued, only to be resumed full force with the Korean conflict. Meanwhile all spare engineering and productive effort was devoted to adapting wartime developments to civilian uses and to supplying consumer products unavailable during the war years. Telephones were needed in huge numbers and radios were in great demand. Soon television made its commercial debut and another boom began. In the next few years millions of television sets were sold, and rooftops bristled with strange shapes wrought of aluminum tubing. Around these new receivers America sat once more, this time in open-eyed wonder. Another tube, the cathode ray tube, with its phosphorescent pictures had joined the audion, further to change our lives.

As electronic devices and systems grew in complexity, their size, power consumption, and, above all, their reliability became serious problems. Whereas a radio set with five tubes was compact, consumed only a few watts, and kept running for months or years without trouble, a computer with ten thousand tubes was huge, consumed tens of kilowatts, and could seldom be kept operating more than a few hours at a time. One of the major causes of failure was the short-lived vacuum tube itself. Paradoxically, the device that had given birth to electronics seemed about to limit its future. At this juncture a brand new device appeared: the transistor.

In the earliest days of radio and wireless telegraphy, crystal detectors had been used. These tiny contacts between a pointed wire and a crystal passed current more easily in one direction than the other and so could rectify radio frequency signals. During the war, silicon crystals were found to be the most satisfactory available device for the detection of the microwave signals used in radar, but still no one completely understood how they worked! Soon solid-state physicists attacked this problem and began to unravel the mysteries. As so often happens, the understanding that followed led not merely to improvement in the crystal detector, but to an entirely new device as well: the solid-state amplifier, or transistor. Whereas the typical small vacuum tube consumes a watt, the transistor needs only a thousandth of a watt to do the same job. It can be made a thousandth the size and with a thousand times the life expectancy. By allowing electronic devices to be made cool, compact, and reliable, the transistor inaugurated a new era in electronics. Solid-state (transistor) computers, much more complex yet much more reliable than their vacuum tube predecessors, are in widespread use today.

In the last few years physical research has given electronics many new and important devices besides the transistor. Probably one of the most important is the MASER (Microwave Amplification by Stimulated Emission of Radiation), which uses a beam of sorted atoms in an excited state, rather than electrons, to provide amplification or oscillation. Masers have much less inherent noise than electron tubes and thus allow the successful amplification of much weaker signals. In this respect they have been a boon to satellite communication and to radio astronomy. Masers also can oscillate at frequencies determined almost entirely by the atoms involved, frequencies that are therefore very stable. These precision frequency-standard masers have given us atomic clocks a hundred times more regular than the rotation of the earth itself, clocks with less than a one-second error in a thousand years.

Recently the principles of the maser have been extended to the optical part of the electromagnetic spectrum. The optical maser, or "laser," produces light of a single frequency, a pure oscillation at 400 to 700 *million* megacycles per second. All other light sources produce what amounts to a band of noise rather than a pure tone. Furthermore, all the energy in a laser beam can be obtained in a single mode of propagation, which means that it can be focused to a point or shot out in beams having very little spreading. Using a laser and a 12-inch telescope, one can produce a spot of light only a mile in diameter on the moon. The laser opens up vast new regions of the electromagnetic spectrum for exploitation by all the techniques used in the radio spectrum. The potential uses of the laser are only dimly appreciated today.

If electronics can be said to depend on physics for its most exciting current developments, it is equally true that physics depends on electronics. Indeed all the sciences—mathematics, physics, chemistry, biology, medicine, geology, astronomy—depend heavily today upon tools that electronics has given them. Almost any physical variable—pressure, displacement, velocity, acceleration, temperature, acidity, magnetic field strength, brightness, color, radiation flux, and many more—can be converted into an electrical signal for measurement, recording, or control purposes. As experiments in any science become more complex, they require more precise control and more sensitive measurements. Since electronics provides these functions, all laboratories today use electronic equipment to some degree, and in many laboratories one cannot see the experiment for the electronic equipment surrounding it.

Missiles, nuclear weapons, and other large-scale, expensive testing programs use enormous amounts of electronic instrumentation. By collecting hundreds or even thousands of channels of data on each test, fewer tests are needed, and this more than makes up for the equipment cost. In a few seconds enough data is recorded to require months for analysis. To speed the analysis, the trend today is to record the data in a form suitable for feeding into an electronic computer, which then performs the desired computations and prints the results or plots the curves directly.

Diverse though the many applications of electronics may be, there is a certain unity about them all. Wherever electronics is found it is concerned with a *signal:* an electrical variable resulting from the detection of some phenomenon. Of course the *apparatus* of electronics is often useful in applications where no signal is involved. For example, high-power oscillators are used to heat metal by induction and to cook food quickly. But these are by-products of an art whose central theme is, as it has always been, the generation, detection, processing, and utilization of information-bearing electrical signals.

The fundamental property of a signal that distinguishes it from the voltages and currents used, for example, in power transmission is that the exact nature of the signal is unknown until it actually occurs. The word "yes" is a signal because the answer *might* have been "no." As a message unfolds, each new symbol resolves the uncertainty, existing beforehand, of what it might have been. Signals are *particular* sequences of symbols or *particular* functions selected from a *set* of possible alternatives. The signaling equipment must be prepared to handle any of the possible signals, not just the one that actually occurs. It is because electronic engineers have learned how to detect, convert to electrical form, process, and utilize so many different kinds of signals, from the atomic flash to the astronaut's pulse, that electronics is found everywhere today.

Just as civil engineering provides the skeleton of our technological body—the buildings and bridges—just as mechanical engineering provides the muscles, so electronics provides the nervous system. It provides the sensory receptors, the transmission paths, the computing centers, and the motor control. Whether our technology, becoming more complex, will demand more electronic interconnection, or whether the existence of such interconnection will permit our technology to become more complex, there seems little doubt that both will happen, and the role of electronics will become an increasingly important one.

The electronics industry has all kinds of jobs to be done and so employs all manner of people. You can be an expert in topology or Boolean algebra, you can be an organic chemist specializing in high polymers, you can be a theoretical physicist working on surface states or plasmas, you can be a psychologist interested in the man-machine interface, you can be a physiologist concerned with the central nervous system, or a high vacuum specialist, or a production specialist, or a patent attorney and still work "in electronics." For, like all large-scale industries, electronics needs the support of professionals in other fields. But if you wish to become an electronics engineer, there is a rather well-defined body of knowledge you must master.

Your first two years in college will probably cover essentially the same material as any other science or engineering curriculum; your choice among these fields will not have to be made until the junior year. By then in math you will have studied analytic geometry, differential and integral calculus, and some differential equations. If you truly master these subjects, you will wonder how you managed to live so long without them. In physics you will have studied the classical areas of mechanics, sound, heat, light, electricity and magnetism, and some atomic physics; and you will think you know more than you actually do about these areas. In chemistry you will have taken general inorganic chemistry, including qualitative and perhaps also quantitative analysis and maybe introductory organic chemistry. In your junior and senior years, you may take advanced calculus, or probability theory and statistics. You certainly *should* take a course in the theory of functions of a complex variable and linear (Fourier and Laplace) transform theory. Of all advanced mathematics these are the branches most used by the electronics engineer. During these years you will also receive your basic engineering courses, including those in circuit theory, electromechanical devices, vacuum tubes and transistors, and transmission lines.

The usual four-year college curriculum does not adequately cover the field of electronics for the good student. He will want to continue as a graduate for at least one year and preferably more. Graduate electronics courses include electromagnetic theory, network analysis and synthesis, electron devices, information theory, and other more specialized topics. In addition, the advanced degree student is required to do a thesis on some subject in his chosen field to show that he is capable of original and significant research. Graduate work often covers much of the same ground covered by undergraduate courses, but on a much more sophisticated level.

Suppose, being fascinated by the subjects mentioned above, you decide to become an electronics engineer. What about the future of the field? Four or eight years from now will you receive your diploma but no offers of employment? Will the field be mature or even old, with all the significant or exciting work already done? Or will we be, as we were in 1940, on the brink of further great expansion in directions as yet unforeseen? No one can say for sure, of course, but all indications are that electronics is still a young and growing field. Even without further innovation the industry will grow severalfold before present developments have been fully utilized, and further innovation will certainly occur. Let us project a few recent trends to see what the future may bring.

Take the area of automatic control. Today a few chemical processes and a few machine operations are automatically controlled by punched tape. But as more and better sensors are developed and as the necessary computers become cheaper and more reliable, the automatic factory will become a reality. Human labor will still be necessary (for a long time) for repair and maintenance, but not for the routine repetitive tasks of production. As automation becomes more widespread, the man-hours it saves will result in a shorter work week and a shorter working age span, but what work there is will be more skilled. This trend is well established. We work two-thirds as many hours per week as our grandfathers did, and for fewer years of our lives.

Computers will continue to invade the industrial, commercial, and business world, and to displace labor there. More and more the world of banking, credit, and accounting is using computers. The telephone company has introduced a new data transmission service. This service is expanding very rapidly. The day may not be far off when more computers than people will be busy on the telephone!

Theoretically, the laser makes it possible to send as many television signals at once in a light-pipe as we now send speech signals in a coaxial cable. Before the television telephone becomes a reality, though, much development will be needed in methods of handling light signals and of switching wide-band signals in exchanges. And even after these problems are solved, the circuits may be loaded not with the video signals of lovers' faces but with the crackle of high-speed computer talk.

As the space program proceeds, more and more complicated operations will be controlled or carried out electronically. It may be years, even decades, before man lands on the moon and Mars. Long before then it is likely that robot devices will have been landed, will have explored the surface, and will have telemetered back almost as much information as a human landing would provide. In fact, many people question the value of the human landing. But whether man lands or not, electronic equipment will.

One of the most vigorous young sciences is radio astronomy. It began about thirty years ago when Karl Jansky discovered that one source of short-wave noise appeared to come, not from anything on earth, not from the sun, but from the center of the Milky Way. Radio astronomy, like television, had to wait out the war, but then the large antennas developed for radar, and the improved ultra high frequency receivers, allowed it to leap ahead. Radio signals from interstellar hydrogen produce a sharp signal at 1420 megacycles, but relative motion shifts this signal in frequency. In this way the swirling of hydrogen in our Milky Way has been mapped. Galaxies so far away that they are receding from us at about one-fifth the speed of light have been discovered by radio. Already we have learned much from radio astronomy about stellar and galactic evolution. Larger antennas would let us learn much more and will surely be built. One day one of these may pick up a radio signal from the stars, one clearly bearing coded information; not a natural signal but the work of another intelligent race. Should this happen it will profoundly affect our culture. We may indeed find ourselves, through electronics, eligible to join a galactic community of intelligent species.

The heart of a transistor, the active part, is less than a millionth of a cubic inch in volume. If we could interconnect transistors and other similar elements without wasting space, we could make computers having 10 billion or more transistors in a small room. Such a computer is so much more complex than anything yet built that it might be capable of kinds of operation —shall we say behavior?—qualitatively different from those of present computers. In particular it might be able to *learn* to perform tasks not specifically built into it at "birth"; adaptive circuits that learn elementary responses already exist. It might acquire memories and habitual patterns of action. It might spontaneously undertake tasks, or stubbornly avoid them. It might compose poetry and music. It might, in short, give every external sign of consciousness. How then shall we say it is not conscious? And if it be, how shall we react: kill it, or improve it? Perhaps organic life, including man, is just a precursor of a later inorganic phase. Perhaps human destiny is to build the super life form out of silicon and copper, a life form capable of self-replication and improvement, of survival under conditions lethal to organic life. In this event electronics would outlive man himself.

Forgive me if these speculations seem too fanciful. I am trying to compensate for my blindness. I am acutely aware of my inability twenty or even ten years ago to predict the present. How can I do better now? I am only sure that electronics will develop over the next decades in exciting ways and that you can share in that excitement. Perhaps the most significant fact is that no one can really tell you what a career in electronics will be like. The art moves too fast.

15 *Communication*

BY JOHN R. PIERCE

DIRECTOR

RESEARCH IN COMMUNICATION PRINCIPLES

Bell Telephone Laboratories

JOHN R. PIERCE

Born: 1910, Des Moines, Iowa

California Institute of Technology: B.S., 1933; M.S., 1934; Ph.D., 1936
Honorary: Newark College of Engineering, D.Eng., 1961
    Northwestern University, D.Sc., 1961
    Yale University, D.Sc., 1963
    Polytechnic Institute of Brooklyn, D.Sc., 1963
    Carnegie Institute of Technology, D.Eng., 1964

Bell Telephone Laboratories:
    Member Technical Staff, 1936–
    Director Electronics Research, 1952–55
    Research Electrical Communications, 1955–58
    Research, Communication Principles, 1958–

Fellow: British Interplanetary Society
    American Academy of Arts and Sciences
    Acoustical Society
    Institute of Electrical and Electronic Engineers
    American Physical Society
Member: National Academy of Sciences

Morris Liebmann Memorial Prize, Institute Radio Engineers, 1947
Stuart Ballantine Medal, Franklin Institute, 1960
Air Force Association's H. H. Arnold Trophy, 1962
Arnold Air Society's Hoyt S. Vandenberg Trophy, 1963
Valdemar Poulsen Gold Medal, 1963
National Medal of Science, 1963

Author: *Theory and Design of Electron Beams,* Revised Edition
    Traveling Wave Tubes
    Electrons, Waves and Messages
    Man's World of Sound
    Symbols, Signals and Noise
    Short stories and articles on popular science

THERE ARE many things that can attract the young engineer
to a particular field of work, and among these is certainly a
sense of importance. There is no question that the field of
communication has this importance. Scholars, educators, and
publicists argue endlessly about the problems of communication
and of mass communication in our world. Diplomats, statesmen,
and politicians follow world events, not only day by day, but
hour by hour, and sometimes almost minute by minute. The
world as we know it has become, not a collection of isolated or
insulated individuals, communities, or nations, but a group of
highly related communities, organizations, and individuals. As
time passes, the interactions between individuals and organizations have less and less to do with physical distance. Indeed, a
businessman may call his headquarters in some far distant city
more often than he calls anyone in a nearby town.

Communication is an essential part of our life. Deprived of
the telephone, we could scarcely conduct our daily affairs; without the resources of electrical communication, nations and men
would lose touch with the world and relapse into static isolation.

The importance of electrical communication has come into
being through the invention and development of the telephone,
and of radio, and of television, and of the auxiliary means of
transmission and switching that have brought the peoples of
the nation and of the world together, voice to voice, and increasingly face to face. It is the engineer who has made possible
this world of communication, and any engineer who works in
the field of communication can have a legitimate sense of pride
in doing something essential to the welfare of man.

Beyond this aspect of service, electrical communication is a field large in scope. In most places in our country, people have a television set and a telephone in their homes. There are over 50,000,000 television sets in North America and over 80,000,000 telephones. There are over 150,000,000 telephones in the world, and the great majority interconnect by short-wave radio or by submarine cable, so that if you have reason to, you can talk from your home to a man in almost any part of the world.

Electrical communication is advancing and expanding rapidly. Transoceanic television has recently been demonstrated experimentally, by means of the Telstar, Relay and Syncom satellites; and, while it is not yet a regular part of our lives, it has proved itself as a part of the great electrical communication system of the world. International telephone calls to and from our country are now commonplace, and their number is growing at a rate of about fifteen per cent a year. The experimental communication satellites and the submarine cable, which is rapidly being extended to all parts of the world, have demonstrated the ease of intercontinental conversation. In fact, as cables and communication satellites give us more circuits, and better and more reliable circuits than those supplied by short waves, world communication will grow even more rapidly. This growth will bring with it a host of fascinating technical problems that the engineer will be called on to solve.

Within our own cities, mobile telephones in automobiles and airplanes are still rare, certainly not so much a part of our lives as the television set or the home telephone. Technical advances and assignments of frequency will overcome this. Besides mobile telephones, we will increasingly have paging devices in our pockets, which, when they ring, will summon us to the nearest telephone. Perhaps we will carry telephones in our pockets as well.

New uses will be found for our world-wide communication system. These will affect businesses and laboratories through the transmission of scientific data and of business accounting information. They will affect us individually as well because we are certain to use some sort of electrical communication, which will perhaps include data transmission, in making reservations and in shopping. Some day, we do not clearly know when, we will also have television as a common adjunct to telephony, not only for seeing the faces of those near and important to us, but also for viewing documents or merchandise at a distance.

Thus, communication is attractive because it is important and because it is widespread and offers many opportunities for providing services better and more economically, and for providing entirely new services. I, myself, have found communication fascinating in another way. Communicators are a world fraternity because whatever language they speak (and a surprisingly large number can speak English), the technical problems are the same. The International Telecommunications Union, which is almost a hundred years old, is far older than the United Nations of which it is now a part. Engineers from many countries meet regularly to discuss standards, and, through international scientific organizations, to discuss the technological problems of communication.

Many men have had a part in advancing the art of communication, but each has worked as an individual and every man who enters this field must himself do some particular thing. All the marvelous machinery of communication science and technology came into being piece by piece through individual advances: a new discovery, a new invention, a new idea opening up a new field and attracting the work of others. Sometimes the advances have come by putting together new and existing ideas in order to provide novel systems or services, as is the case in satellite communication and nationwide distance dialing.

Whatever one does in the field of communication, there is always the problem of getting started. When I joined the Bell Laboratories, jobs were scarcer than they are now. I was told what sort of problems I should work on and was given only a modest amount of guidance. The field to which I was assigned was that of vacuum tubes, one about which I knew almost nothing, but I had to plunge ahead in this unfamiliar field and try to find out how to do research in it.

Today things are quite different. There is great competition for competent technical people in the field of communication, whatever their level of training or field of work, and a man who goes to some company in the field of communication will be shown many projects. Most of these will have aspects that go far beyond any knowledge he can have acquired in a college or university; but because the field of communication is so broad, there is a useful and productive place for anyone with a reasonable degree of natural talent and a desire to accomplish something. There is sure to be some constructive opportunity, whether it be as an originator or executor, as a leader or a doer, whether it be in research, in the design of new systems, in the perfection of old systems, in the devising or construction or manufacture of components, or in the actual supervision of the technical details of operation of some communication system.

Much valuable work in communication has been done by a great number of small companies that make precise measuring equipment, radio sets, or communication equipment for special purposes. Communication systems are becoming ever more complicated, however, and in the future more engineers will probably go into large organizations that have, to some degree, research, development, and manufacturing departments. I have worked for a very large organization ever since I got my doctor's degree in 1936, and it is about life in such an organization that I know most directly.

The Bell Telephone Laboratories, where I work, is part of the Bell System. The parent organization is the American Telephone and Telegraph Company, which owns some 21 operating telephone companies that provide services in 48 states of the Union. The AT&T also supplies long-distance service through its Long Lines Department, and it owns the Western Electric Company, which manufactures all sorts of telephone equipment, from submarine cables that send telephone conversations across oceans, and transcontinental microwave radio relay systems that send television programs and telephone conversations across the nation, to the very telephone sets that you have in your homes. In turn, Western Electric and AT&T jointly own the Bell Telephone Laboratories.

Most of the 15,000 people of the Bell Laboratories are con-

nected with the development, the planning, and the design of
new equipment that will be manufactured by the Western
Electric Company and used in the Bell System. This work includes the development of transistors and other devices that will
be used in such equipment. About a thousand of the people at
the Bell Laboratories work in the research department, and that
is where I have worked.

In research, one deals with what is not yet known or established,
or with what does not yet exist, or with what has not yet been
effectively put into use. When I joined the Bell Laboratories in
1936, one of the great problems was that of providing more
effective, broader-band amplifying devices that were needed in
order to make coaxial cable systems that could transmit hundreds
(and now thousands) of telephone conversations, and television
programs as well, over long distances.

I started out trying to make an entirely different type of
vacuum tube called a deflection tube for this purpose. This deflection tube turned out to be not as good as the ordinary pentode
that was being used, but I did learn something during my work.
That was how to make an electron gun that would produce a
beam of electrons of much higher current than those used in
cathode ray tubes and kinescopes.

This gun proved to be valuable later. During World War II
I was drawn into making vacuum tubes for military purposes, and
my colleagues and I worked out a type of microwave vacuum
tube that was used in all American radar receivers. Successful
operation of this vacuum tube, a low-voltage reflex klystron,
depended on being able to produce the sort of electron beam
that I had learned how to produce in working on the useless
deflection tube. Here we see that research aimed toward one
end may produce unexpected benefits. It has sometimes been
said there is no useless research, and I think that good research
is always useful in some sense, but bad and ineffective research
is always useless.

After the war, the techniques of microwave radio had advanced
considerably through work on radar, and microwaves were put
to use in providing telephone and television transmission. Here

the very tubes that had been built for war purposes played an essential part. But there was another need as well. That was for an amplifier which would amplify a broad band of frequencies.

During the war an amplifier called the traveling wave tube had been invented by Rudolf Kompfner, who worked in a government laboratory in England, and I saw his work there in 1944. The traveling wave tube required the sort of high current electron beam that I had learned to produce. Further, in analyzing and explaining its operation I could draw on my experience in wartime microwave work. At least the next ten years of my life were spent working on traveling wave tubes, analyzing their operation, trying to improve their efficiency, trying to make them less noisy as receivers, trying to increase their power output, trying to devise new forms of this device.

During all of this period, perhaps a score of engineers at the Bell Laboratories were working on the problems of traveling wave tubes. Not a single application was found in the Bell System. Yet all the time we were accumulating knowledge and learning how to do an important thing, that is, to amplify broad-band microwave signals better and in a more controlled manner.

Eventually this work bore fruit. An application was found for the traveling wave tube in a missile system. An application was found for the traveling wave tube in an advanced microwave radio relay system, the TH system, which was introduced in 1961. And, finally, the one and only vacuum tube in the Telstar satellite is a traveling wave tube, which transmits the amplified microwave signal to a station on another continent.

The traveling wave tube has engaged more of my attention during my technical career than any other single idea or device, and I have chosen to say something about it because it illustrates many points about engineering research and about engineering in communication in general.

One of these points is that of continuity and interdependence. The traveling wave tube was not and could not become an isolated and individual product. Its success and utilization depended on Kompfner's invention, on my knowledge of how to form electron beams, on a satisfactory and quantitative theory of its behavior, on many subsequent inventions. It also depended on the application, over a number of years, of many years of background in vacuum tube technology that made it possible to build a structure that could be almost perfectly evacuated, to support and cool the parts in it, and to produce electrons copiously from a cathode. The microwave art associated with the wartime radar contributed principles and measuring equipment that were instrumental in the development of a satisfactory traveling wave tube.

From another point of view, an application was essential to the success of the traveling wave tube. This tube could be useful and important only if it enabled communication engineers to do some job better than they could with other microwave tubes, or to do some job that was impossible with other microwave tubes. Jobs of both sorts were found by men who designed military receivers, missile systems, microwave transmission systems, and the new and unprecedented communication satellite.

Although I spent a decade working on the traveling wave tube, my interest gradually expanded to embrace the fields in which such tubes could be important. This led me to learn something about microwave communication systems, and to meet and talk with the people who planned and designed and built such systems in this country and in other countries as well. For, during this period, research and development in traveling wave tubes went on in Great Britain, France, Germany, Japan, and many other nations, and I have visited laboratories and companies in many of these lands. In doing so, I have been received as a colleague and a friend, and have never felt myself a foreigner in a strange land.

Next to traveling wave tubes, the thing that has most occupied my attention in my own individual technical work has been communication satellites and the possibility of communication systems using them. Here my interest goes back at least to 1954, and was inspired by the knowledge of microwaves and microwave systems to which my work on traveling wave tubes led me. This interest in communication satellites led to the Bell Laboratories work with the first Echo satellite in 1960, and it inspired and laid the basis for the production and the launching of the Telstar satellite in 1962.

I think that to write more than this of my own experiences as an engineer in the field of communication would be a little unfair. Instead, I would like to say something about some of my friends, in order to show the variety of communication work that can take place in one organization. In doing this I don't think that names are important, but I could scarcely conceal the fact that the person who gave us the mathematical theory of communication is Claude E. Shannon.

I met Claude Shannon at the Bell Laboratories shortly after World War II. He was puzzling about various problems of communication systems. What is it that we are really trying to do in electrical transmission? How can we describe the capabilities or limitations of a communication system? Shannon's genius and mathematical talent led him to a solution of this problem, and this led to innumerable books and meetings, national and international, about communication theory, or information theory as it is also called. Here is a career very different from my own.

I have already mentioned Rudolf Kompfner, who invented the traveling wave tube. Kompfner was educated in Austria as an architect and practiced architecture in England, but he had always been fascinated by physics and electronics. Interned during World War II as an enemy alien, he spent his time studying physics, and, on his release, was put into a British laboratory doing radar work. This led him directly to the invention of the traveling wave tube. In 1951 Kompfner came to the Bell Laboratories, where he pursued his work in a broader field, and where he is now Associate Executive Director of the Communications Systems Division in the research department. Kompfner came to the field of communication in a way very different from me, and yet we have ended by working in close cooperation. Certainly, one's career in communication is not a matter of antecedents or of proximity.

When I first came to the Bell Laboratories I shared an apartment with another good friend, C. H. Elmendorf. His career has been very different from mine. He has been concerned with the multitudinous problems of designing and developing complicated transmission systems, including coaxial cable and submarine cable systems. This means that he must devote much time to the study and evaluation of new components, such as transistors, which are built by other departments; to advances in the circuit art of connecting components together to do new things or to do old things better; to standards of performance, many of which have been set on a world-wide basis through the International Telecommunications Union; to the needs for service of the operating telephone companies; and finally, to the feasibility and practicability of manufacture of the systems he designs. In research, we cannot predict when or even whether we will get satisfactory results, and certainly not what the cost will be. Yet, to my friend the matter of meeting a schedule or coming within cost estimates can be the difference between success and failure. Indeed, failure is more likely to be economic than technological.

Some friends of mine work on fundamental problems of physical research in fields that are important to communication, including properties of solid-state materials important to transistors, and the properties of magnetic ceramic materials important in microwaves and in telephone switching and computer-like applications. I know psychologists who work on problems of transmission quality and of telephone design. I know men who use the computer to study proposed telephone rate structures. I know men who understand the logical intricacies of designing automatic switching systems, and I know men who understand the technological intricacies of designing and building switching systems involving these principles. One man who started as an expert in computers is now an operating vice president of a telephone company.

For each of these men there is a fascinating story of work in the broad field of communication. I suppose that one can get rich in this field, although I certainly have not done so. What I recommend to a young engineer is the importance of the field, its immense scope, and, above all, the fascination of seeing new things come into being and into use, however long and painful this process may sometimes seem.

16 _Computing:_
An Alliance
of Man
and Machine

BY EDWARD E. DAVID, Jr.

DIRECTOR

COMPUTING AND INFORMATION RESEARCH CENTER

Bell Telephone Laboratories

EDWARD E. DAVID, JR.

Born: 1925, Wilmington, North Carolina

Georgia Institute of Technology: B.E.E., 1945
Massachusetts Institute of Technology: S.M., 1947; Sc.D., 1950

Massachusetts Institute of Technology:
Research Laboratory of Electronics, Research Assistant, 1946–50

Bell Telephone Laboratories:
Member of Technical Staff, Transmission Research, 1950–52
Member of Technical Staff, Acoustics Research, 1952–54
Supervisor, Acoustics Research, 1954–56
Subdepartment Head, Visual and Acoustics Research, 1956–58
Assistant Director, Visual and Acoustics Research, 1958–
Director, Visual and Acoustics Research, 1958–62
Director, Computing and Information Research Center, 1963–

Fellow: Audio Engineering Society
Acoustical Society of America: Executive Council
Institute for Electrical and Electronics Engineers
Administrative Committee: Professional Technical Group on Information Theory, Professional Technical Group on Audio
Association for Computing Machinery
Biophysical Society
Commission on Engineering Education: Executive Committee
National Science Foundation, Advisor
Psychonomic Society

Author: *Man's World of Sound* (with J. R. Pierce)
Waves and the Ear (with W. A. van Bergeijk and J. R. Pierce)
Articles, monographs, and contributions to technical books

THROUGHOUT man's history, new technology has been the greatest influence on his way of life. Metal tools put him "one-up" in providing food and defense for himself and his charges. Gutenberg's movable type at once made possible the wide dissemination of knowledge, previously available only through precious hand-produced manuscripts. The power-loom sparked the Industrial Revolution and produced an entirely new economic structure. The internal-combustion automobile fathered our modern pattern of city-suburban life. Telephony and radio communication are principal threads in the fabric of commerce and society.

In the years since World War II, nuclear explosives and rocket propulsion have overturned classical concepts of international relations, military strategy, and geographical barriers. However, the most far-reaching new technological influence is less heralded; it is the electronic digital computer.

These computers are, in some ways, similar to the familiar desk-top adding or calculating machine. Desk calculators and electronic computers both deal exclusively with numbers; adding, subtracting, multiplying, and dividing them. Computers, however, are unlike desk calculators in two ways. First, the detailed sequence of operations to be performed must be specified in advance by a sequence of written instructions. This sequence, called a program, is inserted into the computer with the data to be processed so that once a computation is begun, it proceeds without human intervention. Second, computers can compare one number with another, and select the larger, or smaller, one. Subsequent operations can be made, contingent upon the out-

243

come of such a test. This ability enables the computer to deal in logic—if A then B, if not A then C. Herein lies the power of digital computation, for numbers so manipulated can symbolize letters of the alphabet, aircraft in a traffic pattern, neutrons in an atomic reaction, or any one of limitless other possibilities. Thus computers are powerful symbol-manipulators; they are much more than super desk calculators.

However, it is certainly true that computers will not do things that cannot be done in principle by other equipment. Other devices, and people as well, can do arithmetic and logic. But the speed and freedom from error of electronic computers put them in a class apart. It is this swiftness and reliability that makes possible things previously considered impracticable. There are many similar examples in history. The automobile is much more than a super horse. Yet a person given enough time and horses could accomplish just about everything he could with an automobile. Still the automobile has changed our way of life profoundly because it brought mobility within easy grasp of most people.

Computers, too, are changing our way of life. They are aiding human thought and decision-making in research, defense, managerial, industrial, medical, and even artistic ventures. Computers are helping man learn more about himself in psychological and physiological studies. They are reaching into every nook and cranny of his intellectual life, promising to reveal and supplement the innermost workings of the human mind.

The computing field today is populated by a wide assortment of people. By education, they are, in the main, engineers and mathematicians, but physicists and, to a lesser degree, chemists and even psychologists have joined the ranks. In my opinion, however, engineering is the keystone. A strong background in mathematics is essential, but nowadays computing is addressing subjects far removed from numerical and analytical mathematics. Formal logic and grammar are coming to the fore, as is concern with computer systems. A computing system includes the computing machine plus all of its peripheral equipment and utility programs necessary to perform its routine service functions.

This assemblage must be tailored to reconcile somehow the machine's world of cold numbers with man's world of hot problems. This interface between man and machine provides the scope to making computing a truly challenging engineering enterprise.

The notion of mechanized arithmetic began with Leibnitz and Pascal, who in the 17th century built adding machines. These used numbered wheels geared together in much the fashion of today's automobile mileage indicators, to "carry" from one column to the next automatically. Only slightly later came more general mechanical calculators, which could subtract by turning the register wheels backward and multiply by successive additions.

Automatic control for these calculators came from the Frenchman, Jacquard. Around 1800, he developed a loom to weave cloth in a pattern specified by punched cards fed to the loom one after another. If punched cards controlled a loom, they could control an arithmetic calculator, too, causing it to follow a sequence, or program, of operations.

This idea occurred to Charles Babbage, an English mathematics professor from Cambridge University, in about 1840. He proposed to build an "analytical engine," or mechanical computer, having all the essential features of our modern electronic machines. The arithmetic unit was to add, subtract, multiply, or divide successively according to instructions punched on a sequence of cards fed into the machine. The numbers on which the arithmetic was to be performed, as well as the results, were to be held in a "store" or memory unit. Transfer of numbers between the memory and the arithmetic unit was to be controlled also by punched cards. The mechanical unit that was to translate the punched card information into action is today known as the control unit. Babbage decreed that the final results of a computation should be printed out automatically, as they often are today.

Babbage's machine was, in fact, never built, for reasons we shall see later. His invention was eventually forgotten, only to be rediscovered in the late 1930's. Yet his concept of the programmed calculator provided the means to remove much of the push-button drudgery associated with even today's desk-top calculators.

Babbage had another important idea. He realized that one part of the computer program could be used to modify another. To add a column of, say, 1000 numbers, we might instruct the machine, "Add the first two numbers"; then, "add the third number to the previous sum"; and so on. This procedure would take a thousand instructions, and would be laborious and inconvenient. Program modification permits us to tell the machine simply, "Add the following 1000 numbers." The program will then add the numbers cumulatively, in effect counting the number of additions and generating the thousand instructions for itself. Such flexibility is greatly aided if the entire program is loaded into the machine's memory before beginning the computation, for then no "card shuffling" is necessary. Program modification enables the machine to exercise a degree of self-control.

Program control and modification are at the heart of the modern concept of computing, but what about the machines themselves? Though Babbage had anticipated much of modern thinking, he was able to make only a vain effort at actually building his machine. Despite backing from the British government to the tune of $50,000 (equivalent to over half a million today), the necessary mechanical parts for his machine proved to be beyond the technology of the times. It may be hard for us to realize now when gears and mechanisms are so plentiful in our automobiles, clocks, washers, and aircraft that in Babbage's time these things could not be made to the required accuracy by even the most skillful artisans. Babbage was born a hundred years too soon.

The first successful programmed computers were built in the late 1930's and early 1940's. These machines were part electrical and part mechanical. They could add two numbers in less than a second and multiply in five or six seconds under the control of a paper tape on which the instructions were punched.

When relays, gears, and wheels were replaced by electronic

tubes, speeds went up dramatically. The first electronic computer, the Eniac, was built at the University of Pennsylvania just after World War II. It could add or multiply in a fraction of a second, but it took heroic efforts to keep this "model-T" machine in repair (Eniac contained 18,000 tubes). As with early automobiles, the operators had to "get out and get under" too often. One trouble was the immense heat produced by the glowing tubes. Eniac was a potential furnace as well as a computer. Air conditioning and fans kept the machine from melting itself, but heat was still a major cause of failure.

Though later tube machines were far better, drastic improvement had to await the transistor, which produces a great deal less heat than the tube and is faster, too. Today's large computers may contain several hundred thousand transistors, and yet are much more reliable than the earlier, simpler tube machines with far fewer components. Numbers can be added in less than a millionth of a second, while multiplication takes two or so millionths. This remarkable increase in speed is better appreciated by noting that a 600 mile-per-hour jet airplane travels about a mile during the time it took the 1940 brand of computer to multiply two numbers. The same plane would move only about one hundredth of an inch during the time consumed by the most modern machine for doing the same operation.

This speedy performance, which is practically error free, enables modern computers to do tasks that were considered impossible only a few years ago. For instance, during a space satellite launch, the amount and direction of rocket thrust determines the orbit into which the "bird" will be projected. It is vital to know, in planning such a shot, what orbit will result from a particular rocket-thrust sequence. The orbit can be found from the sequence by a straightforward calculation, but over 15 million arithmetic operations are required. This task would occupy a person using a desk calculator for 350 days, if he did one operation each second, 12 hours every day.

It might be possible to conscript some unfortunate person to undertake this job, but the chances of his getting the correct answer would be almost nil. To err is all too human, and millions of consecutive, errorless, manual operations are beyond even the most meticulous of us. On the other hand, typical digital machines can compute orbits in only a few minutes with essentially no chance of error; orbits by the hundreds were produced before Colonel John Glenn's space flight. After he was "safely" in space, computers were vital in rescuing him from that unfriendly environment. Using observations of successive positions of his spacecraft, a computer accurately determined the true orbit, and from this solved for the retrorocket sequence that would bring him safely to earth within retrieval range of waiting naval ships. All these computations were done while Glenn was in orbit; he couldn't have waited for the years required while human calculators did the job. Neither could he have flown his craft "by the seat of his pants," as early aircraft pilots did. The computer is literally the astronaut's compass.

These are essentially numerical feats; what about the nonnumerical capabilities of computers? Inside a computer, there are only numbers, but they can be made symbols of almost any real-world situation. The numbers might stand for the distances between cities, for the letters of the alphabet, or for the successive intensities of a sound waveform. A checkerboard can be laid out in a computer memory just as it can be laid out on a piece of paper; 0's representing empty cells on the board, 1's representing the men. (Each player's men can be stored in a different part of memory to keep from confusing their identity.) Furthermore, the computer can examine the numbers in its memory and decide which are zero. Here is the basis for logic. For instance, a "checkers-playing" program can examine the situation on the board and make a move contingent on the current position. The program must, of course, reflect a suitable strategy for checkers, but in the hands of a clever enough programmer, the machine could play a winning game.

Computers can do more than play games. The flow of traffic along city streets can be duplicated inside the machine by the flow of numbers along simulated streets built up in the memory. Of course, the city map, the rules of the road, the traffic laws, the pattern of daily travel by the populace, and so forth, must be programmed into the set of rules that govern the number flow. By observing this flow at the machine's output, we can watch simulated traffic jams developing, measure the delays involved, and see the effect of proposed changes in traffic routing before they are actually put into practice.

Computers can do logic, just as they do arithmetic, with blinding speed, but let's be skeptical for a moment. With all their agility, what can computers do and not do? An answer was given in the late 1930's by A. M. Turing, a British mathematician. He conceived an elementary computer, now known as a "Universal Turing Machine," which he proved mathematically could compute any quantity for which exact, explicit instructions could be written. Strictly speaking, modern computers are not Turing machines, but do have their generality. Turing's work is important not because he provided principles for designing modern computers, but because he proved that *any calculation* that can possibly be done by machine can be done by a very simple computer. By implication, then, the scope of today's computers is not limited by the machines, but only by man's ingenuity in reducing important tasks to sets of instructions or programs.

Turing threw down the gauntlet and engineers have responded eagerly. In the past decade, they have reduced literally thousands of routine intellectual tasks, and some that are not so routine, to machine form. Computers now keep track of most airline reservations and make the information available to all areas of the country simultaneously over telephone lines. Many of the steps in bringing an electronic system from conception to manufacture—the routine design, drafting, preparation of parts lists, and generation of punched paper tapes to run automatic wiring machines—are all done by computers. They play a key role in keeping track of the position, speed, altitude, and direction of every aircraft in flight near the United States, so that the Air Force can protect the country against attack. Computers are at the heart of the automatic telephone service that permits almost instantaneous routing of calls over the vast countrywide network in response to the twist of a dial. Computers have been programmed to produce near-human speech, to compose and play music, to play a strong game of checkers by profiting from past experience, and to prove geometry theorems.

Yet there are many tasks that have not been reduced to computer programs. For instance, it is not yet possible to obtain a good translation from Russian to English by computer. Though Russian words can be looked up in an automatic dictionary, selecting appropriate English equivalents among the many possible ones and arranging them into sensible sentences cannot be done consistently. The shortcoming is not with the machine but with linguistic theory, which doesn't yet provide a deep enough formal understanding of grammar and meaning in natural languages. Recognition of human faces is not yet feasible either. Psychologists don't know what features of the facial image serve for identification, or how they operate relatively independently of lighting, distance, or aspect. Converting conversational speech to printing, reading handwritten scrawl, recognizing chairs, tables, and other objects in pictures, or playing a fine game of chess, all still baffle computer programmers.

Generally, then, computers can surpass us in much of our routine, stereotyped mental tasks; but we haven't programmed them even to approach our ability to learn and use intuitive strategies and hunches in dealing with the world's diversity. Men are not machines, and machines are not men. Each can do things the other cannot. Together they can surpass either alone. And clearly we are not at an end, for Turing's proof leaves much room for further expansion. We cannot predict what computers will do in the future, but surely human imagination, ingenuity, and zeal will be vital.

In reciting the origins and potentials of computers, I have only hinted at the part people play—their rewards and satisfactions, and their struggles and burdens as well. These are the stuff of which life is made, and they are certainly different in various fields. What would they be like for a person concerned with computers? An answer is best found if we look at how various people are engaged in the computer enterprise.

First of all, someone must conceive, design, and build the machines themselves. At the most detailed level, engineers take devices, such as transistors, and build circuits which add or do logic with speed and reliability at low cost. For example, one of the most significant pieces of "hardware" research was done in the early 1950's when engineers learned how to construct large numerical memories from minute iron oxide doughnuts, called "magnetic cores." Numbers could be stored in the cores by magnetizing them in one direction or the other. Now practically every computer uses magnetic core memory. Certainly there must have been great satisfaction in seeing core storage develop from a mere idea to a key component in modern computers.

One present research and development aim is to compress computer circuits into tiny integrated packages. Another is to utilize light rather than electrons to compute. These activities are concerned as much with electronics and electrical engineering as with computers. Joy in building and experimenting with working models in a laboratory is a vital personal resource in this work.

Engineers are concerned also with the computer as a whole. How should the memory, arithmetic, and control units be organized to assure proper timing between them when each has its own peculiarities and limitations? What instructions should be available to facilitate programming? Considering the diverse applications for computers, what speeds and storage capacities are appropriate? Ingenious answers to such questions can make a new computer extremely powerful and profitable; it may even enable people to attack a class of problems not previously accessible.

Indeed, designing computers for specific purposes occupies many engineers. The heart of the Nike Zeus anti-missile missile system is a computer. It examines radar information as it comes in to identify hostile warheads entering the field of view. When one is found, it is tracked and firing data for the intercept missile is computed. At the proper time, the computer dispatches the interceptor automatically. The Zeus computer is tailored for this one important job. Other machines are expressly intended for compiling payrolls, keeping inventories, running telephone exchanges, guiding air traffic, or controlling chemical manufacturing processes.

Accomplishing these feats calls for a program to bring the machine itself to life. The program must contain instructions specifying exactly what the machine is to do in all situations it will encounter. It is not too hard to imagine, then, that programs can become very long indeed. The Sage program for continental air defense contained many tens of thousands of individual instructions. In the early days of programming, tens and even hundreds of people were employed in a mass push to finish such jobs. Despite their best efforts, schedules could not be met. Calling in even more programmers did not seem to help. Coordinating a mass of programmers, each of whose work had to fit with that of others, proved beyond even inspired and dedicated leadership.

Nowadays, most large, detailed programs are written automatically by a computer from a much shorter description, provided by only a few programmers. This feat is possible because researchers have been able to program general-purpose computers to decipher shorthand descriptions and provide corresponding blocks of machine instructions. These program-writing programs are known as compilers, and they in effect translate between two "languages," one describing the job to be done, the other describing the elementary arithmetic and logic operations the machine can perform.

An engineer working on special-purpose computers finds a real intellectual challenge. He must have an intimate feel for the application, whether it be a telephone exchange, a missile intercept, or a chemical process. He must know, too, about computing equipment—what speeds, reliability, and accuracy are feasible to build and at what cost. He must determine when and how to shift programming responsibility from men to machines. Engineers in this work find it fascinating to watch their brainchildren take concrete shape and finally perform.

The computers we hear about most often are general-purpose, as opposed to special-purpose machines. Special-purpose machines are usually programmed once and for all to carry out their special function. Their programs are rarely changed, and even then only to modify details. General-purpose machines serve a whole community of users, each with his own problems and programs. These general-purpose computers are usually found in computing centers to which users come to run their programs. To take a specific example, over 1000 people make regular use of the Bell Telephone Laboratories Computing Center at the Murray Hill, New Jersey, research and development facility. About 350 individual jobs are processed by the Center every day. These are brought in by users as stacks of cards and tapes holding their programs and data. Getting these into the machine and retrieving the results presents a major logistics problem.

The main computer at this installation is so fast and its time so valuable (about $600 per hour in rental fees), that it cannot be permitted to wait while program cards are slowly tallied or a typewriter is printing results. As an aid to matching man's world of seconds to the machine's world of microseconds, three small, slow computers are used to feed the main machine. Dispatchers collect tapes and cards from the users and take them to one of the small machines that condenses a batch of them into a smooth flow. When the main computer is ready, an operator switches this flow to its input. The output flow as it spews forth is caught by one of the small machines that stores it and prints out individual results for each of the users.

The "turnaround" time between a user submitting a job and receiving his results can be as short as one hour. The Center operates some 12 to 15 hours a day and has a staff of 50 to 60 people. The rental charges for all the equipment exceeds $100,000 per month (many computers are rented on a monthly basis rather than being bought outright). There are several hundred such centers in the country, some much larger and some smaller.

Fittingly enough, most of the center operations are controlled by the computer itself under the direction of a monitor, or executive, program. This program enables the machine to pick up jobs one after another with little time wasted in between and treat each appropriately. The housekeeper of the center is the executive program. It is also the interface between the user and the machine. The monitor has many utility functions that the user can call into play. He can obtain his results in a wide variety of forms, including graphs or curves on microfilm. He can ask the monitor for intermediate results to help him locate faults in his program. But most importantly the executive program can call on compiler and assembler programs to translate commands written in a convenient shorthand to the form appropriate for the machine. This facility greatly eases the users' task in writing their programs.

The design of compilers and assemblers is a research field all on its own, and I shall have more to say about it a little later on. The point here is that the executive, compiler, and assembler programs are just as important as the machine itself to the user. These programs are often called "software" to emphasize their unity with the "hardware," or the machine itself. (This word, "software," is not yet to be found in the dictionaries; it denotes those programs that remain "permanent" accessories for the machine, and become an integral part of it as far as the user is concerned.) In bringing his problem to the machine, the user takes advantage of this integrated hardware-software system. He can, by simple commands, ask this system for any of those convenient above-mentioned extras that render the machine more accessible and useful. The user does not have to program these extras himself each time he wants them, but can merely call on the lists of software instructions already in the machine. Thus if the software is inadequate, the user is likely to find the machine unwieldy and inconvenient. Indeed, software determines the machine's "personality." It makes the machine appear to be a much more sophisticated and usable machine, one that would be altogether uneconomical to build. People specializing in software design are sometimes called system programmers. They attempt to span the gap between user needs and existing hardware capabilities.

Some computer engineers know how to tailor a computing center with several machines, and with their peripheral equipment, so that all can be efficiently operated and are easy to use. These engineers may be salesmen for a computer manufacturer or they may be responsible for the operation of a center for an industry or university. In sales, the engineer may make a great deal of money if he is sensitive to customers' needs and has an attractive hardware-software package to sell. Also, of course, he must have thorough knowledge of what computing systems can and can't do.

The engineer who runs a computer center will be aided by a substantial clerical staff, as well as system programmers. People to keypunch cards, to operate printers and card-readers, to see to magnetic and paper tapes, to maintain and repair the machines themselves all hover about, interleaving their work. Obviously a flair for organization and dealing with people, backed by a deep engineering knowledge of computers and programming, is very useful. The director of a center must be constantly on the lookout for new possibilities to extend the machine's capabilities. Since users themselves are not likely to know what is possible with computers, the director's foresight is important. Experimentation and research are often appropriate.

For instance, a few years ago it became clear that conventional input-output by punched card, magnetic tape, and printer were not sufficient. How was one to put seismograph signals, sound and speech, radar data, and photographs into the machine and retrieve processed versions? Though there was little demand for such inputs at the time, a group of far-seeing engineers suspected that more versatile input-output would open a whole new dimension in computer usage. They proceeded to build the necessary sound and light transducers and to use these in conjunction with the computer. Through their efforts, the computer is now much in demand as a laboratory tool to study speech, vision, underwater sound, geology, and picture transmission, to name a few examples.

Currently researchers in computer operations are striving to bring man and machine closer together. They visualize a situation where many people are using a large, fast machine simultaneously, each communicating with it via a telephone line using a typewriter, or using a pointer called a "light pencil." The computer would send back messages to the typewriter, or pictures to be seen on a television screen. Of course, a sophisticated executive program is needed to bring peripheral typewriters and oscilloscopes to life, and a completely satisfactory one is yet to be achieved. Should present efforts be successful, however, computer service could become as accessible as the electric outlet on your wall. Thus in the operation of a computer center, research has a significant role. The engineering challenge is to achieve a flexible and convenient coupling between the machine and the user's world.

The user's world is essentially a world of programming. A computer without a program is merely a magnificent pile of senseless complexity. With a program, the computer can become a fine-honed tool to probe the unknown. Programming can provide a career on its own.

Programming has at least three distinguishable steps. First comes an analysis of the problem to be programmed. This stage is a crucial one, for it is here that real-world situations must be idealized to computational models. If the programmer overlooks some important influence so that the model is oversimplified, the computed results will be incorrect or, worse still, misleading.

Next comes program planning. Here the programmer must decide which of the available programming languages should be used to implement the model. He must then outline the sequence of program steps to do the intended job. A well-planned program is one that uses the machine's time efficiently. There are many ways to skin a cat or solve a problem; often an ingenious way yields a much shorter computation time than the obvious first choice. One major programming challenge is to find such time savers, for computing time may cost many hundreds of dollars per hour.

The third step in programming is coding. Here are written the actual commands that will be translated to machine instructions. The programmer's commands must accurately and exactly specify his desires. Coding requires meticulous care, for *every* command must be correctly written. If a command is left out or misplaced, for instance, the machine may solve some problem, but not the one the programmer intended. Chances are the output, if any, will be meaningless garble.

The programmer can be a person of broad or narrow interests. Because programmers are in demand, they are free to associate with a vast variety of enterprises in business, science, economics, physics, biology, library science, and on and on. The programmer can stick closely to one of these or change to others as opportunities arise. At every stage, however, he must understand both the original problem and its machine counterpart. If he views the original subject superficially, he is likely to obtain an elegant solution to the wrong problem. If his knowledge of computing techniques is not deep, he will often come up with an inefficient, wasteful solution to the right problem. Certainly he must be intimately acquainted with his particular machine, with its idiosyncrasies and internal workings. He also should have a bag of computing tricks to call upon when faced with a knotty problem. The former takes study and interest, the latter experience and ingenuity.

Also, the programmer must not mind buckling down to write the command code for the machine, clear up the inevitable errors, get the program to run, and interpret the results. There is real satisfaction in carrying this chain of events through to its end and seeing the machine jump through the hoop. A programmer can have a varied and active life, or he can pursue a particular subject deeply. Programming is a particularly fine field for women. Many of the very best programmers are women; somehow they seem to be especially adroit at it.

So far I have been talking about programming for users in business, science, and engineering itself. But there is also programming to produce aids for other programmers. I introduced this field of advanced research earlier in referring to compiling, or translating, programs. These are often known by unfamiliar names, symbolic names, such as FORTRAN, ALGOL, BLODI, LISP, and so on. Regardless of these names, compilers permit programmers, in essence, to write their program commands in a convenient shorthand language tailored to their particular problem. The compiler translates a program written in shorthand into instructions for the machine. Among the many compiler languages now available, there are those especially suited for programming the computer to simulate electrical signaling systems, to do algebra, to produce animated moving pictures, and to make "electronic" music.

The people engaged in compiler research are concerned essentially with translating one language into another. These are not natural languages, such as English and Russian, but they are not entirely unlike them either. Programming languages must be unambiguous; they therefore tend to be stylized and stereotyped compared to natural language, but the same considerations of grammar and syntax are involved. In fact, a parsing section is one of the keys in a compiling program. The parser analyzes commands written in programming language so that their meaning in terms of machine instructions can be established.

Advanced programming research in general aims at keeping programming time and effort within reason as we undertake more and more ambitious tasks on computers. As the Sage experience shows, even if programs are conceived with inspiration and planned with care, they cannot in practice always be coded by hand. Indeed the future of computers hinges on new linguistic devices for shorthand programming.

I have tried to intrigue you with my story of computers—with the notion that it is much easier to show what computers can do than what they can't. If I have succeeded, you may well ask, "What kind of education do I need to enter computing?" Much of the hardware aspect is based upon electrical and, to a lesser degree, mechanical engineering. Electrical engineering can also provide a good background for software and programming work, provided a generous dose of mathematics is included. In some universities, computing departments with their own faculties are beginning to appear. Probably it will not be long before computer-oriented curricula are available at many places.

With all this talk of hardware and software, I have run the risk of making computation appear formidable. Is computing too demanding for a mere mortal to contemplate? Certainly not. A person can approach the whole in easy stages, and at each step be able to do something that is both useful and intriguing. Perhaps, too, some aspects of the computer enterprise may seem over-specialized. But there is no need to tread one path to the exclusion of others. Perhaps the most valuable person is one who can cover many facets of computing—hardware and software, transistor circuits and compilers—contributing to each. Certainly, there is a place in computing for all sorts of engineering talent, whether one's interest is narrow or broad, whether one is highly mathematical or intuitively practical. And what has been done is nothing compared to what will be done.

Computing and engineering seem to go together. Above all, engineers want to do things that are useful and will work. This is the approach that will benefit computation. As Turing hinted, the computer can do things in bewildering variety. With such a versatile toy it is all too easy to spend one's life in amusing nonsense. Yet it is just the computer's vast horizon that provides the opportunity and challenge to achieve the unlimited.

17 _Information Engineering_

BY CHARLES STARK DRAPER

DEPARTMENT OF AERONAUTICS AND ASTRONAUTICS

Massachusetts Institute of Technology

CHARLES STARK DRAPER

Born: 1901, Windsor, Missouri

Stanford University: A.B., 1922
Massachusetts Institute of Technology: B.S. in Chem. Engineering, 1926;
M.S. in Aeronautical Engineering, 1928; Sc.D. (Physics), 1938

Massachusetts Institute of Technology:
Professor, 1939–
Head, Aeronautical and Astronautical Dept., 1951–
Instrumentation Laboratory, Director, 1948–

Operated Laboratory to develop infra-red signaling devices for U.S. Navy,
1927
Consultant U.S. Navy, also U.S. Air Force and commercial organizations
in fields of aeronautics and control

Member: American Physical Society
Institute of Aeronautical Sciences (Honorary)
Instrument Society of America, Honorary Life Member
American Academy of Arts and Sciences
American Society of Mechanical Engineers
Institute of Radio Engineers
National Academy of Sciences
National Inventors Council, Chairman
American Ordinance Association
American Institute of Consulting Engineers
International Academy of Astronautics, President

Awarded Exceptional Civilian Service Award, Dept. of the Air Force, 1951
Navy Distinguished Public Service Award, 1956, 1961
Air Power Award of Massachusetts Wing, Air Force Association
Thurlow Award, Institution of Navigation
Air Power Trophy, Air Force Association
Holley Medal, American Society Mechanical Engineers, 1957
Blandy Medal, American Ordinance Association, 1958
Godfrey L. Cabot Award, Aero Club, New England, 1959
Potts Medal, 1960
Sylvanus Albert Reed Award
Medal for Merit
Space Flight Award, American Astronautical Society, 1962

Author: Numerous articles in field of aeronautical instruments in technical
journals

IT IS the purpose of this chapter to describe a field of engineering that is both very old and very modern. The field deals with the use of information in understanding and controlling the behavior of both animate and inanimate systems. The writer has found information engineering an interesting and rewarding profession for some thirty-five years, and during this time the field has expanded rapidly, with new tasks of ever-increasing challenge appearing with the development of modern technology.

In our consideration of information engineering, we must take into account that every complete system, that is, every complex of components and subsystems organized to serve some need or desire of humanity, must include two particular subsystems. They are the *director* subsystem, which generates commands for controlling actions, and the *effector* subsystem, which is a means for carrying out these actions and achieving desired results.

For example, an automobile with its engine, wheels, frame, body, and so forth, is an effector serving the purpose of transportation in the sense that passengers and inanimate items placed on board can be carried from place to place. But an automobile without a driver to provide the director function of controlling speed and direction is useless as a transportation unit.

The case of the automobile is typical of all operating systems. Man is another example, with his bones and muscles, serviced by lungs, digestive organs, heart, blood vessels, and so forth, making up the effector system, and his nervous system and its various parts serving the director function. In man, the director system output has the form of nerve impulses which serve as command signals for the muscles of the effector system.

When primitive man looked at a mountain he acquired information as to its direction and distance and recorded it in his mind. The information might only have increased his general knowledge and had no other significance to him; but it might also have been used to influence his decision to walk toward the mountain, actually starting him on his road and then keeping his steps directed on the proper path. This simple example, drawn in terms of a human being, illustrates rather fully the elements of information engineering.

The eyes of the man sense light from the mountain and generate signals of transmission over nerves to the brain, where the pulses represent information. The brain processes the pulses and gives an understanding of the external situation, which is combined with stored information on desires and plans, producing signals that represent walking commands for the muscles. The nerves then carry these signals to the muscles, and the erect, stabilized posture of the man is changed into motion toward the mountain.

As the man moves, his eyes sense position and speed, feeding these back through nerves and brain for comparison in regard to position, direction, and all desired conditions. This comparison gives information on any deviation, and the information then causes the brain to send guidance signals to the muscles. The muscles make whatever corrections are needed, producing guidance signals that keep the man moving along his proper path toward his destination.

Processes like this one have been enacted as human activity for the unknown thousands of years that man has been in existence. In this, as well as in inanimate processes, the director systems must perform all the actions necessary to generate commands for their associated effector systems, if these two subsystems together are to be effective in causing the over-all system to achieve desired results.

Commands of proper quality are possible only if they are based on the acquisition, thorough processing, wise evaluation, and effective application of all available information associated with the existing environment. Also, they are possible only if they take into account the situation of the effector, the performance characteristics of the operating elements involved, and the results desired from the effector.

Director systems may be made up almost completely of human beings, and throughout millennia of human progress they *were* made up of men. For example, in the early military systems, spies, scouts, and observers collected the information about the enemy. Generals, with their staffs, received this information, combined it with orders and advice from their governments, considered the size, weaponry, logistics, morale, equipment, and so forth, of their own forces, then formed judgment of possibilities, built up campaign plans, and issued orders that were finally carried to the troop commanders by messengers.

It might well be pointed out that the functions just named serve to illustrate that the director system deals with information rather than the power for action that is associated with the effector system. It is an ordinary rule that director systems, whether formed entirely of human beings, of both men and inanimate devices, or entirely of inanimate devices, all deal exclusively with information whose power levels are just sufficient to represent signals.

Besides using director systems made up almost entirely of men, humanity through the years has depended very strongly on director systems built around men using inanimate equipment. For instance, the ships that have been the effectors of waterborne transportation have always depended on human pilots. In the beginning, the pilots had only their natural equipment of sense organs to receive information, brains to collect, process, and evaluate the sensed information, and to determine commands that applied to the effector by muscle forces exerted on the rudder, or by words spoken to a helmsman.

Later, the director function was divided among several components, navigators using telescopes and sextants to improve observations, using computing aids to speed up position determinations, and power steering to make guidance commands effective. As a result of many developments, occurring principally during the first half of the present century, inanimate systems capable of high performance as automatic pilots for ships are presently common on large vessels.

Automatic director systems are now being widely used for the vehicles of modern transportation ranging from ships, automobiles, and airplanes, through rocket-powered missiles to the space craft. Many of these vehicles present director system problems that are beyond the abilities of human pilots unless they have aid from inanimate equipment. High performance airplanes must have power boosters to supplement the pilot's muscles, while an array of instruments to aid his senses is necessary if he is to fly all-weather missions. Ballistic missiles and many space craft do not carry human pilots, so that their director systems must be comprised entirely of inanimate components.

The trend today is to design flight vehicle director equipment capable of completely automatic operation, with optional configurations adapted to provide assistance for human pilots when they are present and desire personally to carry out any part of the over-all director functions. With an arrangement of this kind, man has complete mastery of his machine.

It was perfectly natural that, in early times, the simple wheeled vehicles and sailing ships should have been controlled and guided by human pilots. It was natural, too, that later, when trains, steamships, and airplanes appeared, they also should be guided by human pilots, even though increasingly these pilots were aided by inanimate controls. However, it is only within the past half century that technology has reached a state of advancement that permitted the realization of completely inanimate systems for dealing with information. This circumstance, coupled with new requirements for performance that are beyond the capabilities of human beings, has resulted in much new technology and in the emergence of information engineering as the really important field of activity that it is today.

In any discussion of information engineering there are numerous factors that must be taken into account. Important among them are measurement, control, and guidance.

The process of measurement came into existence with modern science itself and continues to hold a primary role in all scientific development. In addition to the highly refined measurements of advanced research, which require very accurate and generally expensive instruments, there are gauges of many kinds for temperature, pressure, humidity, light, speed, distance, and so forth, which are supplied to the public by an active and intensely competitive industry. The engineering of measuring instruments continues to be a field of many opportunities.

The second factor mentioned above is control, which represents the interface between the information handling elements of the director system and the high power components of the effector system. Thus the control system of a rocket missile includes the components that receive command signals and change the direction of thrust as necessary to propel the missile along a path that carries it toward accomplishment of its mission. Amplifiers, wires, angle sensors, mechanical elements, valves, and so forth, are combined to adjust thrust directions as such changes may be needed.

A minimum requirement for control is that the effector system must be constrained to operate continuously near some equilibrium condition. In the rocket, for example, the vehicle must fly consistently along some equilibrium direction; that is, it must rise vertically from the launch pad without significant oscillations and it must continue to move smoothly in all parts of its trajectory during which control is desired. The process of achieving this necessary condition is called stabilization.

It is important to notice that all operating systems with animate, inanimate, or mixed components must be stabilized if they are to be of practical use. Thus an army made unstable by mutiny and lack of discipline will obviously be a most unsatisfactory effector system. An airplane oscillating because of severe flutter is similarly not in stable operation, a condition of operation that must be reached before the vehicle can effectively follow any command signal.

Until the 1930's human pilots using manual controls provided all the information involving services required by aircraft. This situation was obviously unsatisfactory as it limited flying to times of good visibility and was very tiring for pilots on flights of long duration. All aircraft were designed to be fairly stable with respect to the air masses through which they moved, in the sense that they tended to remain fairly close to smooth equilibrium paths. However, this so-called aerodynamic stability was never good enough for the pilot to desert his controls for long because the equilibrium path always deviated from straight and level and always required correction. So long as pilots could see the ground, their sensing processes enabled them to make these corrections without difficulty; but once they could not see the earth, these processes had to be supplemented by sensor devices not depending on visibility.

The problems both of stability and of direction indication were solved for human pilots by providing gyroscopic instruments, which are instruments of information self-contained within the airplane to show angles with respect to the earth. This made it possible for the human pilot to stabilize airplane positions and directions of motion by looking at his gyroscopes and operating his controls according to their readings and without being dependent on the visibility of the earth.

The next step in the progress of information engineering was to eliminate the need for a human pilot in the requirement of stabilization. This was done by connecting signals from the gyros to power boosters for operating the aircraft controls. In effect the amplifier used for the correction replaced the man because it could tirelessly perform, as its sole ability and duty, one of the capabilities of a human being. The amplifier, being an inanimate system, can do its job continuously without loss of attention or deterioration in performance even after many hours of operation.

Automatic pilots of the 1930's were effective for relieving the human boredom associated with continuous stabilization, but their capabilities did not include accurate guidance for aircraft making extended trips. On such trips, it was necessary for the human pilot to use all available navigation information for establishing position and working out guidance commands for the aircraft control system. In generating these guidance commands, the pilot dealt only with his sensing and processing of information. No force-level operations, such as the manipulation of controls, entered the problem.

Actually, guidance, the third basic factor, is the process of generating command signals for the purposes of control. This process involves only information and consequently needs power levels no greater than those required to satisfactorily represent information. Thus, the ships of a naval force are guided by orders generated in the admiral's staff, while the actions of the admiral himself are guided by orders from Washington. In this process, computers and communication equipment must be used to couple all the elements of the system into an effective operating chain.

The development of guidance systems has been so rapid that ballistic missiles now carry guidance systems that generate command signals for their control systems. All the necessary actions must be carried out by inanimate systems for the simple and compelling reason that no man is on board the missile, which must therefore depend on self-contained equipment. In addition, the geometrical problems involved are too complex to be solved with the required speed and accuracy by human calculators on the ground when radiation links are used to transfer signals to and from a missile. Operational orders, which are essentially the guidance commands for complexes of military weapons, must today be generated by or under the supervision of men, but as technology develops, inanimate devices will surely play increasingly important roles.

Under the stress of World War II, and along with the advance of technology, the decade of 1940–50 was a time of remarkable development in information engineering, particularly concerning fire control, flight control, and inertial guidance.

At this time, the author took advantage of the already developed ideas of gyroscopic devices and applied them to gunsights that were successfully used by the navy for defending naval vessels from multiple attacks by aircraft. The same principles were incorporated in airborne sights for fighter aircraft that later were effective in the Korean fighting.

All these fire control equipments belong to the realm of information engineering because their operation involves only the sensing, processing, and application of information. In general the units were self-contained and of necessity were small and simple. In fact, only analog principles were applied in the gunsights.

During the 1940's another factor of tremendous influence in information engineering came into effect and must be mentioned here. It was during this time that great developments in the new field of electronic digital computers were started and continued to important usefulness. It should be pointed out, however, that this early usefulness was limited by a somewhat less than acceptable reliability coupled with the considerable size and weight of the computers themselves; yet the trends toward digital operations, that are of such great practical importance today, were started at this time.

About 1945 the author became involved in the new field of inertial guidance, a segment of information engineering that has undergone spectacular developments that are continuing at the present time. Inertial guidance depends upon gyroscopic principles accurately to stabilize a mechanical member in a known orientation with respect to space coordinates, and applies digital signals from high performance accelerometers as computer inputs. By digital counting in the computer (which also corrects for the effects of gravitational fields that may be present), the motion and position of the craft carrying the inertial system may be computed during considerable time periods without the need for external contacts.

The Instrumentation Laboratory at the Massachusetts Institute of Technology designed, built, and tested the first inertial guidance system for aircraft with flights during 1948. This equipment incorporated a celestial body tracker that added this reference to the inertial quantities. Later aircraft systems in 1954 and 1957 gave improved performance for reduced weight and size. The aircraft inertial guidance system continues today with operations extended to the reaches of space for greatly prolonged periods of time.

Inertial Guidance Equipment studies for ballistic missiles were started by the Instrumentation Laboratory during the early 1950's for the Atlas Intercontinental Ballistic Missile, but the first actual applications were made to the Thor missile in 1957. Success with the Thor equipment was followed by Polaris and Titan inertial guidance developments that are today also giving good performance in operation.

Soon after the national decision to develop the Apollo Spacecraft for carrying men on journeys to the moon and return, the National Aeronautics Space Administration assigned full responsibility for development of the Apollo Guidance Equipment to the Instrumentation Laboratory. The mission included launch, insertion into earth orbit, refinement of earth orbit, departure from earth orbit, midcourse travel, entry into moon orbit, refinement of moon orbit, despatch of Landing Excursion Module to the moon's surface, launch from moon's surface, rendezvous with module in moon orbit, despatch from moon orbit, return midcourse, re-entry into earth's atmosphere, and landing at a designated spot on the earth's surface.

When one takes into acount all the functions incorporated into one piece of equipment that is designed to use inertial principles, optical lines of sight to celestial bodies, reference points on moon or planets, telemetry, radar, radio, lazars, one can then at least partly recognize the quality and breadth of understanding required. When it is also remembered that the machine must communicate easily with men, while men must effectively control the machine with the same degree of facility, the complexity of the over-all problem appears.

It is only within the last few years that information engineering has emerged as a distinct field. Many subfields are involved; communication engineering, computer engineering, and instrumentation engineering, for example, belong to the broader field of information engineering. These and other areas are now highly developed and are still expanding. The primary function of information engineering is to integrate the essential components provided by more specialized activities into director systems needed to work the effector systems that serve the needs and desires of society.

Information engineering involves basic ideas that have been associated with over-all systems having fantastic performance even by the standards of recent times; indeed, information engineering is often largely responsible for the development of these systems. The concept involved is simply that of a procedure in which all the problems of dealing with information for any complete system are treated as a single coherent field. Sensors, communication systems, computers, data storage units, signal conditioners, couple elements, amplifiers, and so forth, are all regarded as components to be combined into a pattern giving optimum performance. This means that for each particular case the engineer responsible must have enough understanding of all the essential principles to design and bring to realization a system that takes full advantage of the resources available from science and technology. When these resources do not provide the means for achieving adequate performance, this fact must be realized and proper steps taken in research and development to remedy the recognized difficulties.

All operating systems that fail to give peak performance represent chances for information engineering to improve control, command response, and direction. Since few systems of today have complete information equipment, and much less refined equipment, it is obvious that great opportunities exist for the information engineer.

Power stations, chemical plants, steel mills, factories, ships, submarines, airplanes, missiles, space craft, and all other operating systems can profit from information engineering. Business and industry are just beginning to take advantage of the improvements that follow systematic treatments of information to give improved results. The real work of information engineering has just begun in terms of operating patterns, system mechanization, components of smaller size and cost, and general advances toward optimum systems. The paths of progress are clearly visible ahead, and it will surely be many years before information engineering can catch up with existing problems. There is no chance that the information engineer will work himself out of a job in the foreseeable future.

_18_ _Engineering in the Sciences of Life and Man_

BY WALTER A. ROSENBLITH

BY WALTER A. ROSENBLITH

DEPARTMENT OF ELECTRICAL ENGINEERING
AND
CENTER FOR COMMUNICATION SCIENCES
(RESEARCH LABORATORY OF ELECTRONICS)

Massachusetts Institute of Technology

WALTER A. ROSENBLITH

Born: 1913, Vienna, Austria

College education in France, degrees in communication engineering

New York University: Research Assistant, Dept. of Physics, 1939–40
University of California at Los Angeles: Lowy Scholar; University Fellow; teaching fellow in Physics, 1940–43
South Dakota School of Mines and Technology: Assistant Professor; Associate Professor; Acting Head Department of Physics, 1943–47
Harvard University: Research Fellow, Psycho-Acoustic Laboratory, 1947–51
Massachusetts Institute of Technology:
   Associate Professor of Communications Biophysics, Department of Electrical Engineering, 1951–57; Professor, 1957–
   Research Laboratory of Electronics, Staff Member, 1951–
Harvard Medical School and Massachusetts Eye and Ear Infirmary:
   Research Associate in Otology, 1957–

Committee Memberships:
   National Academy of Sciences-National Research Council:
      Hearing and Bioacoustics, 1953–59
      Use of Electronic Computers in the Life Sciences, 1960–
      Computers in Science, Education and Research, 1962–
   American Standards Association, Panel Chairman, 1952–58
   American Academy Ophthalmology and Otolaryngology, Conservation of Hearing, 1953– (consultant)
   President's Science Advisory Committee: Life Science Panel, 1961–
Professional Memberships:
   Institute of Electrical and Electronic Engineers
   Biophysical Society: Council and Executive Board, 1957–61
   Society of Experimental Psychologists
   International Brain Research Organization: Central Council, 1959–; Executive Committee, 1962–
   International Organization for Pure and Applied Biophysics: Council, 1961–
Fellow: American Academy of Arts and Sciences
   World Academy of Art and Science
   New York Academy of Sciences
   Acoustical Society of America

Author: Numerous book chapters and articles; editor *Sensory Communication* and *Processing Neuroelectric Data*
Editorial Boards: *Information and Control; Biophysical Journal; Kybernetik; Daedalus*

MANY OF YOU may have come across one or more of the following expressions: biomedical electronics, biomedical engineering, biological engineering, human engineering, biotechnology, life science engineering, engineering biophysics, bionics, and other names that are comparatively new but that denote an interface—a boundary or a crossing area—between engineering and biological science.

When you heard or read one of these terms for the first time, you probably were intrigued and maybe even puzzled. What has engineering to do with biology? It is far from obvious how various engineering specialties relate to the multiple subdivisions of biology and medicine, or how they are concerned with the ways in which men react, reason, and live in social groups. You may have gone on to ask whether there exist professional groups of engineers whose primary concern is with these interfaces between biology and engineering. Finally, you may have wondered whether there are colleges and universities with curricula that lead to careers at this most recently discovered frontier of engineering.

This chapter is written by one whose training was in prenuclear physics and communication engineering and who is now trying to learn more about how our brain processes the information that our senses provide. It is thus a rather biased view of how you may proceed if you prefer the excitement and uncertainties of something that is obviously new, rather than the relative security of more established fields and disciplines. Changes in these latter fields also are rapid but perhaps they are qualitatively less compelling than in a field where one starts from "near zero."

Different individuals learn about problems that involve both engineering and biology (or engineering and medicine, or engineering and social science) in different ways. I, for instance, was offered three distinct chances to become involved with them —all three, by the way, after I had my engineering degrees. Since each of the experiences can convey something of the grain or fabric of the problems, I shall recount them in a manner not unlike that of a lawyer or physician who reports case histories in detail instead of trying to pontificate in often fragile generalities.

My first opportunity came when a physician, who headed a consulting service for industrial medicine, had the notion that high noise levels might be related to the frequency of accidents in a given factory. This question proved too difficult for direct investigation because a factory in which work of comparable hazard could be carried out in the absence of noise could not be found. However, my employer was also interested in demonstrating physiological effects of noise that were less dramatic than accidents. Hence, for each member of a population of factory workers I determined his exposure to noise and his hearing for pure tone. On the basis of these data, I was able to establish that for this population the amount of permanent hearing loss suffered was, in a statistical sense, related to the severity of the noise exposure.

Earlier observers and investigators had already suggested in qualitative terms that severe exposures might be responsible for hearing losses suffered in industry. Our data, however, because of their more quantitative nature, seemed to warrant the conclusion that steady, lifelong exposure at even relatively low noise levels could produce—at least in susceptible individuals— appreciable hearing losses. Such a conclusion indicated that measures to protect man's hearing, either by reducing unnecessary noise or by providing ear protection, are required for human welfare, or at least in order to guarantee reliable auditory communication.

To understand how prolonged noise exposures affect man's hearing requires that we know more about the normal changes that aging produces in man's auditory capacities. As longevity becomes more prevalent, engineers who design communication equipment, such as telephones, hi-fi, and television sets, certainly need to know how different age groups differ in their abilities to communicate via their sensory channels. This is a clear instance of the relevance of biological data to the engineer, though it is also true that most of these data on human sensory performance require sophisticated engineering equipment for their measurement.

The problem of noise obviously concerns both man and machine, and thus clearly involves other factors than just engineering. Whatever the practical and even social significance of the conclusions of my investigation concerning the effects of industrial noise exposures, they were overshadowed in my mind by a single finding. The observed hearing losses did not occur in the frequency region in which most of the acoustic energy of the noise had been concentrated. How was one trained, as I had been, in physics and communication engineering to interpret this apparent paradox?

Von Helmholtz, whom most people today consider the earliest great biophysicist, formulated about one hundred years ago a resonance principle to account for man's ability to resolve complex sounds. This resolving power is based on certain features of the anatomy of the inner ear. The hearing losses that appeared to be caused by prolonged exposure to industrial noise seemed to violate certain aspects of the Helmholtz theory. The clash between the Helmholtz theory and these empirical findings made me curious: How much of man's hearing is a more or less *direct* consequence of mechanical events in his ear? How much depends upon the way in which the ear's output is handled by that part of the nervous system that is more particularly concerned with hearing?

This autobiographical story is told here for two reasons. One is to give an example of how engineering and the life sciences can blend. Another is to suggest how an engineer, who started out by measuring the distribution of power in the audible frequency range, may find himself involved in the study of biological mechanisms on which evolution has been at work for millions of years.

My second engineering encounter with biological problems came two years later while I was working in the New York University Department of Physics on certain engineering aspects of a Van de Graaff High Voltage Generator. Surprisingly (at least to me), I found myself drawn into a research program on electric fish! For more than a century and a half, natural scientists have been fascinated by these creatures that are capable of generating electric discharges which apparently serve both for defense and communication.

Since the specialized electric organs that the various species of electric fish possess are well adjusted to the environment in which each species lives, the study of each species needs to take into account their normal habitat. The team of physicists and biologists that I joined was studying electric eels that came from the fresh waters at the mouth of the Pará River in Brazil. There the eels grow to a length of six to eight feet; they are capable of delivering up to several hundred short (2 millisecond long) pulses of electricity per second; these pulses range as high as 500–600 volts, and, at the peak of the discharge, current as high as ⅓ ampere has been recorded.

My first task was to measure the speed at which these electric pulses travel along the eel's electric organ, which is several feet in length. With the aid of well established engineering techniques, we found that this speed was about several thousand feet per second, a figure much greater than the speed with which the electrochemical changes called nerve impulses were known to travel. More thorough analysis then revealed that the apparent speed we had obtained (which had been done by dividing the distance the pulses travel by the travel time) was misleading. This engineering "error" had a biological reason, for eels apparently make use of a delay mechanism that prevents the front end of the electric organ from firing until the tail end is almost ready to do so. By insuring almost simultaneous firing of the entire organ, a more efficient mechanism of pulse delivery is provided than our initial, not very subtle calculations, had assumed.

After this contact with what is probably the most potent source of biologically generated electricity on our globe, I next became interested in electrical events in the micro-volt-range. My wife, then a student of psychology, dealt in her senior thesis with the following topic: How do changes in the electroencephalogram, popularly known as "brain waves," relate to changes in man's metabolism? As my wife told me about the experiments that had been done in order to relate biochemical and electrical variables, I became intrigued with the description and analysis of the electroencephalogram as a signal that changes from instant to instant and is, therefore, rather unpredictable. How was one to describe such a signal in mathematical terms? This set of problems has fascinated me ever since and I have worked on certain aspects of it since I came to MIT.

Considerable progress has been made in understanding the problems of the brain in the last two decades, but we are still far from having found adequate mathematical formulations for even its most important characteristics. The human brain contains billions of neurons whose activity is at least in part symbolized by patterns of electrical events that vary both in time and space. In physics we have learned over the centuries to express in mathematical form the properties of a gas, or a fluid, or a piece of solid material; we do this in terms of the properties of the atoms and molecules that compose it. An adequate description of the brain as a collection of intricately organized and highly specific structures, capable of a multitude of communications and control functions, would require that we be able to derive the brain's over-all properties from the properties and connections of the neurons that compose it.

It is clearly impossible to deal with this incredibly difficult job as a single problem. Instead, brain researchers have tried to tackle, both experimentally and theoretically, subtasks that were simple enough to give hope of making some progress. In recent years the availability of computers has added a most powerful instrument to these investigations. Indeed there are many who feel that without computers it would be practically hopeless to try to make mathematical models for, or to write mathematical descriptions of, even the simpler workings of the brain.

The above three examples represent only a minuscule sample of the many opportunities for contact with bio-medical topics that engineers can find, or make, if they so desire. The opportunities range over the enormous expanse of the biological and social sciences, extending from service and support functions in medical practice to participation in basic research.

Let me caution you to understand that the engineering frontiers I have been discussing are increasingly recognized and appreciated. Quite a few institutions accept graduate students who want to work in these areas under a variety of departmental or interdepartmental committee labels. However, there are as yet no standardized, accredited curricula that lead to undergraduate degrees; and there are as yet only a few well-established career channels in industry, universities, and hospitals.

To become an engineer in this field, or in any other, and to remain a live one throughout one's career, requires more than the acquisition of certain skills and a knowledge of the canons of engineering practice in any given field. The contemporary engineer can remain contemporary only if his initial understanding of the scientific fundamentals of the problems he deals with continues to be deepened by new learning that is related to advances in the relevant sciences.

Most often when people use the word science, they have in mind the physical sciences and mathematics; but in this chapter we need to go beyond physics, mathematics, and chemistry. We need to take into account the fundamentals of what are called the life or biological sciences, as well as certain aspects of the medical, behavioral, social, and perhaps even management sciences.

You recognize that one could enter here into a quasi-academic discussion regarding the extent to which there is justification for the use of the term *science* for these fields. The term is perhaps less well defined than most of us suspect, but we live in a decade in which the label "science" has clearly become a symbol of prestige. Yet a good deal more important than a precise definition is the fact that the word symbolizes an attitude of commitment to rational, unbiased, and unselfish search for principles of order in all of nature. Science provides us with the most objective and economical way of organizing knowledge and perhaps even with the most civilized way of dealing with our own mistakes.

Not so long ago, people tried to label a given field of scientific inquiry or technical competence rather meticulously: it was usually identified with a particular discipline or profession, which in turn belonged either to the pure sciences, the applied sciences, or to engineering. More recently it became evident that many problems in nature are so comprehensive that they cannot be dealt with successfully by a single scientific or engineering discipline. Since then, terms such as "the earth sciences," "the space sciences," "the material sciences," "the communication (or information) sciences," and so on, have been coined. The use of the plural itself is not insignificant, but even the expanded names do not make clear how much engineering is an organic part of these "sciences." Indeed, the necessity for a close coupling of engineering with the search for basic knowledge is precisely what the title of this chapter tries to convey.

In this search, there is both curiosity and necessity to know more about the characteristics of human memory, of learning, of the principles of sensory communication, and so on. To these various studies, well-trained engineers can contribute in a variety of ways. There is, for example, the maker of mathematical models (who may often call himself an applied mathematician, a computer scientist, a systems engineer, or an operations analyst), who knows how to manipulate abstract symbols without particular concern for the physical structures involved.* If the model

---

* There are of course also *physical* models such as wind tunnels, model airplanes, or miniature space capsules. But whether a model be physical or abstract, in a mathematical sense, if it is a good model, it will make us appreciate what the "real thing" might do by imitating (or simulating) it in simplified but essential ways.

maker is creative and serious about a problem area, he may try to define a new specialty—such as "artificial intelligence," or new organizational entities such as engineering psychology or mathematical psychology. Such groups exist already in some places and include, in addition to people trained as engineers or mathematicians, increasing numbers of young people whose formal education has been in psychology.

Next let me mention a friend of mine, an applied mathematician with an engineering bent, who is concerned with the principles of visual pattern recognition in man. To be more specific, he tries to formulate these principles by programming a digital computer so that it can distinguish and identify—some might prefer to say "read"—hand-written words. He and his engineering students have also described and analyzed the actual movements that are involved in handwriting; they found this physiological description useful in improving their computer program. But my colleague was not satisfied with these quasi-engineering achievements; he tried to infer, and to verify experimentally, whether his computer program proceeds by steps that are similar to those men take when they try to decipher handwriting.

In another area, several of my closest colleagues and I have been interested in how sensory events in our environment are translated or "coded" into patterns of electrical events in our brain. In such a study of what might loosely be called the language (or at least a dialect) of the nervous system, one encounters a broad range of questions: Are, for instance, identical acoustic events—stimuli, as psychologists would call them—translated into identical patterns of pulses in the fibers of the auditory nerve? Are there common principles of coding to the several sense modalities; that is, for sound, light, touch? Are there common elements of coding across species; that is, do corresponding structures in the sensory nervous system of cats and frogs behave in an identical manner? Are various species preferentially "tuned" to sounds made by fellow members of their species? Are sensory events coded differently when they signify danger from when they signal a mate? Does coding remain invariant when an animal pays attention, when it is asleep, or when it is bored by constant repetition of the same signal? Are there ways in which the patterns of electric activity can be described mathematically in a manner that will yield insight in the mechanisms of this type of coding?

Communication engineers for a long time have been concerned with many aspects of the process of speech communication. In recent years they have tried to produce so-called synthetic speech by computer-controlled electronic circuitry and associated acoustic devices. In this pursuit they felt the need to describe the mechanical events that accompany the production of human speech more precisely than had seemed necessary up to this time to anatomists or physiologists. The engineers seem to have gained a sufficiently good understanding of the mechanical aspects of speech production and are now ready to join hands with interested neurophysiologists and medical scientists in inquiring into the ways in which these mechanical and acoustical phenomena are controlled by the nervous system.

Finally in this enumeration, I think of some colleagues who are designing quite powerful general-purpose computers so that biological and medical researchers may handle them like laboratory instruments, and of other colleagues who are using up-to-date transducer and data processing technology together with principles of human information processing to design sensory aids for the blind.

The above examples, chosen from work with which I am more or less directly familiar, cover only a modest region of today's bio-engineering interface. It seems to follow that to be an engineer at this interface requires more than the taking of a few biological or premedical survey courses. Serious biological problems are, on the average, at least as tough as those engineers traditionally encounter; hence there can be little expectation of help from prefabricated or slightly used solutions.

Yet, while the biological sciences certainly lack cohesion and unity, each problem is not so different from all others that one can afford always to start from scratch and to ignore its biological context. Some of the characteristics of the more highly evolved biological systems that render analysis so difficult may be stated as follows: they are not devices that have a single purpose or use; they have many inputs capable of absorbing information from the outside world; and, besides carrying on the business of living, they have a repertory of behaviors with which they can affect the world (the engineer might say: they have many outputs).

Brains of higher mammals with their billions of nerve cells, or neurons, offer prime examples of types of organization that evolved in response to varied needs for rich interaction with an organism's environment. These central nervous systems are not just collections of haphazardly connected neurons; instead they consist of carefully organized subunits that relate to each other in a hierarchical, quasi-military manner. However, this organization is not rigid, and in response to different needs or tasks the subunits are capable of reorganization, of cooperating in new and adaptive ways. To analyze such a system is, of course, much harder than to analyze the systems or devices engineers are used to. Hence we should only rarely expect to do a piece of elegant engineering design by imitating the way that the organisms themselves actually carry out a particular "engineering task." Everybody knows that we do not build airplanes like birds, that our cars do not walk on legs, and that there is rather little resemblance between calculating machines, or even electronic computers, and brains. In all these instances there is little resemblance so far as the *physical* appearance is concerned; the similarities relate to specifically defined and isolated *functions:* both planes and birds fly, both computers and brains are capable of carrying out certain logical operations, and so on.

Let me continue for a moment this digression concerning analogies between engineering and biological systems. There is much talk today that during the next decades engineers will get their best ideas from the study of organisms. I feel certain that engineers can learn much from a serious study of man's sensory, motor, and even cognitive behavior (behavior that relates to the manipulation of symbols), and from the study of structures in animals that subserve these or similar behaviors. These researches will help engineers to understand better how to match their machines to human needs and may even give them ideas of how to achieve certain engineering characteristics in an unconventional way. But I would hate to have to justify biological studies in terms of the possible payoff in engineering design. I would at the same time avoid handicapping the engineer who is trying to build a device that can perform a function that organisms also perform. He should not be forced to flatter nature by imitating it in trivial and perhaps irrelevant ways.

An engineer needs to be free to create his devices in the most rational way in relation to the specified task. A good computer program designed to play checkers should not also be required to yield a deep understanding of man's brain as a by-product. Work in artificial intelligence is variously motivated, and to the extent that the purpose is to develop technological tools for the manipulation of symbols, we would be stunting its growth if we viewed its contribution to brain *science* as its primary goal or justification.

From my own experience I believe that the proper study of higher organisms requires peculiarly a multiplicity of approaches, techniques, and methods. How else can one deal with the several levels of biological organization, with the variegated properties of biological materials, and with the rich repertory of behaviors of which individual organisms or groups of organisms are capable? This evaluation leads me to a pluralistic strategy when faced with questions that aim at a basic understanding of the nature of life and man. There is thus hardly ever a single *right* approach, and there is an even greater premium than elsewhere in science and engineering at being ingenious by combining boldness and soundness.

One final comment. There has been much concern about the split between the so-called "two cultures"—the one of science and technology, the other of the fine and creative arts and humanistic pursuits. Originally science and technology seemed to be predominantly dealing with the non-living world and to be capable of supplementing man's muscle only. Today things have changed; no society can claim to possess a truly unified and harmonious culture unless science and technology have a place in that culture. Science and technology are uniquely effective agents in satisfying human needs, whether the need be mere thirst or thirst for knowledge.

Today science and technology do not just permit us to control inanimate nature and to fulfill our material wants; instead, they enable us to have rich sensory and esthetic experiences and to live in societies of the complexity to which we seem to aspire. Yet we must always remember that science and technology are not agents of inevitable progress unless we use them better to understand the nature of life and man, both of individual man and of man as a member of organized society.

19 *The Profession of Engineering*

BY NEWMAN A. HALL

EXECUTIVE DIRECTOR

Commission on Engineering Education

NEWMAN A. HALL

Born: 1913, Uniontown, Pennsylvania

Marietta College: B.A., 1934
California Institute of Technology: Ph.D., 1938
Yale University: M.A. (privatim), 1956
Marietta College: D.Sc. (honorary), 1959

Queens College, New York: Instructor, 1938–41
University of Minnesota: Professor of Mechanical Engineering, 1947–55
  Head, Heat Power Division, Mechanical Engineering Department
New York University: College of Engineering, Professor of Mechanical
  Engineering, 1955–56
  Assistant Dean in Charge of Graduate Division, 1955–56
Yale University: Strathcona Professor of Mechanical Engineering, 1956–64
  Chairman, Mechanical Engineering Department, 1956–62
Chance Vought Division, United Aircraft Corporation: Research Engineer,
  1941–44
Research Division, United Aircraft Corporation: Research Engineer and
  Head, Analysis Department, 1944–47
Commission on Engineering Education, Executive Director, 1962–

Consulting Activities and Service on Government Commissions:
  United Aircraft Corporation
  General Electric Company
  Fairchild Aircraft and Engine Corporation
  General Mills Corporation
  Combustion Sub-committee, NACA, member, 1947–50
  Engineering Science Division, Office of Ordnance Research, U.S. Army,
    Director, 1952–53
  Scientific Advisory Board, Rock Island Arsenal, U.S. Army, member,
    1953–58
  Aerophysics Division, Naval Ordnance Laboratory, Consultant, 1950–62

American Society of Mechanical Engineers
Society of Automotive Engineers
American Institute of Aeronautics & Astronautics
International Combustion Institute
Engineers' Council for Professional Development, Education and Accredi-
  tation Committee
American Society for Engineering Education

Author: *Thermodynamics of Fluid Flow*
  Engineering Thermodynamics (with W. E. Ibele)

ENGINEERS have an essential place in our modern society. The tangible results of their endeavors surround us, and almost every aspect of our daily life has been influenced by their ac- complishments. Yet the average individual has little personal con- tact with them professionally. Many of us, more or less frequently, consult a doctor or a lawyer, but it is unlikely that we will seek personal services from a professional engineer, even though our mode of living may, at times, be even more dependent on the success of the engineer in his job.

Everywhere one turns, the handiwork of the engineers is evi- dent, whether it be in such household appliances as washing machines or television sets; in private and public transportation; new roads and buildings; the services that supply power and water; or in the newer technological advances, such as nuclear energy and space satellites. We are aware of these accomplish- ments, and, if we happen to think about them, we know that the engineers are at work behind the scenes; but actually we are more conscious of the occasional dramatic engineering failure than of the continuing successes that have become so necessary a part of our living.

There seems to be considerable confusion about what engi- neers do and where their responsibilities lie. Everyone is agreed that engineers are concerned with technological accomplishment, but beyond this there are misunderstandings. One reason for this is that many individuals who are titled "engineers" hold positions, both in business and industry, that really are quite outside the areas of professional engineers.

In an effort to identify the actual professional engineer, suppose we consider the positions of *all* who are given the title of engineers and divide their activities into four main categories:

1. Operations and maintenance.
2. Distribution and installation.
3. Design and production.
4. Research and development.

The professional engineer is concerned primarily with the last two categories, although the other two must necessarily enter into his planning if his results are to be effective.

The first two categories include the largest number of individuals identified by the general public as engineers. In the first group are the men who operate and maintain the bewildering variety of devices and systems that are basic to the functioning of our technological environment. They must be able to supervise the work of mechanics or electricians, to handle various emergencies that may occur, and to follow very faithfully the exact way in which these systems are to be used. The success of the men in this group is substantially based on their being trained for a specific type of activity without any consideration of the steps that were involved in its development. With long experience these men are apt to acquire a well-developed knack in handling their machines or systems. The professional engineer becomes involved with this group when he is called upon to evaluate the efficiency of a certain activity, or when he must specify, at the outset of a new operation, the exact procedures that must be followed in order to carry it through.

In order to make clear the difference between these highly-trained technical men and the professional engineers, let me suggest that we consider the diesel engine. The man who drives this engine is called an "engineer," and no one should quarrel with the use of the term; most certainly no one would detract from the work of this man or question its high value in our industrial society. Our only concern here is that the name "engineer" for the man who drives the engine causes confusion when we consider the man who designed it.

Many another man who has a job pertaining strictly to the

operation of machinery, such as the supervision of the machinery in some plant, is called an engineer. Also in some of the great airplanes, one of the crew members may be called an engineer. But in this chapter when we refer to "engineer," we are thinking of the creator rather than the operator; we are referring to the man who took a blank piece of paper and designed the diesel engine, or the man who designed the machinery system of a plant, or designed an actual airplane. Later, he also played his part in supervising the building of the necessary models, checking and testing them, and then acted as a consultant on the building of the engine, the machinery system, or the airplane. Such a man is a professional engineer and is a part of the *profession* of engineering.

The men mentioned in the second group in the list above are concerned with the distribution and installation of products. They are sometimes called "sales engineers," or "field engineers," but their responsibility is more often related to business transactions than to any technical activity. They must be familiar with the capabilities of a product in order to demonstrate and install it, and also in order to interest potential customers, but almost certainly they had nothing to do with the design of the product or with its development. That is the responsibility of the professional engineer, and whenever questions arise concerning design and development, the field man, despite the name of "engineer," most likely will have to turn to the actual engineer for the answers.

In the third category, that of design and production, we come to the heart of the work of the professional engineer. As he encounters a technological situation, he is confronted with a multiplicity of decisions. In some cases he can draw on his past knowledge so that the situation may involve only minor modifications of previous designs. In other cases, he may be required to accommodate for totally new specifications that will call not only for the highest degree of creative ingenuity but also for use of the very latest scientific discoveries. The process of establishing his course of action is often identified as that of preparing a design, and designs are so varied that they can represent a complicated piece of mechanical equipment, a highly developed electronic computing system, the layout of a new highway, or the more efficient operation of an industrial distribution system. The design is the engineer's description of the way in which a particular situation can be met.

After a design has been formulated, the engineer has the responsibility of following it through to its realization. He consults with his professional colleagues and works closely with people who can provide expert technical knowledge or information pertaining to other aspects of operations, so that, in the end, the product of the design can be achieved. However, throughout the time of the production, and despite the involvement of other people, the continuing participation of the original engineer is very important, since there may arise unforeseen problems which will require design modification. It is also necessary for him to apply his technical knowledge during development to insure that there is no misrepresentation of the procedures he has conceived.

The last category of engineering activity, research and development, is the base upon which every other engineering endeavor ultimately rests. The technological advances that occur in our modern world are dependent upon a continuing development of information, and development engineers must be conversant with the total store of engineering and scientific information that is being accumulated. At the same time, they must be conversant with the needs of society.

Research undertaken today by an engineer as part of a development effort frequently verges on what used to be purely scientific inquiry, but there is this major difference: an engineer seeks to further his understanding of natural phenomena in order to meet a present, or anticipated, need in actual development. It is his job to translate the formulae presented by the scientists into the nuts and bolts of our everyday life. The dizzy pace of technological change has been the result of the vast resources that research and development engineers have made available for designs and production.

It is clear, then, that there are two types of engineers: those who carry out the detailed steps that require special skills and training in operations, maintenance, service, and distribution; and those who, because of deeper and more extensive education, are equipped to advance our civilization by their understanding of new needs, and by their new approaches to new possibilities.

The vast increase of knowledge in both engineering and pure science makes it almost impossible for one man to know all the facts pertaining to any new development. Consequently, engineering activity most often takes place as a team effort, and engineers have developed the ability to work easily and effectively with their colleagues. This means that there must be a highly organized distribution of responsibility; neither the project engineer, who has direction over a large effort, nor the routine analyst, whose contribution may be very small, stands alone in pursuing the task. The project engineer must rely very heavily on the material provided by his associates, and they, in turn, having confidence in his ability to direct the whole effort, must be willing to pursue the routine jobs assigned to them. The cooperation of the engineering team may well determine the success of the devices and systems with which they deal.

The organization of an engineering effort is generally initiated by the management of an industry or a government establishment, which may already have a nucleus of engineers equipped to carry out the needed research, or it may hire the talents of some more specially trained person or group. The team then undertakes inquiries, carries out analyses, performs tests, assembles information, and, finally, examines and reviews ideas and results for decision.

In his professional responsibility, a paramount obligation of the engineer is maintenance of technical integrity. The physical world is very intolerant of error, yet every engineering decision cannot be reviewed or checked, even though the price of technical failure may be high. The successful engineer, therefore, is one whose performance can always be depended on, without someone necessarily coming behind him to make certain that he has done his work well and accurately.

In order to be prepared for his job and to maintain his competence, the engineer must, of course, have basic aptitudes and a thorough education; but he must also have a determination to maintain his study and constantly to re-examine his technical competence. This competence depends, in part, on an awareness of change in his own engineering specialization, but it also has to do with his knowledge of developments in other engineering fields and in science, as well as his understanding of the increasing interaction between technology and science. Actually by his own development, and by his development of new products and new systems and services, the engineer is continually rendering obsolete his own technical and scientific knowledge. The opportunity for creation, to move constantly in new directions, and at times into new areas, is obviously one of the most satisfying challenges of the profession.

A new factor, and a major concern, in engineering today is the influence of social, economic, and political forces on the technological decisions that an engineer must make. At one time mechanical and structural devices could be designed and produced without consideration of any implication beyond their immediate use and behavior. The systems produced by the engineer today, however, often have effects far beyond their immediate structure and operation. Except for the simplest situations, it is no longer possible to say with certainty that any decision can be made on a purely technical basis. The location and design of a highway affects many people; a weapons system inevitably becomes an element in international politics; the automation of a factory is a vital consideration in labor relations; and the design of private automobiles is a major factor in the air pollution of our cities. These examples, and a host of others, confirm the responsibility of the engineer to make his decisions with the fullest realization of *all* their consequences. He must be sure his personal preparation is broad enough to meet this challenge, and he must cultivate every means to increase his awareness of, and his sensitivity to, the total environment in which he operates.

The engineer will surely continue to be one of the more decisive influences in the development and progress of our society and economy. His opportunity for productive contributions is almost without limit; his obligation to judge wisely and imaginatively is profound.

20 *Engineering and Science: A Sum and Not a Difference*

BY WILLIAM O. BAKER
VICE PRESIDENT, RESEARCH
Bell Telephone Laboratories

WILLIAM O. BAKER

Born: 1915, Chestertown, Maryland

Washington College: B.S., 1935; Sc.D. (hon.), 1957
Princeton University: Ph.D., 1938
Honorary: Stevens Institute of Technology, D.Eng., 1962
  Georgetown University, Sc.D., 1962
  University of Pittsburgh, Sc.D., 1963

Bell Telephone Laboratories: 1939–
  In charge Polymer Research and Development, 1948–51
  Assistant Director Chemical and Metallurgical Research, 1951–54
  Director of Research in Physical Sciences, 1954–55
  Vice President, Research, 1955–

Member: National Academy of Sciences
  President's Foreign Intelligence Advisory Board
  National Science Board of the National Science Foundation
  President's Science Advisory Committee, 1957–60
  Consultant to Special Assistant for Science and Technology
  Consultant to Department of Defense
  Air Force Systems Command Board of Visitors
  Science Advisory Board of the National Security Agency
  Liaison Committee for Science and Technology, Library of Congress
  Committee on National Defense, American Chemical Society
  Committee on Science and Technology, U.S. Chamber of Commerce
  National Research Council:
    Committee on Physical Chemistry of Division of Chemistry and
      Chemical Technology
    Advisory Committee to Office of Documentation
    Advisory Board on Military Personnel Supplies
  Visiting Committee for Chemistry: Harvard, Princeton
  Visiting Committee for Metallurgy: MIT
  Board of Governors of Scientific Research Society of America
  American Chemical Society
  American Physical Society
  American Philosophical Society
Trustee: Mellon Institute; Rockefeller Institute; Aerospace Corporation

Harvard Fellow, 1937–38; Proctor Fellow, 1938–39
Perkin Medal, 1963; AIC Honor Scroll

Author: Various science articles
Contributor: Four books on polymers

MANY MEN of an earlier day, in trying to distinguish engineering from science, pictured the scientist as a man who discovered laws of nature, such as Newton's law of gravity or Mendel's law of heredity. The scientist was said to be motivated solely by curiosity, or by sense of order or beauty, or by a desire to know the truth. In contrast, the engineer was pictured as a doer, equipped with handbooks, slide rules, drafting instruments, and transits, who built railroads, or electric power systems, or airplanes. Somehow the engineer managed to pick up and exploit the discoveries of science for the use and profit of mankind. According to this early concept, the engineer performed a useful service or produced a useful product for which his fellow men were willing to pay.

The world has never been as simple as this. Many eminent scientists of an earlier day showed a great concern for the practical consequences of their work. Pasteur found vaccines for anthrax and rabies. Lord Kelvin remedied defects of the early submarine telegraph cables. And engineers have contributed to mathematics and science. Nonetheless, in that earlier day, a separation of science and engineering seemed reasonable. It was easy to believe that engineers and scientists should receive very different training, pursue very different careers, and accomplish very different things.

Ours is a time of learning and of governments in which this historic and once rational detachment of science from engineering is outdated. This outdating came fast and recently—when those with political power saw in the technology of rockets, missiles and satellites, nuclear weapons and electronic automata, a road to national security or to international conquest.

299

A grave result of the adoption of technology as a chief tool of world power has been a distortion of the purposes of both research and engineering. The role of scientific research in today's world is not oriented by any clear promise of usefulness, or profits, or of accomplishment, but by national goals. Because science has produced so much in this century, it is pictured as a miracle maker that can produce anything demanded of it. It is the very bounty of twentieth-century science, especially in the second half of the century, that has led to two entirely new aspects of science—assigned missions or goals, and large-scale demonstrations of "technical feasibility."

As to the first, society, and specifically our government in the United States, has begun to assign missions to science. Deciding how to accomplish these missions is just as difficult and obscure as progress toward any of the intuitive goals of individual research always has been. Some elements of our national space program show this. It is particularly true of many aspects of manned space flight and of planning toward interplanetary missions. We still know so little about both space and space technology that longe-range plans cannot be based on sure knowledge and demonstrated technical capability. Besides this, we should also think of the recurrent directives by the Congress to do things that are perhaps even further from our grasp—directives to the National Institutes of Health to produce cures for cancer and the common cold, statutory bids for control of the weather, including one to the National Science Foundation, assignments to the Atomic Energy Commission for the production of economic nuclear power generation, and others for "ultimate weapons" to the Department of Defense.

A second new aspect of science, the demonstration of technical feasibility, has led to an expanded science that is a big business, engaged not only in production of ideas but also in production of full-scale apparatuses and systems embodying these ideas and intended to demonstrate their effectiveness in achieving the missions that have been assigned. This big science has learned to take (at government expense) big risks, and it has learned to succeed in some of these.

Thus, ours is a world of a big science that is directed toward space, defense, and other governmentally determined goals, and that is pushed to expensive operating devices and systems—whole mechanical orbiting laboratories and the vehicles to launch them, as an example.

What of engineering in this world of big science and its big demonstrations of technical feasibility? In an earlier age, the engineer shrewdly surveyed the findings of the scientist. He quite independently advanced, modified, and applied them to produce useful and profitable things: cars, radios, mines, bridges, telephone systems, and highways. The scientist explored nature, impelled by curiosity, with confidence that an extensive corps of engineers would review his results and derive proper values from them. But lately, these roles have been somewhat varied. Many factors have caused this, but one is certainly big science projects that have as their goal merely a demonstration that, granted sufficient time and money, some stated objective can be achieved. This situation strikes severely at the classic aims of engineering to translate new technology into practical use in manufacture, in transportation and communication facilities, in public health, in power generation and distribution, in farming, and the like.

The philosophy of measuring our technological progress by demonstrating the technical feasibility of rather arbitrarily chosen goals is probably only beginning to show its impact on science and engineering, on public affairs, and on education. Yet we are already given a strong impression that if the engineer is to succeed in this world of big science he should not think of the economics of his art, or, indeed, of whether or not it will provide society with everyday products or services, such as the automobiles or telephones. Conversely, the scientist is persuaded that he should work on particular specified and organized programs because they have some sort of political and sociological virtue, and that he must carry his work in these domains through to publishable and picturable, if not to workable, models—models that he once confidently and gladly left to the engineer. This then is the present disturbed state of science and engineering.

This disturbance comes at an unfortunate time because of the crucial decisions being forced upon us. Through research and development, both our capabilities and our problems will multiply. We now have the capability to guide a vehicle to the moon, the capability to explore the Antarctic, the capability of making 100-megaton atomic explosions, the capability of communication around the earth by satellites, the capability of transplanting vital organs among living creatures. The next phases of this advance may be vastly more intimate and personal than the present ones of space voyaging and nucleus splitting. The elements of the genetic code in deoxyribonucleic acid are gradually being revealed. Who knows when the capability of controlling heredity and preselecting the characteristics of successive generations will be displayed? The decisions for action that such capability may engender could cause our present dilemmas to pale into triviality.

Only the most expert summing of science and engineering can deal with such issues successfully. Those who become engineers and scientists must understand this and make it clear to others. Leaders in both government and education, as well as in industry and public affairs, should learn, and then learn to say, that we must combine and sum up qualities of science and engineering. Then we will meet new duties and attain the new aims that are upon us without losing our system of personal liberty and industrial enterprise. If you who read this become engineers, you can resolve to work toward this summing, and a glorious new balance can be created between what is worth doing and what is imaginable.

The historic roles of science and engineering must be altered. The needs and wants of people and of government must be jointly assimilated, understood, and acted upon by the scientific and engineering community. This is in contrast with the present. The wants of government are now largely directed toward the scientific bodies, because government aspirations for space voyages, for ultimate weapons, for the eradication of human ills, have become so futuristic, so wishful, so far removed from the possibilities of our everyday life, so aimed at demonstration of feasibility of things that the government arbitrarily deems important. And with the wants of the government go its almost limitless resources.

But the wants of people are generally, in the Western world, expressed through the free market and the industrial development path, at the top of which stands the engineer. It is the engineer who provides people with light, heat, cars, planes, refrigerators, telephones, roads, and bridges. Yet neither through financial support nor by tradition has the engineer been encouraged to take the bold, if sometimes dubious, steps that big science has undertaken.

The main chance of our succeeding in the huge tasks ahead lies in the calculated, educated, prudent risk. This, the heart of modern scientific research, must be extended to and adopted by engineering. This sounds like rabid heresy, since engineering has nearly always been thought to proceed only with highly probable or even certified success in its use of knowledge and direction of effort. Now we are saying that there must be a bolder use of chance and a wider stake in medium or even low probabilities when these probabilities reflect both scientific resources and human utility. In this way, engineering can regain the part in human achievement for which it once had public recognition, and can cast off the obscurity it has sunk into because of the public glamour of the nuclear and space scientists.

Happily, several new resources are available to the engineer who wants to be both bold and successful in working with science and for man. These resources are themselves among the most exciting intellectual movements of our time. They include particularly interdisciplinary or uncompartmented education, research, and engineering in what were recently highly fragmented and separated branches of learning. As our understanding of various sciences becomes deeper, we see that they are closely related and interdependent—that to understand one we must understand several. The engineers of the future must, collectively or individually, understand and use them all. Today we can see clearly the importance of various relations between and combinations of the physical and life sciences, involving collaboration among biological, medical, and engineering sciences, and a whole field of materials research and development that brings together the physical sciences and engineering.

Second, there is the profound influence of computing machines and related automata on data processing and information-handling systems. Use of non-numerical computing—mechanized information handling—will be a major revolutionary element in engineering operations within a few years, particularly for simulation of the function of proposed devices, structures or systems, whether they be communication systems or load-bearing structures; for the analysis of the behavior of interconnected systems, such as communication or transportation systems; for the optimization of the design of devices, structures or systems for manufacture; and for the control of some manufacturing operations.

The third major support for the summing of science and technology is different from, and more artificial than, the great movements of interdisciplinary or unified science and the advent of computers or automata. It is the role of engineering and science in government.

Whatever nostalgia we might have for an easier, more independent, more modest era of science and engineering, it is with government support that we have cast the country's fate, along with its dollars. For government support is to be the principal support of engineering and scientific research. By sheer probability, the engineer of tomorrow will work for the government, either directly in a government laboratory or in industry financed by government contracts.

This totally revolutionary "science administration" could have been a deadly hazard for the well-being of science and engineering if it had been organized in a monolithic, centralized, bureaucratic way; but I think we have safely crossed the danger zone. Instead of a supersafe set of checks and balances administered through a single central Department of Science, which would be sure to sanctify a cautious and riskless certainty of science for every man, I believe we have constructed a system of the highest level in the executive office of the President through the Federal Council for Science and Technology, through the President's Science Advisory Committee, and through the independent National Science Foundation, which will cultivate courage, initiative, and careful explorations by engineers and scientists. Indeed, the way for this was shown by the preservation of scientific freedom by the NSF during its whole decade of operations.

So far we have sketched out compelling bases for leavening science and engineering each with the other, and also have suggested three major social and intellectual elements that favor this movement. My plea is that if you make your way into the community of the technical professions, you will as engineers be as bold, and as carefully calculating in it, as the practitioners of big science have had to be in the past two decades (since the nuclear era began). Also, I beg any who become scientists to be as responsible, and reliable, and orderly, and as conscious of human values, as the engineers have been since this century began.

In these ways, engineers can and must relieve any despair that the mighty force of scientific research and application has passed them by. They can recall how adroitly the founders, indeed the inventors, of modern engineering, of engineering as a profession, adapted the scanty understanding of nature, which science gave them, to the problems of the real world. With far less knowledge than we now have, engineers built steamships, railroads, canals, dams, transcontinental highways, airplanes, and telephone systems that link many nations together. Now, when the world seems over-occupied with pure and applied science, the engineers will be as able as ever to cope with the flooding tide. But they must perform the selection, the assimilation, and pick the bold chances to understand and to meet the two great classes of needs that press upon us, those of people and those of nations.

The formula for success that we have outlined has three chief ingredients: (1) the unified interdisciplinary resources of science and engineering in training and practice, (2) the computer-based exercise of science and engineering, and (3) the federalized support of, and nationally made policies for, science and engineering. All of this is perhaps abstract and difficult to grasp without concrete examples, and I propose to give some.

The solid-state era, now historic, is a notable example of a combination of basic scientists from physics, metallurgy, and chemistry outrisking the engineers in the very subjects that the engineers, with their superb radio work of 1917 onward, and later microwave and other electronics, could have been the chief sponsors. The operation of the transistor depends on the apparently absurd notions that crystals can be made of such purity and perfection that electric charges can be distributed in controlled regions, and that mobile charges of opposite sign can coexist for appreciable periods. It was this reckless presumption that led to the intensely practical revolution that the transistor and its numerous derivatives have worked in electronics. Still more recently, others of our associates (and they were men who were not working on government contracts of programmed development) conceived the notion that the quantum electronic energies in both solids or gases could be distributed in states defying the presumably relentless rules of the Maxwell demons and could be made to possess, in effect, negative absolute temperatures. Solid-state devices, and microwave masers and optical masers, or lasers, are the result of these wild, though different, conjectures.

Engineers should and can react zestfully to this amplification and generation of coherent light by lasers. Although this is one of the most beautiful manifestations of modern quantum theory, it is just as accessible to present-day engineers, as part of their arsenal of knowledge, as the steam tables or the elastic limit lists were to engineers of a few generations ago. The solid-state microwave maser is already the nerve center of our satellite communications receiver, which first operated in the Echo experiment nearly four years ago and which responds to the 10^{-12} watts of signal power from the Telstar satellite.

In all this preparation for the forthcoming tides of new knowledge from interdisciplinary research, the engineer must not become over-committed or narrowly specialized in what is most popular at the moment. He must be as good a gambler in the breadth of his personal education as in the choice of his career aspirations. He must try to equip himself to respond as well to the needs of superconductor electric power line transformer or solenoid as to a role in the fluid mechanics and geophysics of the MOHOLE penetration of the earth.

From the nearly 1000 superconducting alloys or elements now known, there are emerging the fantastic high field superconductors from which magnets of negligible power consumption, but of field strengths of 100,000 to 200,000 Gauss, can be prepared. If there is controlled nuclear fusion, it is expected to come from within magnetic containers, themselves a result of interdisciplinary science. So here again are essential ingredients for a liaison of science and engineering, in which the engineer who takes the big chance in understanding and working with these new systems (which presently require cryogenic surroundings, itself a great new branch of heat engineering) may also find that he has revolutionized the transformer art for power distribution.

Engineers must move quickly, but dauntlessly and wisely, into all new elements of potential national and industrial strength. Daring among engineers must be exercised promptly in order to associate properly with the new biophysics. The biomedical engineering implications of genetics control, as well as a readiness to respond to other great discoveries that are impending from the life sciences, must be faced by a new generation of engineers, who will perhaps also understand and use the phenomenal timing sense of living matter, the biological clocks that reflect a behavior still baffling to our engineering senses.

Thus, I am preaching a merger of all that is useful in science and engineering, and I hope you feel that we are not speaking of any minor conjunction in urging a merger that only an Injustice Department could oppose! This is a key problem of our time. We must say again that it should be settled by the reaction of engineers with their concern for both sciences and human values, much more than by the diversely guided politics and pressures that are emerging as the other great force in scientific and technical affairs.

Lately the very essence of design engineering has been approximated by "design-a-mation" computer programs. These have achieved automatic design of complex electronic systems, specifying the position of circuit packages on a chassis for economical wire routing between them, the connections within the circuit packages, the parts lists to be used in the manufacture of the equipment, and finally the drawings and diagrams which are automatically printed out. This method has been largely used for design of computer-like systems, and is, in fact, astonishingly close to the von Neumann concept for machines that are able to design (if not to reproduce) other similar machines.

Here the actual results achieved are useful and economical, and the engineering options are incalculable. Should not a new generation of engineers and scientists propound seriously to the nation the issue of whether the effort in major production of automata should compete with national resources for a manned space program, in some future priorities? The combination of computer-based information processing and self-reproducing machines could, of course, dominate the mass-production facilities of the world. Is competition of this kind in the face of the enormous developing world markets, and equally rapidly developing competing economies, not also crucial for the survival of our nation? Is it not also a subject of high prestige content?

A new generation must lead us past the primeval prejudice against automation and its alleged threats to employment, which must have existed during the invention of the wheel, the domestication of the horse, and in every significant state of man's advance. It is the computer-based organization of knowledge and method of executing routine engineering design, as well as of numerical analysis, that can equip civilization to feed and clothe, house and govern its hordes.

The future and its wonders depend on two elements, engineers and scientists who are wise and congenial, and adequate financial support for their work. The federalized policies that favor a combination of science and engineering are, of course, outgrowths of the international and national aspirations we noted in the beginning. Fortunately those policies now have a considerable ingredient of proved values in the national educational and industrial interest. The Director of the National Science Foundation and the National Science Board have adopted a policy that research in engineering will be supported in a broad range of subjects, of which the following are examples:

a. The development of principles and techniques in systems engineering design.

b. The development of principles and a philosophy for creative engineering.

c. Interdisciplinary research related to such matters as biomedical engineering, transportation, urban planning, fire prevention, and so forth.

d. The principles of generation and control of energy systems and information systems.

e. Analysis and synthesis of processes and systems that contribute to mastery of the environment.

This is a new and exciting recognition by our government that for the public welfare a new intellectual junction of engineering and science must be forged.

Thus we have from nature, and from the techniques of science, and from the actions of governments, means for the joining of engineering and science. If able and enterprising young men become engineers, and if as such they participate in this program, we may accomplish that age-old aspiration of man—to find at last a whole that is greater than the sum of its parts.

21 Engineering Obligations in Government and Public Affairs

BY JAMES R. KILLIAN, JR.

CHAIRMAN OF THE CORPORATION

Massachusetts Institute of Technology

JAMES R. KILLIAN, JR.

Born: 1904, Blacksburg, South Carolina

Massachusetts Institute of Technology: B.S., 1926

Sc.D.: Middlebury College, Bates College, University of Havana, Cuba, Notre Dame University, Lowell Technological Institute, Columbia University, College of Wooster, Oberlin College, University of Akron, Worcester Polytechnic Institute, University of Maine.

L.L.D.: Union College, Bowdoin College, Northeastern University, Duke University, Boston University, Harvard University, Williams College, Lehigh University, University of Pennsylvania, University of Chattanooga, Tufts University, University of California, Amherst College, College of William and Mary, Brandeis University, New York University, Johns Hopkins, Providence College, Temple University, University of South Carolina, Meadville Theological School

D.Eng.:Drexel Institute of Technology, University of Illinois, University of Massachusetts

D.Appl.Sci.: University of Montreal

Ed.D.: Rhode Island College

HH.D: Rollins College

Massachusetts Institute of Technology:
10th President, 1949–1959 (on leave 1957–59)
Chairman of the Corporation, 1959–

Special Assistant to the President of the United States for Science and Technology, 1957–59
President's Science Advisory Committee: Chairman, 1957–59; Member, 1959–61; Consultant-at-large, 1961–
President's Board of Consultants on Foreign Intelligence Activities, 1956–1959; Chairman, 1956–58
President's Foreign Intelligence Advisory Board, Chairman, 1961–63

Director: American Telephone and Telegraph Company
Cabot Corporation
General Motors Corporation
Polaroid Corporation
Trustee: Educational Services, Inc. (Chairman and Trustee)
Institute for Defense Analyses
Mellon Institute
MITRE Corporation
Mount Holyoke College
Alfred P. Sloan Foundation

AMONG THE CURRENTS flowing through our times and affecting us most profoundly are the exponential growth of knowledge in science and technology; the enormous increase in useful energy; the "eclipse of distance" and nearly instantaneous communication of events the world over; and the consequent global dimension of the human community, in which all people are involved and their aspirations mutually stimulated and amplified.

The engineer has helped to create these conditions, and in turn they steadily augment his role in our society. He still designs and directs the building of roads, bridges, and vehicles for land, sea, and air, and power plants; but in addition, he now designs and directs the building of missiles, rockets, space vehicles, communication systems, radio telescopes, radar, nuclear reactors, supersonic planes, and a myriad other advanced products of the research that he joins the scientist in conducting.

But increasingly his role embraces more than researching, designing, building, and producing. It also includes the responsibility to help society appraise, assimilate, and wisely use the torrent of new technology available today. Increasingly he is called upon to administer great teams of people or industrial organizations that both use and create this advanced technology, and to serve as an indispensable consultant and adviser to government and private organizations, thus helping to shape both public and private policy. Increasingly, he deals with men as well as things, with policy and planning as well as products.

As the late Professor Hardy Cross once observed, "It is customary to think of engineering as a part of a trilogy, pure science, applied science, and engineering. It needs emphasis that this

313

trilogy is only one of a triad of trilogies into which engineering fits. The first is pure science, applied science, engineering; the second is economic theory, finance, and engineering; and the third is social relations, industrial relations, engineering. Many engineering problems are as closely allied to social problems as they are to pure science." *

The engineer's concern for social problems must grow steadily greater as his work affects society more profoundly. His professional status and his influence on the society of our time has come to be not unlike those of the lawyer and the doctor in their importance to our continuing prosperity and health. Engineers today must not only work in the laboratory or in the field, but they must also be available to assist our governments at all levels, and many other institutions in our society, to make the complex decisions that are required to insure that science and technology will be put to work for social purposes. The revolutionary thrust of science and technology is constantly creating new conditions with which these units of government must deal, and they have had, consequently, to devise methods of drawing upon the scientific and engineering communities for advice and analysis. Much of the subject matter of modern science and engineering is, in its details, outside the purview of the generalist policy maker, who has to depend upon expert advisers to make the complexities meaningful in terms of their usefulness and relevancy to matters of government. In consequence, both the scientist and the engineer, in recent years, have found themselves more and more called into the public arena to make their expert knowledge available and to assist in dealing with the great variety of policy problems with a scientific or engineering component.

Although our nation today needs both scientists and engineers in the public service, it particularly needs engineers and the engineering point of view. By this I mean that it needs that kind of professional advice that has had experience in making things work, in weighing their value against their cost, and in

* Hardy Cross, *Engineers and Ivory Towers* (New York: McGraw-Hill, 1952), p. 55.

exercising judgment as to their practical utility and their attainability within the present "state of the art," and within a given schedule and budget. So far, in our government at the national level, it would appear that the scientists have been most called upon or most readily available for policy-making, advisory, and administrative roles. This has imposed an undue burden on the scientific community, and it has also denied the government enough of the special skills, insights, and experience of the engineers. This is not a situation that should continue if we are to have the best balanced technical judgment available to our top policy makers. I do not mean to imply that engineers have not been playing a crucial role or that there is competition between scientists and engineers as advisers. Throughout the federal government today we find hundreds of engineers among those serving in advisory capacities or holding appointive posts. Two of the four men who have served United States presidents as advisers on scientific and technical matters from the 1940's into the 1960's—Vannevar Bush and Jerome Wiesner—were engineers.

Both the scientist and engineer have become explicitly coupled to high policy making in the federal government. For example, the President has, as I've already noted, his Special Assistant for Science and Technology. He also has a seventeen-member Science Advisory Committee. These advisers usually deal primarily with problems of applied science or engineering, even though many of them may actually be scientists or identified with the scientific community. At the time that I am writing this chapter, the President's Science Advisory Committee includes six men trained as physicists, four as chemists, two as biologists, two in electrical engineering, and one each in chemical engineering, geophysics, and mathematics. I have mentioned engineers serving as advisers to presidents. It is also worthy of note that one of those who recently served as science adviser to the Secretary of State was a chemical engineer; one must also note, however, that the two men who have held the post of Director of Defense Research and Engineering in the Department of Defense, where again the matters dealt with are primarily engineering and applied science, were both educated as physicists.

Because of the great size of the research and development program of the federal government, it is of the utmost importance that the government have available appointive personnel who have the experience, the knowledge, and the skills to manage this program well. This need has led the executive branch of the government recently to seek out scientists and engineers for appointive posts in what might be called "the Little Cabinet," to serve at the assistant-secretary level in the various government departments. For example, the Department of Commerce now has an Assistant Secretary for Science and Technology, who, incidentally, is an engineer and whose job it is to supervise and give policy direction to important scientific and engineering activities such as the Bureau of Standards, the Weather Bureau, the Patent Office, and the Coast and Geodetic Survey. The Director of Defense Research and Engineering in the Department of Defense is, in effect, third in command in the civilian secretariat of that department. One can go on through the government departments, the Post Office and Department of Interior and so on, and note that each now has subcabinet-level appointees who are exercising their skills in helping the government deal more effectively with its huge engineering and scientific responsibilities. A study by Michael E. Smith in 1958 showed that 17 of the 63 bureau chiefs had been trained as engineers or technicians, and 9 held advanced degrees in the social sciences. This is a total of 26 scientists and engineers compared with 9 economists and 8 lawyers.

The federal government, however, is by no means the only public-service user of engineering talent. Our states, cities, and other government units, of course, employ engineers in substantial numbers to carry on such activities as highway designing and building; the design, building and management of water-supply systems; and the host of duties having to do with environmental engineering, sanitation, and public health. Engineers must share in the development and administration of building codes and in the study and improvement of traffic conditions. When state governments become involved in the development of sources of power, as, for example, those the State of New

York has undertaken, some jointly with Canada, along the rivers of its northern boundaries, engineers play a key role both in advising the state and in designing and building these state-managed projects. In all of the manifold activities of Robert Moses, he has had available to him able engineers who have helped plan the development of parks and parkways, recreational facilities, freeways, bridges, airports, new power sources, and so forth.

Some of the most difficult decisions with which public bodies are faced today involve engineering on a large scale: decisions in regard to new water supplies for our great cities, the location of highways and airports, air-traffic control, and many aspects of urban renewal.

At the federal government level, of course, many fateful matters require engineering inputs. The question as to whether we can safely agree to a nuclear test ban is one example; selection between competing weapons systems is another. The planning and design of great dams, such as the Grand Coulee, for reclamation, irrigation, and power is still another. Often these problems are highly controversial, and it is vital that the government units have available technical judgment that is free of political considerations, of personal gain, or any other kind of influence that might distort the objectivity of the adviser.

In quite another way the engineer plays an important role in our public life today. This is in his responsibility to deal sensitively with esthetic and human values. There are many impressive examples of his success. In the Brooklyn Bridge, the Golden Gate Bridge at San Francisco, the George Washington Bridge spanning the Hudson River in New York, and many other great bridges, American engineers have produced some of the most beautiful structures of all time. I cite also the work of the great Italian engineer, Pier Luigi Nervi, whose inherent sense of design and mastery of reinforced concrete has led to the construction of some of the most beatiful buildings of our time— buildings in which function and structure are blended, through the arts and skills and science of this gifted engineer, to architectural beauty of the highest order.

Frequently, engineers have fought hard, not only for economy and utility, but for these more subtle values. Robert Louis Stevenson, in his reminiscent writings about the engineering careers of his father and grandfather, provides an eloquent description:

> Even the mechanical engineer comes at last to an end of his figures, and must stand up, a practical man, face to face with the discrepancies of nature and the hiatuses of theory. . . . the civil engineer . . . is always the practical man. The rains, the winds and the waves, the complexity and the fitfulness of nature, are always before him. He has to deal with the unpredictable, with those forces (in Smeaton's phrase) that "are subject to no calculation"; and still he must predict, still calculate them, at his peril. . . .
>
> It is plain there is here but a restricted use for formulas. In this sort of practice, the engineer has need of some transcendental sense. . . . The rules must be everywhere indeed; but they must everywhere be modified by this transcendental coefficient, everywhere bent to the impression of the trained eye and the *feelings* of the engineer. . . .
>
> Perfection [with a capital P and violently under-scored] was his [Robert Stevenson's] design. . . . On this consistent idealism there is but one thing that now and then trenches with a touch of incongruity, and that is his love of the picturesque. As when he laid out a road on Hogarth's line of beauty; bade a foreman be careful, in quarrying, not to "disfigure the island"; or regretted in a report that "the great stone, called the *Devil in the Hole,* was blasted or broken down to make road-metal. . . .*

However, we must admit that there are examples where engineers have not been adequately mindful of the human or esthetic impact of their endeavors. The location of highways, under certain circumstances, have destroyed scarce recreational facilities or substituted ugly structures for the beauties of nature or destroyed wildlife and other natural resources. Massive public housing projects in some of our great cities, constructed without

* Robert Louis Stevenson, *Records of a Family of Engineers* (London: Chatto & Windus, 1912), pp. 83–89.

due consideration of human needs for beauty and privacy, have, in many instances, become "cement jungles," producing neighborhoods as inhuman as those they replaced.

As we build more highways and as urbanization grows and spreads over the land, there will be many great challenges to the engineer to make our urban concentrations more humane. He has a superb opportunity to demonstrate the insight, the taste, and the sense of cultural responsibility to combat bulldozer brutality, ugliness, and deterioration in our environment. Working closely with architects and city and regional planners, and participating in environmental planning for conservation of wildlife and other resources of natural beauty, the engineer is in a key position to help us realize and preserve those values that promote beauty, "commodity and delight," and humaneness in our living. There is an esthetic power that belongs in the domain of the engineer along with physical power, and it is his duty to employ both for the use and convenience of man. As one of my humanist friends has remarked, the great opportunity for engineering today is to help humans to be more human.

Our efforts as a nation to be helpful to the new emerging nations of the world is yet another activity of our time calling for special public service on the part of the engineer. In providing the technical assistance needed in the economic development of these countries, the engineer has a new and enormous contribution to make. Not only must he be prepared to make available our technology in the most useful and practical sort of way in these countries, but he must also, through study and careful preparation, develop his knowledge and insight of these alien cultural environments in order to work sensitively and effectively in them.

American engineers today are working in many strange and exotic places and in a number of different ways to help raise the standard of living of peoples in these less-developed parts of the world. An American engineer helped to build great dams in India and Pakistan, and to shape the imaginative goals of the Indus River development. Other engineers are helping to develop the resources and generate economic growth in many countries in Africa and the Middle East; helping them build roads, water supplies, and better inexpensive housing from indigenous materials; helping to build aluminum and fertilizer plants and paper mills, electric-power generation and distribution facilities, and oil refineries and pipe lines, and teaching their people how to operate them efficiently.

American engineering professors are assisting in the establishment of two modern institutes of technology in India. They are engaged in similar cooperative efforts to establish schools of agriculture and engineering and technician-training in other countries that heretofore have had to export their young people to receive this education. The list could go on and on, but the point is that to an unprecedented extent, we see the nations of the world calling upon our engineering community for assistance, and we see our engineers responding to one of the greatest challenges they have ever faced.

What I have been saying about the role of engineers in public life clearly implies that their range of skills and education must be exceptional, that those who are to be effective in the public domain must be something more than technicians and specialists. They must have a deep sense of social responsibility; they must be able to accept and withstand the buffeting of political life; they must be able to interpret seemingly esoteric science and technology to policymakers; they must be sensitive to the mores, the social conditions, the needs and outlooks of many peoples; they must be skilled in the arts of management; and, finally, they must have a professional outlook, that is, a sense of public mission. In the professional estate, a man's mission overrides his personal welfare in many circumstances because he accepts an overriding responsibility to see that the public welfare is served.

In 1962, W. L. Everitt, Dean of Engineering at the University of Illinois, made a forecast that in fifty years "engineering will be acknowledged as the most learned profession." "The explosion and the breadth of knowledge," he said, "needed for [engineering] practice will have made preparation for an engineering career both rigorous and extensive. Full professional recognition will be available, except in unusual cases, only to those who have completed formal educational programs . . . equivalent to or exceeding our present doctorates." *

Perhaps Dean Everitt overstates the burden resting upon the engineer of the future or the amount of education he will acquire, but certainly he reflects the growing responsibilities and opportunities that face this profession, and the great contributions that engineers must make to our society.

* W. L. Everitt, "Engineering Education—Circa 2012 A.D.," in *Proceedings* of the Institute of Radio Engineers, Fiftieth Anniversary, May 1962, pp. 571–72.

22 *Engineering in an Evolving World*

BY JEROME B. WIESNER

DEAN OF THE SCHOOL OF SCIENCE

Massachusetts Institute of Technology

JEROME B. WIESNER

Born: 1915, Detroit, Michigan

University of Michigan: B.S. in Electrical Engineering, 1937; M.S., 1938; Ph.D., 1950

Honorary Degrees: Polytechnic Institute of Brooklyn, 1961
Lowell Technological Institute, 1962
University of Michigan, 1962

University of Michigan Broadcasting Service: Associate Director, 1937–40
Library of Congress: Chief Engineer, 1940–42
University of California, Los Alamos Laboratory, 1945–46
Massachusetts Institute of Technology: Radiation Laboratory 1942–45
Professor of Electrical Engineering, 1950–; Chairman of Department, 1958–61
Research Laboratory of Electronics: Associate Director, 1949–52; Director, 1952–61; Institute Professor, 1962–
School of Science: Dean, 1964–

Von Neumann Committee, 1954
U.S. Delegation to the Conference of Experts on Methods of Preventing Surprise Attack: Staff Director, 1958
Special Assistant to the President for Science and Technology, 1961–64
Office of Science and Technology: Director, 1962–64
President's Science Advisory Committee and the Federal Council for Science and Technology: Chairman, 1961–64
President's Science Advisory Committee, 1964–
Army Science Advisory Committee: Member, 1956–61
Television Electronics Fund, Inc., Advisory Board
Sprague Electric Company, Director
American Foundation for the Blind, Technical Advisory Committee
Weizmann Institute of Science: Board of Governors, 1964

Fellow: Institute Radio Engineers
Member: American Academy of Arts and Sciences
Geophysical Union
American Society of Engineering Education
Acoustical Society of America
National Academy of Sciences

Electronic Industry Association, Medal of Honor, 1961
Presidential Award for Technical Contributions to the War Effort, 1946
Government of Pakistan, "Star of Pakistan," 1963

Author: Numerous technical papers

IT MUST seem unlikely that there can be any new opportunities left in engineering in addition to the full range of those covered in the earlier chapters in this volume. Still, there is something left to be said about the very important need that exists for broadly trained engineers to fulfill the integrative role in the application of technology to the problems of society; the need for someone with broad understanding of the technical possibilities, plus sensitivity for the great social needs of our time, plus the vision to perceive bold solutions and the resolution to see them through.

As the earlier chapters have indicated, the past two decades have seen major changes in the character of engineering activities and of the education regarded as adequate to prepare an engineer for his place in the modern world. Today adaptability is the key word; change, adaptability, and breadth describe the modern technological setting and the determinants of a modern technical education.

Two generations ago the picture was very different. An engineering education was expected to provide the basic information needed for a lifetime. A communication engineer, a civil engineer, a power engineer, or an aeronautical engineer was expected to get a solid, derivative education that provided the foundation for a lifelong career with little danger of obsolescence. To be sure, changes occurred and progress required the acquisition of some new knowledge, the mastering of new techniques, and the adaptation of new tools; but the changes were slow and orderly and generally were of such character that little new understanding of basic science was required for their assimilation.

325

Contrast that with the period that has followed World War II. Since 1946, techniques, technical capabilities, and even the dominant problems have changed so dramatically that the language of today's engineering sounds foreign to a student of the earlier period. Today's world of engineering involves the intimate and continuous exploitation of basic scientific knowledge and broad systems concepts, an interplay of technical capabilities and mathematical analysis. While engineering has always been based upon existing scientific knowledge, there is a qualitative difference between modern engineering and the profession of two decades ago. Two factors are responsible for this difference. First, and probably most important, is that the understanding of many natural phenomena is much more complete than it was; indeed, today it is sufficient to permit understanding of most physical properties of materials and the quantitative prediction of many. Consider, for example, the engineer's approach to the properties of solids such as metals or insulators or semi-conductors, which are so important in both mechanical and electrical engineering. Not so long ago the engineer had to accept these substances as they were found in nature or as they were modified by well-organized alchemy. Neither the physical nor the electrical properties of matter could be explained in terms of the atomic constituents of a material or the forces acting between them. In this circumstance the engineer was content to be, indeed compelled to be, satisfied with a good phenomenological description of the properties of the materials available for his use. There was little point then in understanding the quantum theory or the experiments in solid-state physics that eventually led to the comprehension we now have of such fundamental material properties as strength, ductility, electrical conductivity, magnetic behavior, and many others. In contrast, solid-state physics has advanced today to the point where it is possible to explain and predict the characteristics of most materials and often to tailor them for special needs. The modern engineer whose work involves the application of materials needs to stay abreast of this rapidly changing subject.

Similarly, the understanding of complex systems has progressed to such a degree that the behavior of intricate mechanical, electrical, or combined systems can be simulated on computers. In this way the operation of such systems, whether they are supersonic aircraft, ballistic missiles or an automatic control system, can be studied thoroughly without ever being built. This requires a knowledge of feedback theory, automatic control theory, numerical analysis, and computer programming.

The second point of difference I would stress is the increased complexity of the engineering problems of today over those of twenty years ago. Today's problems require the collaboration of numerous specialists, each of whom must have some understanding of many related disciplines in order to contribute effectively to the whole creative task. Furthermore, someone must orchestrate the effort, visualize the fitting together of the disparate technologies that must contribute to the solution and select the best one; that is, the solution that represents the optimum matching of technical possibilities, needs, costs, time required, and any relevant social factors.

In choosing a career and learning a profession, you seek a way to earn a living and to be a useful member of the society in which you live. The engineer has played a particularly important role in the industrial development of our country, for it has been his application of scientific knowledge that has helped create the modern world. Those of us who have chosen engineering careers are particularly fortunate because they are personally rewarding as well as constructive. Technical and scientific work is usually fun. In fact, creative technical work provides much the same satisfaction that is obtained from painting, writing, and composing or performing music.

As the world becomes increasingly dependent upon technology and the possibility of its serious misuse becomes an ever greater threat to our society, there is a growing need for engineers and scientists to become involved in the social problems associated with our rapidly changing society. Furthermore, in my experience a creative contribution to those special problems involving both technology and the general welfare is even more rewarding than making a new scientific discovery or finding an especially clever engineering solution to an important technical problem. This is a vital aspect of the exciting scientific race in which we are all involved, and by which we are all affected. While most engineers will probably have to—and probably prefer to—spend the major part of their time on fairly specific technical problems, they are peculiarly able, because of their technical understanding, to appreciate and to enjoy the important human drama unfolding about us.

We are living during what certainly must be considered one of the most exciting periods in man's history; the most exciting, the most challenging, most dangerous and most hopeful. And technology makes it that way. We appear to have within our grasp the realization of many of man's fondest dreams and most urgent hopes; yet simultaneously there is ample reason to be concerned about our very survival. Throughout history there have been threats and challenges, and the survival and growth of civilization must often have looked hopeless. Yet our ancestors somehow managed not only to survive but also to leave something more than they found, so that opportunities for all of us have steadily increased.

During recorded history, societies have faced two hostile environments, the unpredictable and usually harsh natural world and the societies of men that often were crueler than nature at its worst. Human knowledge has provided us with the tools to master the physical environment, but unfortunately in doing so has greatly aggravated the problems man faces with himself, so that his welfare and probably his continued existence depend upon the outcome of a race between the achievement of greater and greater ability to manipulate the physical world and the evolution of a social and political structure capable of controlling the great forces that have been unleashed.

I am intrigued by the analogy between biological evolution and the present human enterprise, particularly in the application of technology, and I believe that there is much to be gained from an appreciation of the similarities. Man represents the culmination of an awe-inspiring process of growth and development that has taken millions of years, starting with single cells, which apparently found survival easier if they joined forces and developed differentiated members of the group with special talents. Sir Charles Darwin pictured a world in which all of the organisms were involved in a bitter struggle for survival, made necessary by a given earthly space able to support only a limited population without privation for all. He found that species changed, apparently in a random manner, and that occasionally the changes gave their possessors a slight competitive advantage, which put some individuals and their descendants slightly ahead of others in the struggle for survival. Ultimately, the successful species became dominant.

In the process of selection described by Darwin those characteristics were accentuated that made members of a group better able to survive. At the same time that animals and plants were evolving to improve their survivability, the physical conditions on the earth were also changing, so that the evolutionary process had to adapt to changing climatic conditions, and the living creatures (our ancestors included) were faced with an ever-new environment. Fortunately, the physical conditions—temperature, amount of water, amount of vegetation, and so on—changed so slowly that evolutionary adaptation by our ancestors successfully coped with the problems created by the changing environment. This was not true of a great many species whose ancestors made wrong turns and chose the road to extinction. There is very little detailed knowledge of man's ancestors or of his early history, but it is clear that those who followed the succesful path placed a higher premium on cunning than on physical prowess.

Relatively recently man made one of his most vital discoveries —agriculture. Even today the development of agricultural techniques must be regarded as one of the most important steps in the development of human society, an event at least as significant and far-reaching as the scientific revolution we are now living through. It may seem strange for me to rank that prehistoric and accidental development ahead of all the great scientific discoveries and marvelous inventions of recent times, and yet I really believe we should. To be sure, it was not the result of organized effort; it didn't emerge from a famous laboratory; it wasn't planned by a committee; and it certainly wasn't financed by a government contract. Nonetheless, it marked a turning point in history. I believe that without this early discovery, none of the rest would have followed. Cultivation and organized agriculture made possible the next steps in human development. There could be no organized society before man learned to plant foods and harvest crops. The nomads roamed over vast areas searching for enough food to support even the smallest tribe. Without cultivation, a patch of forest or plain could support just a few people and social groups had to remain very small. Furthermore, life was very precarious and survival a matter of extreme good fortune. A harsh winter or a few seasons of drought were enough to decimate a tribe. Under such circumstances there was essentially no opportunity for the development of specialized skills. Only after the appearance of cultivation do we find other evidence of the renewed development of civilizations. The formation of villages, the fashioning of crude tools, the emergence of the artisan, were all made possible by the increased margin for survival. As agricultural techniques improved, so did the lot of man. Even today there is a direct, reverse correlation between the economic well-being of a society and the portion of its total effort that must go into raising the food it needs to stay alive. In the United States today, less than ten per cent of the work force is engaged directly in agriculture; in the underdeveloped countries as much as ninety-five per cent of the manpower is involved in raising food, leaving little or no resources for other forms of development.

Biological and social evolution continued along together for a very long period of time, although during the period of history for which we have significant records, the last five or ten thousand years, social evolution progressed so rapidly that there are few if any concurrent signs of biological change in man. It is interesting to note that most of the social progress in this period, until the Industrial Revolution, which began only about two hundred years ago, involved improvements in our ability to make do with what we had. For energy we were dependent upon our own muscle and that of animals we tamed and on the use we could make of materials found in nature. As skills were developed and the arts and trade grew, the land could support more people, and the population of the towns increased. Nonetheless, the same harsh laws of nature that had limited the size of nomad groups controlled the growth of the more highly organized communities, and they were equally affected by natural or man-made disasters that reduced food production.

Such was society until the beginning of the Industrial Revolution; primarily agricultural but with an important element of crafts and trade. Then came the Industrial Revolution, brought about by the introduction of a series of ingenious and important inventions—the steam engine, the loom, and many other machines —leading to the organization of the factory and the development of the industrial society.

Concurrently, experimental science was beginning to develop. Newton did his famous studies on gravity, optics, and mechanics during the period from 1665 to 1704. At almost the same time, Faraday, Henry, Oersted, and many others were beginning to explore electrical phenomena. Their motivation was entirely one of scientific curiosity, an insatiable desire to explore and understand some mysterious aspect of nature. However, it was not long before inventors began to exploit these interesting scientific discoveries. Samuel Morse invented the telegraph in 1832. Thomas Edison and his contemporaries invented in rapid succession the telephone, the electric generator, the electric motor, the electric light. The internal combustion engine was invented at the turn of the century. At the same time that this start was being made in the exploration of the physical world and in the useful application of the new ideas, a similar awakening was occurring in the understanding of living things. Experimenters explored and explained the complexities of the human body, the germ theory of infection was proved, Mendel did the plant-breeding experiments that led to his now famous gene theory illuminating the transmission of inherited characteristics. As in the case of discoveries in the field of physical sciences, so in the life sciences; the new insights were quickly exploited in both medicine and agriculture. This, too, is recent history. Just one hundred years ago the Department of Agriculture was established to make possible the widespread use of new varieties of plants and new agricultural techniques.

So began the scientific revolution—a few curious scholars trying to understand the physical universe, and a few ingenious inventors who put to work every new idea that came their way.

Earlier I said that these modern developments can be viewed as an extension of biological evolution, and now I would like to explore this idea a bit further. Many of the most significant innovations of the last century are really means of extending or amplifying our individual capabilities. The internal combustion engine and the electric motor are devices for allowing us to do more work than our own muscles or even the muscles of our domesticated animals can do. The automobile, steamboat, airplane, and train are means of greater locomotion. Radio, telephone, and television extend the distances over which we can communicate. Chemistry has extended the usefulness of the minerals that make up the earth around us. Research in the life sciences has revolutionized agriculture and medicine. The collective impact of this century of discovery and invention has been to produce a much greater mastery of nature and more secure living for the citizens of the nations that have been fortunate enough to participate fully in this revolution.

Agricultural and industrial evolution have not produced Utopia. The process has been so rapid that society often has not been able to anticipate the problems that have accompanied the exploitation of each new technical achievement, and even if it were possible to anticipate the difficulties, the immediate advantages of a new development may be, or at least appear to be, so important that the long-term liabilities would be tolerated.

We are all aware of the fact that the war potential of the major nations is almost sufficient to annihilate the human race and is still growing.

The air pollution problems and congested cities are unexpected by-products of the automobile. Many knowledgeable people are predicting serious consequences as a result of the widespread use of insecticides in agriculture. And, as we look to the future, we are sure to encounter more such problems. Many of the technological innovations introduced to solve one of the problems facing society create other problems that may be even more severe. Unless we come to understand this paradoxical situation and learn to deal with it, we will have created a most unstable system.

The labor problem posed by automation is probably the most serious domestic manifestation of the dilemma caused by modern technology. Computers in a sense complete the man-made additions to our senses, for they are used to extend or substitute for our innate mental capabilities. They can replace workers engaged in simple repetitive activities, and they can be used to aid a skilled mathematician confronted with an otherwise insoluble problem.

How should we view this problem? If we take the short-range view, we must be very concerned with the dislocations of laborers caused by automation. Yet in an evolutionary sense, automation represents another important step in the continuing effort to increase individual productivity and, consequently, the general economic level of the country. By encouraging its development we are tacitly agreeing to further changes in the society. The increased complexity of the industrial enterprise leads to the consequent need for a more skilled and more professional work force, fewer man-hours of work to produce a given volume of goods, and directly to the realization that new occupations must be developed in order to keep the available work force fully occupied.

The trend toward an increasingly skilled industrial work force is clearly visible. As this chapter is being written, our American employment statistics show that the total work force is at a peak. More than sixty-three million Americans are at work today. Yet during the last two decades, while we have been establishing this record high, the total number of unskilled workers employed has actually been dropping, and the most highly skilled group—the technical manpower—has been rapidly increasing. In fact, while the population of the country is now doubling roughly every forty years, the engineering manpower group is doubling once every twelve years. Yet there is no danger of there being a surplus in the engineering profession, for our best estimates indicate that there will continue to be a technical manpower shortage for the foreseeable future. In fact, I believe this feature is built into the system because individual technical workers on the average generate more good ideas than they can explore or develop. Consequently, productive engineering opportunities will continue to exist for all available technically trained people, and as long as their work adds to the general welfare, the society will undoubtedly continue to find ways to finance it.

As science increases the productivity of the farms and industry, society has available an increasing fraction of its labor force for forward-looking activities. In recent times much of this margin has been going into expanding technical activities that have led to new industries. As the manpower pool grows and as automation techniques make industrial production ever more economical of manpower, there will be a continued need for major new industries. If such new industries are not provided, we face mounting unemployment. Concurrently, as an alternative we may curtail working hours, but such a course presupposes the unwarranted assumption that every human need has been satisfied.

Since World War II, much of the science and technology that has provided the stimulus for new industry has been the result of the impact of large-scale governmental military research activities. Science and technology provide the basis for the military protection to our nation and its institutions, and in turn the federal government finances the research and development for that purpose. Fortunately, much of this effort contributes to technological development in other sectors of our society as well, most notably civilian industry and university scientific and technological activities. It is doubtful, for example, that we would have modern antibiotics, or electronic computers, or jet aircraft, without military demands that have brought forward immense public investment in pure research.

In spite of these large expenditures by the federal government, most of our outstanding technological successes have been produced through private initiative. The development of electric power, the electric light, the railroads, the telephone, radio and television, medicines, the automobile, automation in industry and other labor-saving devices—all of these were the creation of private initiative. Individuals or groups of individuals, of their own initiative and at their own risk, exploited new ideas in order to satisfy what they believed to be important needs, and private research and development to produce new products and better processes for the old ones will continue to be the backbone of our industry and private enterprise system.

There exist a growing number of important needs that cannot attract private industry and are only now being recognized as urgent public problems.

Consider, for example, the broad area of natural resources. In this category are such diverse problems as maintaining adequate water supplies for a growing population, protecting the atmosphere from pollution, maintaining the productivity of the agricultural lands, ensuring adequate supplies of raw materials to meet the ever-growing needs of our industries, and preserving wilderness and recreation land for the enjoyment of the ever-increasing population of our cities.

Some of these represent extremely acute needs in some countries and whole regions of the world, but as far as the United States is concerned today not one of them is truly a critical need. Yet, in time, each one of them is almost certain to become critical here in the United States as our population grows and the demands upon our resources increase. And if we wait until they become critical, each one of them may by that time be extremely difficult or even impossible to cope with. To maintain the productivity of agricultural lands, for example, is a task well within the current resources of science and technology. To restore lands that have been depleted or to replace topsoil that has washed away is a far more serious problem, and I am not sure that we will easily learn how to go about it. The total water in the United States is much more than adequate to meet current needs, but as our population grows we will need to manage this now bountiful resource with great care. Studies made by a Select Committee on National Water Resources of the Senate, headed by the late Senator Robert S. Kerr, have called attention to the need for a major research effort—now—to develop the means of managing this problem and the even greater need for engineers educated to deal with these problems. But scientific hydrology is in its infancy; there are only a few scientists engaged in research in this field, and the facilities available to them are inadequate. Few universities or colleges educate students for work in this field, or do research leading to an understanding of the problem. And similar deficiencies exist in the fields of atmospheric sciences, for example, and environmental health.

All of these areas have a characteristic in common: they do not promise sufficient financial return to make the necessary large-scale research and development efforts attractive to private investors. I can imagine a period some time in the future when there might indeed be great financial return to the man who can provide water where it is desperately needed, but by then it may be too late, or too expensive for the boldest entrepreneur. But at the moment these problems must be met, if they are to be met at all, by means of a public effort to which the private profit motive is not central. Such a public effort would clearly be fruitful. Recent developments in technology have provided the tools for dramatic advances, if these tools could only be grasped. In the atmospheric sciences, for example, satellites make possible world-wide observation, and sounding rockets can sample atmospheric conditions at all altitudes. The federal government now supports a substantial effort in these fields, but I expect that a far greater effort will be needed in future years.

I have written so far of *problems* that the scientist and engineer can hope to solve. But there is still another viewpoint to consider: what new science and technology can be turned to the creation of direct benefits? In reference to atmospheric pollution, I mentioned the contributions that might be made by satellites and sounding rockets; these same devices offer great promise for the creation of a truly scientific, truly predictive meteorology. Vast amounts of data can now be collected, and large computers then make it possible to use those data to create and test mathematical models of weather systems. I do not know what might lie at the end of this road. At the very least, there can be immensely improved weather prediction, with all the convenience and the commercial advantages that might accrue. It is even possible, as some experts hope, that we might learn to control the weather to some degree.

The resources of the oceans have never been thoroughly tapped, except in the most direct and primitive ways. We know a great deal less about the oceans than we do about outer space, and we are certainly learning about outer space a great deal faster than we are learning about the oceans. Yet they are a good deal closer at hand; they cover some four-fifths of the earth's surface, and they are extremely rich in food, in chemicals, in energy, and in almost everything that man has learned to put to use. Here, too, the great tools are close at hand, and the present administration is making great efforts to put them to use.

Here again, we can scarcely look to private initiative to do the necessary work. It is true that the potential returns are great, but they are too general, too diffuse, to encourage venture capital in the vast amounts that would be necessary. As for the degree of public support that would generate massive government involvement, it is not easy to win public support for an unspecified future benefit, as certain as we may be that the benefit, somehow or another, is there to be grasped. So once again we find ourselves confronted with great potentialities, and yet somehow without the means to realize them.

One of the most challenging opportunities for engineers, another one that provides a challenge for both technical and social engineering abilities, is found in our commitments to the less-favored nations of the world.

We have already seen that the principal advantages of technologically advanced societies over those with a traditional rural or village structure based primarily upon agriculture are found in the exploitation of technology. To move forward to meet the demands of this century, the developing countries must achieve a technological base side by side with their traditional culture, and the countries of the West are pledged to help. They need capital, capital of two kinds. The hardware, the factories, the roads, the dams, are all obvious needs. But the human capital—

trained technicians, agriculturalists, doctors, engineers and scientists—is no less important. The technicians and the engineers must be present if the plants are to be built and run; the agriculturalists must learn to support urban populations with a diminished farm labor force and often to support the whole population more adequately; the scientists must provide foundations for the indigenous development of special local industry.

In the short term, much of this human capital must come directly from the industrialized nations, as must many of the teachers required to build a local educational system. Here, then, is still one more opportunity for engineers and scientists in a world full of exciting and interesting and rewarding tasks to be done.

Engineers will play a most important role in all of the areas I have mentioned. As we contribute to and influence the evolution of society, there is always a need to be conscious of the wide impact of our work. Our creations can provide the means to an ever-better society and a happier life for our fellow men. But they also hold serious dangers. There can be few isolated acts in this modern interdependent world, and so we must be conscious of the long-range consequences of any endeavor. The engineer must therefore become social innovator and leader as well as technical inventor and implementor and thus contribute his part to the continued progress of society.